The Analysis of
Information Systems

Information Sciences Series

EDITORS

Robert M. Hayes
Director of the Institute of Library Research
University of California at Los Angeles

Joseph Becker
Director of Information Sciences
Interuniversity Communications Council (EDUCOM)

CONSULTANTS

Charles P. Bourne
Director, Advanced Information Systems Division
Programming Services, Inc.

Harold Borko
System Development Corporation

The Analysis of Information Systems

A Programmer's Introduction to Information Retrieval

Charles T. Meadow

Federal Systems Division
International Business Machines Corporation

John Wiley & Sons, Inc.   New York · London · Sydney

SECOND PRINTING, MAY, 1967

Copyright © 1967 by John Wiley & Sons, Inc.

Library of Congress Catalog Card Number: 66-28760

Printed in the United States of America

Information Sciences Series

Information is the essential ingredient in decision making. The need for improved information systems in recent years has been made critical by the steady growth in size and complexity of organizations and data.

This series is designed to include books that are concerned with various aspects of communicating, utilizing, and storing digital and graphic information. It will embrace a broad spectrum of topics, such as information system theory and design, man-machine relationships, language data processing, artificial intelligence, mechanization of library processes, non-numerical applications of digital computers, storage and retrieval, automatic publishing, command and control, information display, and so on.

Information science may someday be a profession in its own right. The aim of this series is to bring together the interdisciplinary core of knowledge that is apt to form its foundation. Through this consolidation, it is expected that the series will grow to become the focal point for professional education in this field.

Dedicated to the memory of Abraham Meadow

Preface

This book is intended to supply the background needed for participation in the analysis and design of information-handling systems and for understanding the literature in the field. I have tried to present a unified approach to the subject and to the relation of information retrieval to other disciplines and an appreciation of the importance of this interdisciplinary relationship. I hope that the scientist or computer programmer, newly interested in information-retrieval problems, as well as the librarian, will find the book of value.

Information retrieval is a relatively new field of study, and although it is concerned with the application of electronic data processing to library functions all aspects of the problem of human communication must also be considered. In the context of information retrieval this is largely a process that may range from communication between a seeker of information and a card file on one level to a conversation between a man and a computer on another. The emphasis is on how languages and files can be organized to make this communication effective.

The basic library functions performed even in a mechanized library are probably as old as writing. However, in coupling computers with libraries, the developers of information-retrieval systems have not produced consistent terminology and standards of performance. We also have the problem that terms meaningful to the programmer are not always so to the librarian and vice versa. In writing this book I have been somewhat dogmatic in usage, but I have discussed in one consistent terminology a broad range of topics which contribute to information retrieval.

This is not a book on library science, although, clearly, it and information retrieval are highly related fields. I have attempted to reduce the array of different names which I have found applied to what, to me, seems to be a relatively few basic concepts. This is the essence of the scientific approach—the recognition of similarities in apparently diverse systems. Therefore I have often lumped under a single heading concepts that librarians may identify by several terms.

This book is divided into three parts. The first, *Information Retrieval and Communication,* emphasizes the human communication aspect of information retrieval. It covers languages used, document indexing, and problems of searching for information. Part II, called the *Organization of Information,* explains how information is organized for storage and retrieval by the use of computers. Part III, *Processing of Files and File Sets,* is concerned with machine processing of stored information, including search and retrieval.

Exercises at the end of each chapter provide an opportunity to practice the ideas presented. Information retrieval is not a contemplative science; it requires practice and participation, of which these exercises are designed to be the second best form.

Because this book is partly about language, in general, and partly about computer language, in particular, there is a special problem of differentiating among various uses of words. I have adopted the following conventions. *Quotation marks* are used (in addition to denoting quotations) whenever a word is presented in some sense other than its literal or most common meaning. *Italics* are used for emphasis, to denote foreign words, or to denote that a word is used as a sign representing a word itself, not the word's referent. For example, later in the book, we say ". . . the word *definition* needs definition first." **Boldface** is used to denote a word being used as a value of a variable or field or as a search term. (Although a man may live in New York, when he completes a form calling for his address the value of the data item called *city* is **New York.**

I should like to acknowledge my great indebtedness to Dr. Robert M. Hayes, of the University of California, chairman of the advisory board for this series, for his many valuable suggestions and for his encouragement when it was most needed. My thanks also to my colleagues at IBM who read and criticized the manuscript at various stages: Dr. Claude E. Walston and Messrs. Leo E. Davis, Jr., and Matthew J. Perriens. Finally, my thanks to the many others at IBM who helped at various stages to get the manuscript ready for publication, particularly Mrs. Ruth Telfair, Miss Joanne Wagner and Mrs. Eva Lambert.

Charles T. Meadow

Washington, D.C.
October 1966

Contents

PART III   PROCESSING OF FILES AND FILE SETS

The Analysis of
Information Systems

I

Information
Retrieval and
Communication

1

CHAPTER 1

Introduction

1.1 INFORMATION RETRIEVAL AS A COMMUNICATION PROCESS

Information retrieval is the process of recovering information-bearing symbols from their storage places in response to requests from prospective users of the information or from librarians on the users' behalf. The basic thesis of this book is that information retrieval is part of a complex communication system existing between the authors of information-bearing documents and their readers. We treat the book, research paper, or other document as a message to be communicated from the author to the reader, usually via one or more communications centers. Although we often make reference to a library and to books or other "hard copy" documents, the principles espoused here apply as well to photographs or to systems in which all data are stored in a computer and no reference to external documents is involved.

Our primary concern is with the organization of information to facilitate its retrieval. As a preliminary to this material, we shall review some basic principles of the languages used in information retrieval, the creation of index records, and the retrieval of information from index files. We then proceed to the organization of information and, finally, to the processing of it. Our first concern is with the basic notion of information and of the information retrieval process.

1.1.1 Concepts of Information

One of the most intriguing aspects of information retrieval is that it deals, through a variety of tools, with only one substance or material—an abstraction called information—and we know so little about it. Shannon[2] provides a measure for information but does not define it. He does, however, point out that his concern is not with *meaning,* or the semantic aspects of information but with the engineering problems of

3

transmitting it.   He states that

> The fundamental problem of communication is that of reproducing at
> one point either exactly or approximately a message selected at another
> point.   Frequently the messages have *meaning;* that is they refer to or
> are correlated according to some system with certain physical or con-
> ceptual entities.   These semantic aspects of communication are irrele-
> vant to the engineering problem.[3]

Warren Weaver,[4] although tending to agree, points out the important
fact that accurate physical transmission is a requirement if the semantic
meaning is to be communicated.   Weaver, in fact, defines three levels
of the communication problem: the *technical* problem of physical transmission, the *semantic* problem of conveying meaning by names of transmitted symbols, and the *effectiveness* problem of influencing the conduct
of the receiver.   The latter two aspects of communications are essentially
those defined by S. I. Hayakawa[1] as the *informative* and *affective* functions of language.   The word *affective,* according to Hayakawa, refers
to the arousing of response, not to efficiency, effectiveness, or strength
of the responses as might, he feels, be implied by the word *effective.*
Nonetheless, both authors agree that one function of language is to
influence behavior.   Although information can be measured, in an engineering sense, and its problems and functions defined, we are still unable
to describe it well analytically.

In this book we generally try to follow Weaver's resolution of communication into transmission, semantic, and effectiveness problems.   We
have no definition for information either, but we assume that, whatever
it is, it is communicated only in terms of structured sets of symbols
which are *representations* of information but are not the *same as* information.   If the reader of a book feels he has found information therein,
so be it.

The function of an information retrieval system (which might be
no more than the reference librarian at the village library) is to locate
and recover information from a store.   To do so, the patron issues a
request describing his wants in some way that may vary from, "I want
to know Napoleon's birth date," to "I want a good mystery."   Often,
and this is our principal focus, the patron uses this request, or *query,*
to locate and recover some string of symbols which might, by our two
examples, range from a single number to a shelf of books.   If the retrieved symbols add nothing to his store of knowledge, he may challenge
their veracity or accuracy, this being his prerogative.   On the basis of
new information contained in the patron's rejection of the first retrieved
message, the librarian can help him to perform another search and per-

haps retrieve another, more palatable string of symbols. The patron's rejection, and the reason therefor, constitutes effective use of language—its use to induce the librarian to make another search.

1.1.2 Transmission of Information

According to Shannon,[5] the communication process requires five elements: a *source,* or originator of a message; a *transmitter,* which usually modifies the form or coding of the message, enabling it to be sent out; a *channel,* the medium through which the message is conveyed and which may introduce noise into the system; a *receiver,* which reconverts the form of the message; and a *destination,* the recipient of the information. These are illustrated in Figure 1.1. An example of a communication system is a man as a source, his speech organs as a transmitter, air as the channel over which sound waves are transmitted, the auditory system of another man's body as receiver, and the brain of the receiving person as destination. Many systems actually involve a chain of transmissions, receipts, and retransmissions. A microphone is both a transmitter and receiver, receiving sound waves and transmitting electric power. Figure 1.2 illustrates how a conventional communication system can, almost arbitrarily, be subdivided into smaller, linked systems.

Because communication system elements can perform dual roles, we can visualize a system as consisting of a set of basic elements, each a generalized signal transducer which has an input, an output, and a functional role to play in converting the input to the output. This is the "black box" concept illustrated in Figure 1.3. The description fits a transmitter, receiving a signal from the source and converting it for dispatching through the channel. The channel performs a different conversion role; it physically displaces the signal in space and, although less important to this definition, often attenuates or weakens the signal. The receiver very often performs an inverse function to the transmitter. A radio receiver, for example, converts electromagnetic signals back into sound signals very similar to those originally spoken

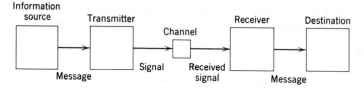

Figure 1.1 Schematic diagram of a general communication system (after Shannon[5]).

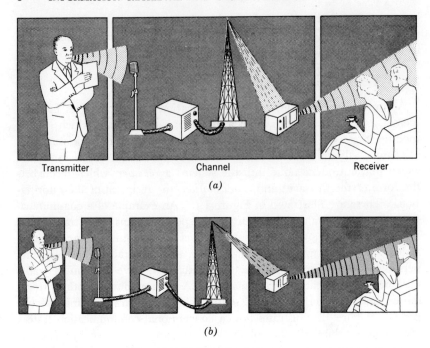

Transmitter   Channel   Receiver

(a)

(b)

Figure 1.2 The arbitrary nature of the transmitter-channel-receiver designation: (a) The studio announcer is the transmitter. The entire broadcasting process may be viewed as a channel and the listener at home, the receiver. (b) The announcer's vocal chords are the transmitter of air pressure variations, air, the channel, the microphone a receiver of sound waves and a transmitter of electricity, and so on, until the listener's inner ear sends electrical signals to his brain.

into the microphone. If we adopt this convention, the Shannon definition of communication amounts to a requirement for five basic, black-box elements in series, as shown in Figure 1.4, which is not dissimilar to Figure 1.1. An advantage of this notation is that, rather than concerning ourselves with sources and destinations, we can treat both the input and output of any communication link as messages subject to some forms of transformation, and we need not be concerned with the identity of

Input (message)   Output (message)

Transducer

Figure 1.3   Transducer.

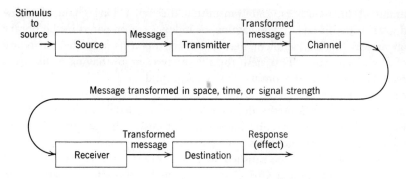

Figure 1.4 The communication process as a chain of transducers.

the message originator or ultimate reader. This represents only a symbolic departure from the Shannon definition for he goes on to talk of a source as a processor by which signals or symbol sequences are generated by selection from a finite set of possible symbols. This *process* may be represented by one of our black-box elements if we assume that the input is the set of possible signals, that the transducer performs the function of selecting one signal and rejecting all others, and that the output is the selected message.

No real communication can have taken place unless the transmitter and the receiver are making use of compatible codes or schema for symbolic representations of information. Identical codes are not always a requirement, but communication cannot have taken place unless the destination is sent the codes it is prepared to recognize and act upon. We often find that when a bridge player has apparently failed to catch and properly respond to his partner's bidding signal the partners have learned their signals from different bridge books and are using the same symbol to mean two different things. Here, we are interjecting semantic information connotations into the question of physical communication; that is, the bid has been uttered and heard. For engineering purposes a message was sent and received and technical communication was accomplished. Semantically, the received message sounded reasonable— was a legal bid and not a nonsense signal—but the receiver did not recognize the meaning that the transmitter intended. Thus *semantic* communication was not accomplished but the transmitting partner was unaware of this. As a result, *effective* communication was not accomplished—the receiving partner did not respond as the transmitting partner expected.

The documents stored in a library are messages, originating in the brains of their authors, and transmitted through a long chain of transducers to the library. The catalog, or index, card prepared in the library on arrival of the document may be looked upon as a further encoding of the document. This new form is arrived at by having a librarian read (transmit to the brain) the message and recode it, classifying the subject content and recognizing the symbols that denote author, publisher, date, or title of the document. The recoded form is then stored in the library for the convenience of patrons. The patron comes in, sometimes for specific facts and sometimes for broad knowledge. In the first case he may be satisfied with a phrase from a single book. In second, he will want a variety of books on his subject. In either case it is his function to communicate his needs either directly to the librarian or to the card catalog or index file. Any fuzziness of definition of his subject can often be resolved in a conversation with the librarian. However, if communication is to be directly with the catalog, the user must be able to translate the language he normally uses to describe his subject into the language of the catalog. This is not so easy as it sounds, and it is especially important to realize that ability to state questions accurately to a card catalog is not necessarily correlated with performance ability in the subject discipline. A brilliant physicist is no more innately endowed with this sort of communications faculty than he is with the ability to communicate with his professional colleagues in Iceland, using their native language. The language of the library is a different language from everyday English, and skill with its use must be acquired.

1.1.3   The Library as a Switching Center

Large, true-life communication systems tend not to be just simple links from A to B or even from A_1 to A_2 to $A_3 \cdot \cdot \cdot$ to A_n. They often have node points where more than two lines meet. These are switching centers without which modern communication—telephone, telegraph, mail, or even network radio and television—would be impossible. A switching center essentially makes use of some attribute of an incoming message to determine the disposition of the message. In a simple, two-input, one-output switch the first message to arrive, over either channel, may capture the output line, and, if a second message arrives on the other line while the first is being sent, the second message may be lost. A more complex switch may require more than one message to make a decision. An example is a modern, stored-program communications multiplexer which can accept messages from any one of over a hundred input lines and use a computer program (itself having been entered into the computer as a message) to decide on priorities and dispositions.   To help visualize the role of a library as a communication center, let us contrast its operation with another center for communication of documentary data, a post office.   We find the following major points of difference:

1. The post office finds an explicit address on each item of mail (leaving out illegible addresses and other error conditions).   Even "junk" mail is addressed to a street address, the name of the resident being redundant, except for a multiple dwelling or office for which the addition of an apartment number is sufficient.   Books, on the other hand, are addressed to the library, not to the library's patrons.

2. A postal patron gets all mail addressed to him, and only such mail (again, leaving out deviant cases).   He cannot be selective.   He cannot cut off the flow of third class mail or refuse to accept bills.   He cannot ask for more Christmas cards than are explicitly addressed to him.   A library user not only has these selectivity powers, but he is actually required to exercise them if he is to receive any messages at all.   Nothing is delivered by a library to a patron without some form of request by the patron, and this request must describe the nature of the material he wishes to receive.   A library patron, then, uses his description of desired messages as an "address," requesting all documents that fall into a given, figurative pigeonhole to be given to him.

3. The post office is not very selective on its input.   It prohibits certain materials (e.g., matches) in the mail and limits the size of parcel post packages.   It bars obscene or seditious written material from the mails, but it does not rule on subject matter.   Obscenity or treason, for example, are permissible as *subjects*.   The ban is on writings for which these terms describe *properties*, not *subjects*.   Libraries *may* also impose restrictions on the properties of books but *must*, to meet the requirements of their patrons, exercise control over the subject matter.   They must do, or try to do, just what the post office cannot do—try to find out what kind of messages their patrons would like to receive and see to it that these are the kinds of messages that are acquired.

4. Both must contend with ambiguity in addressing—the post office with poor or smudged writing, the library with poorly defined topics of interest in queries or subject matter of books received.   The manner of resolving these problems is quite different.   The post office can assume that an item of mail was directed to a specific person or address, even if a misspelling or digit inversion mars the accuracy of the address.   The library faces a different problem.   Neither the topic sought by the client nor the topic written about by the author necessarily fits into any unique, predefined pigeonhole; that is, the "address" or subject category need

not exist before receipt of the book at the library. It is an intellectual exercise to express a subject in terms of the library's language, the classification system.

5. Some of the library's search problems derive from the fact that it accumulates its input, while the post office, of course, passes its receipts along as quickly as it can. The growth of a collection intensifies the search problem. For example, if there is a pigeonhole for *biology* and one for *physics,* then *biophysics* can go in either category or a new pigeonhole can be created for it. As the volume of material on *biophysics* grows, some documents will be more "biological," some more "physical," and some will be misclassified. A cluster will develop, and although users will soon learn that all biophysical material is somewhere in the *physics-biology-biophysics* classes, there can be no guarantee which, if any, single subject will contain all the material. Both librarians and users will grow accustomed to this ambiguity. This is a natural trend. Certainly, the meanings of words in natural language tend to change over the years as once erroneous usages become proper because of repeated use. With no accumulation, even though the post office may make errors of interpretation, it is not likely to create adaptive processes by which early errors reinforce the tendency to repeat the errors and to endow these errors with authenticity through usage.

1.2   THE INFORMATION RETRIEVAL PROCESS

In Figure 1.5 we show a highly oversimplified, schematic representation of the information retrieval process. The purpose of this diagram is to illustrate the organization of this book, not to attempt to represent all the many activities and interrelationships that contribute to the successful communication of information through the medium of a library.

We base our description on the flow of information into and within a library, and we continue to make reference to a library throughout the book. However, we mean to imply a library in the most general sense—an organized collection of documents and an organization to handle both documents and the information requests made to a collection. Thus an information system in which all "documents" are files stored within a computer falls under this definition.

Part 1, which is comprised of Chapters 1 to 4, is concerned largely with human communication—the problems and techniques of communication among authors, readers (or users of a library), and the staff of the library who must classify, catalog, or index incoming material and help to search for information wanted by patrons.

The retrieval process may be deemed to start with the creation of

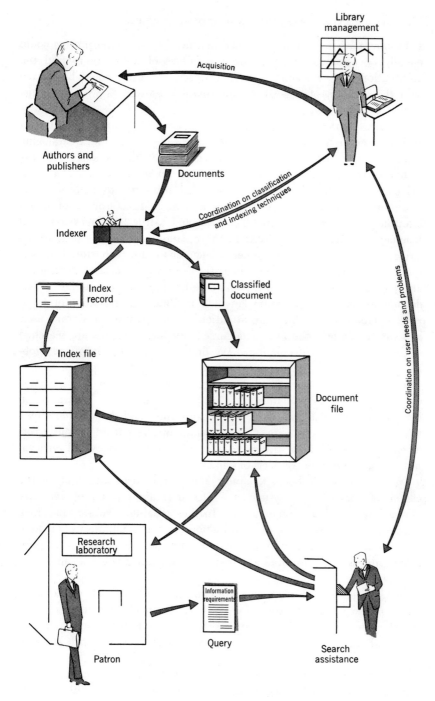

Library
management

Acquisition

Authors and
publishers

Documents

Coordination on classification
and indexing techniques

Indexer

Index
record

Classified
document

Coordination on user needs and problems

Index file

Document
file

Research
laboratory

Information
requirements

Query

Search
assistance

Patron

Figure 1.5 The information retrieval process.

11

a document by its author. We say "deemed" because the process could equally be assumed to start with the failure of a library to find the information a user wants. In other words, the cycle could be started with the creation of a need for information, as well as with the satisfaction of this need.

The next major step is to create an index record for the document as it arrives in the library. In our usage *indexing* includes cataloging and classifying, as they are more conventionally understood. This explanation is amplified in Chapter 2. The index records, collectively, make up an index file. This file is used primarily to help find the information stored in the documents and as a direct source of useful information. Chapters 2 and 3 are devoted to the languages used and language problems encountered in the creation of index records to describe documents. The documents themselves are also stored in the library. We repeat that the schematic form we have chosen does not imply that documents must be books or other hard copy materials. The documents can be in computer language and machine readable form.

In Chapter 4 we shift our attention to the patron, or library user, and we discuss how the files of documents or index records are searched in the quest for his information. We find, here, another language problem. The searcher must communicate his wants to the index records and in doing so must use a language compatible with the language used in the index. He must also expect to meet some frustration in his efforts to find his information. Because his search is not guaranteed to "work" perfectly, he must be conscious of the nature of the errors he can make and plan a strategy to overcome them. Errors and retrieval strategy are among the subjects of Chapter 4.

In Part II of the book, Chapters 5 to 8, we focus attention on the center of the retrieval system, the files that are created by indexers, and are searched by system users. In these chapters we are concerned primarily with structures of information-bearing symbols, rather than with library users or activities. We are also more concerned with computer processing of information than with human processing and communication.

In Chapters 9 and 10, which are contained in Part III, we combine some of the subject matter of Part I of the book with that of Part II. Here, we discuss file operations both from a theoretical point of view and that of library management who are concerned with the economics of retrieval system operation.

This material must, of necessity, be presented one topic at a time. The reader should ever bear in mind that a real and successful information retrieval system is highly dependent on informal communication.

The lines of communication, or data flow, we have illustrated in Figure 1.5 are the formal lines, mostly characterized by having one form or another of written record transmitted through them.   The informal lines of communication may include conversations among indexers (e.g., how to classify a given book), or between a patron and an indexer or library manager.   We do not describe this aspect of information in detail.

We have now briefly discussed the basic nature of information, communication, and language.   We have described information retrieval, largely by analogy, as an activity equivalent to the operation of a very complex and somewhat unusual switching center.   In this center patrons communicate with library files by using a special language to find and read books written in natural language.   We shall now examine the documents, the special languages, and the operation of the searching system in detail.

REFERENCES

1. Hayakawa, S. I., *Language in Thought and Action,* Harcourt, Brace & World, New York, 1949, p. 82.
2. Shannon, Claude E., and Warren Weaver, *The Mathematical Theory of Communication,* The University of Illinois Press, Urbana, Illinois, 1959, p. 18 et seq.
3. *Ibid.,* p. 3.
4. *Ibid.,* p. 95.
5. *Ibid.,* p. 4.

EXERCISES

1. Make a study of the flow of material in the library you regularly use. Describe how books are procured, cataloged, stored, and accounted for when lent. What are the various rates of book transactions, reference queries, special purchase requests? Who are the most frequent users of the library? Why? What classification system is used and why? Begin the study by compiling a questionnaire to be used to record information and, in the process, justify the questions asked and the choice of persons to be queried (e.g., librarian, clerk, user). This study can be done individually or as a group effort.
2. Recommended reading:
   S. I. Hayakawa, *Language in Thought and Action,* Harcourt, Brace & World, New York, 1949.
   J. R. Pierce, *Symbols, Signals and Noise: The Nature and Process of Communication,* Harper & Brothers, New York, 1961.

CHAPTER 2

The languages of information retrieval

2.1 INTRODUCTION

To retrieve desired information from any large collection of documents we require two things of that collection. First, the collection must be ordered so that when we know what we want we will know where to find it. Second, we must have a means of searching and matching, some way of recognizing whether or not any given document contains the information we want. Reading a document in its entirety is one approach to the latter requirement, but, in addition to its obvious deficiency from the point of view of time, it still does not guarantee the searcher that he will recognize the material he wants. Suppose, for example, he wants some tutorial material on data processing and he comes upon a book on computer programming. If he is totally ignorant of the field, it will not be obvious that the book at least partially answers his needs. To resolve both the time and the recognition problems, we use an *index,* or *catalog,* as a tool for locating desired information. In this sense an index or catalog is basically a list of the documents in a library which contains some descriptive material about document content and the location of the documents. We shall enlarge on and formalize this definition later. We call each entry in the index an *index record.* An *abstract,* or natural language *summary* or *condensation* of a document, performs some of the functions of an index record, and, in certain of its uses, can be considered a form thereof.

In the context of our analogy of information retrieval as a communication process both an index record and an abstract are messages. They are created by a specialist in indexing or abstracting, upon his receipt of a new document. Both are further transformations of the author's original mental concept which he transformed into the document. The usual purpose of creating an index record or abstract is to inform the reader about the document, not about the concept symbolized in the

14

document. Although the document serves the end of informing its reader about a concept in the mind of the author, the index record or abstract informs its reader that a document is available on a given subject or with given characteristics. If the index record or abstract performs this duty then the reader will use it to decide whether he wishes to select the original document from a store of documents.

There are two major uses for index records and abstracts. In the first they are stored in a file called an *index file* which may be searched by a person looking for information. Here, indexes are used to help find information. A searcher uses the file to help him decide what documents he wants to retrieve and to tell him where these documents are. The second major use is to indicate what information is available in a library—a *holdings list* of all material on hand, or an *accessions list* which is disseminated to library users, and tells them about new material acquired by the library. In an index file search the prospective information user takes the initiative in seeking out information. An accessions list represents the library's initiative in telling its users about information of potential interest. In a *selective dissemination system* these approaches are combined. Here, the user tells the library of his general and continuing information needs. The library disseminates to each user only new acquisition data which fall in his self-defined area of interest. To do this, of course, the library must go through a search procedure but one in which document index records are used to search for user interest records which they satisfy.

An index has special language requirements. As a gross generality, an index record will simplify those attributes of a document it is describing, making the search of the index easier by reducing both the amount of material to be searched and complexity of the search process, thereby reducing the time required to perform a search. As we pointed out in Chapter 1, the use of this intermediate communication channel requires the use of a language or coding that is comprehensible to all parties to the communication, in this case the searcher, the cataloger or indexer, and the documents being searched for. This chapter is devoted to the languages used in this special communications situation.

In traditional library usage a *catalog* is,[17] "a list which records, describes, and indexes the resources of a collection. . . ." A catalog entry, such as the familiar catalog card, is made up of a number of elements descriptive of subject matter, publisher, physical size, and so on. Making up this entry is called *descriptive cataloging*. One element of a catalog entry is often a *classification code*. In conventional library work, in addition to serving as an aid to describing content of a book, this code is also used to determine placement of the document on the shelf. For this reason, only one classification code is affixed to a document. This does not imply, although it often results in the conclusion, that each document neatly fits into one and only one subject class. We shall consider this topic at greater length later in this chapter. In library usage, an *index* is often a file used to find information in another file, and does not necessarily contain much descriptive material about the document ultimately sought.

We prefer to generalize these concepts and to stress the similarity among *index, catalog,* and *classification,* rather than their differences. We use the term *index* to encompass both the meanings of *catalog* and *index* as given above. An index, then, contains some descriptive material about records or books in a file or library, and may give some information about their location. An index can refer, not just to the main document collection of the library, but to any collection of records within it, such as the card catalog itself. We shall use the term *index record, index of a document,* or *index* (when the context makes clear the difference) to refer to an individual record or entry in an index file. We shall treat the words *indexing* and *cataloging* as synonymous.

Classification, as we shall see, is treated in this book as one, out of many, ways of describing a document for use in an index. We do not accept that there exists a unique classification for each document, but we respect the operational problems of a library which make the use of a single code desirable. Classification, then, we treat as a part of the indexing or cataloging process.

2.2 ATTRIBUTES OF INDEX LANGUAGES

2.2.1 The General Nature of Index Languages

Almost all index languages in use are to some extent artificial. A natural language, although hard to define, is easy to illustrate. English, French, and German are natural languages. They are the languages that people "naturally" speak. Index languages are invented, not for general communication, but for a very special form of communication— that of enabling indexers and library searchers to communicate with each other and, in a sense, with the documents of the library. The particular role that the language is to play will vary with the library, the collection, and the users. Selection or design of an index language is probably the single most difficult step in designing an information retrieval system; in our opinion, the biggest single reason for this is our general inability to predict the performance of human beings when faced with a communication system different from that with which they have become familiar. Our approach here is to present some basic principles for the design and use of these languages, leaving it to the designer of an individual system to apply them to each local condition.

2.2.2   Index Language Requirements

Some of the attributes of any language in which an index is expressed are the following:

1. Index records usually are to be read by a human searcher at some point in his interrogation procedure. Hence, they must use a vocabulary and syntax that can be understood by the searcher. If the patrons of the library are the general public or any large, not specially trained group, this implies that the index language should approximate natural language, or be otherwise easily learned.

2. Some index files, and these are our primary concern here, are also intended for computer searching. This means that the format, syntax, and vocabulary of the index language must be comprehensible to a computer, just as they must be to men. Usually, this implies more rigidity in the language than is needed for a manual, or nonmechanized system.

3. The records or messages written in index language must be sufficiently descriptive of the corresponding documents to provide for accurate retrieval, yet not so detailed and cluttered as to slow searching or index composition to an uneconomical rate. Descriptiveness implies not only degree of detail but also concentration on the "right" subject. The "right" subject of concentration for an index varies among user groups.

4. Some indexes are to be prepared by a computer and then are to be searched by man or machine or both. The language of a computer-prepared index is limited by the analytical capability that can be built into the index preparation program. This is not to say that a computer-prepared index must always use a rigid language, for the automatic abstracts produced by Savage et al.[15] are in natural language. But Savage used the exact language of the author. His program is able to select rich, descriptive sentences, if they exist, from the original text, to form the abstract, but the program cannot modify a sentence to make it a better descriptor of the document.

5. Because the individual index records are to be grouped into a file, they must use a format and a physical storage medium that eases file organization. For example, the three-by-five inch cards traditionally used for library catalogs contain information that follows a defined format which greatly speeds perusal of the card during a search. Figure

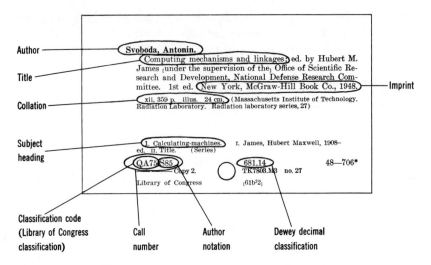

Figure 2.1   Library of Congress catalog card.

2.1 shows the format of an index card produced by the Library of Congress. As to the importance of the physical medium, it can readily be seen how the use of nonuniform card sizes or even use of lighter paper stock could slow the search process.

6. Languages change, index languages among them. A properly designed index language must contain provisions for its own modification, as the language of the documents or of the users changes.

The foregoing list is in terms of results we would like to see from our index language. We shall proceed, through this and the next chapters, to develop a basis for selecting a language capable of giving the required results and for ways of using the language to achieve them.

2.2.3   The Structure of Index Languages

We are concerned with two major components of language—vocabulary and syntax. Indeed, because we are working only with written languages, we may treat these as sole components of a language. A *vocabulary* is the set of words that is used in a language. As applied to natural language, this is a fairly self-evident term. We shall apply it as well to index languages. The set of numeric codes of the Dewey Decimal Classification is, in our usage, a vocabulary for that index language. The set of headings used to describe businesses in the yellow pages of a telephone directory constitute a vocabulary which, although not the most precise language for describing businesses, is apparently quite effective. The vocabulary of an index language, then, is the set of words that is or may be used to describe a document in an index record.

The *syntax* of a language is the set of rules for combining elements of the vocabulary into language units with meanings not expressible by the basic vocabulary. We call these units *syntactic units*. A syntactic unit, typified by a natural language sentence, or the concatenation of a classification code and author code into a unique call number, is, then, a means of extending the descriptive capability of a vocabulary. If we admit, as nouns, *tree* and *water,* and as adjectives *green* and *blue,* we can use syntax to convey the images of *blue water* and *green trees,* which the basic vocabulary cannot convey. The word *syntax* is also used to refer to the particular construction of a sentence, phrase, or other syntactic unit.

In the artificial languages of indexing an authority for vocabulary and syntax is a vital part of the language. These languages derive their usefulness by being restrictive in usage and by expecting of their users fairly rigid conformance to formal definitions and syntactic rules. We generalize the word *dictionary* to include all lists or books specifying a vocabulary, rules of syntax, or general word relationships and include a dictionary as a vital element of an index language. Dictionaries are discussed in Section 2.6 where we further define this tool and diverge even more from the conventional meaning of the word.

We postulate that our readers will accept the expression *word,* as used in natural language, without formal definition. We define the expression *descriptor* to be a word in an index language. A descriptor may have semantically meaningful subdivisions, but it need not have. Most of the time it will imply a single word, number, or code, but, as we shall see later, it can include larger syntactic units as long as they are not subdividible within the vocabulary of a given language. We define a *term* as a syntactic unit composed of descriptors in a language. In natural language a phrase or sentence falls under our definition of *term*. We define an *index phrase* as a set of index terms somehow linked together. Hence our phrase is analogous to the grouping of sentences into a paragraph or of phrases into a sentence. Note that in natural language there is little syntactic relationship between phrases and none formally defined between sentences, whereas there is a complex syntax among the words of a phrase or sentence. We shall see a similar phenomenon in index languages.

In natural language the word *term* can mean a single word or a phrase. We carry this ambiguity into our own usage because it is so common. More formally, we allow for the possibility that a term is composed of only a single descriptor, in which case we can use either word to describe it.

2.2.4   Measures of Index Language Effectiveness

There is no single scale on which languages can be compared, in general. There are many, often not fully separable from one another. Furthermore, the importance of any given factor will vary considerably with the particular use of the language. A crossword puzzle author makes use of certain redundancy characteristics of a language, and a specialized scientific writer may use a subset of a natural language, a jargon, to convey very precise meanings to other specialists. Index languages perform a special limited role; hence they are more amenable to an analysis of their effectiveness than are natural languages in general use. The particular value or relative importance of any factor remains a function of the individual application.

We use four language attributes as a basis for comparison: expressiveness, ambiguity, compactness, and cost. We caution the reader to be aware, in considering the definitions to follow, that these attributes are not independent or mutually exclusive. A language can be expressive, yet have much ambiguity. The compactness of the words in its vocabulary is not what determines its cost of usage.

Expressiveness is the ability of a language to identify a subject, to distinguish between fine differences in subjects, and to describe a subject to differing levels of detail. We are, of course, concerned with the potential of the language to be expressive and not with the skill of the user or the degree of skill involved. A language such as the Dewey Decimal Classification is not very expressive, whereas natural language is highly so.

Ambiguity, in the sense in which we use it, connotes both a word or syntactic unit having more than one meaning and a meaning that can have more than one symbolic representation in the vocabulary of a language. Ambiguity is caused by *synonyms* and *homographs.* Two words with the same meaning are synonyms. When one word has more than one meaning, it is called a homograph. In spoken language we have *homonyms,* which are words that sound the same but have different meanings. Synonymy and homography can exist in syntactic units larger than individual words. "My book is colored red," and, "Red is the color of the book belonging to me," are, for all practical purposes, identical in meaning. The sentence, "He covered the field," can refer to literature searching, crop dusting, or baseball, and is a full-sentence homograph. The extent to which synonyms and homographs can occur in a language is independent; that is, they neither exclude nor imply each other. Ambiguity is not necessarily an undesirable quality in language, for although it can blur meanings and cause misunderstanding its existence and recognition puts language users on guard that whether meanings are the same or different depends on context and user. A language without synonyms or homographs will require of its users a number of quite arbitrary decisions on word meanings.

Compactness refers to the physical size or length of an index term or record that is required to convey a certain amount of information. A highly compact language is in use by telegraph companies which permit a customer to select from among a set of standard messages, then transmit a message *number,* but deliver to the ultimate addressee the full, reconstituted message. This example also illustrates why we consider compactness—because the physical memory requirements for storing index data and the communication requirements for transmitting them can become significant in the design of an information retrieval system.

Cost refers to the cost of the decision-making process when an indexer or searcher is faced with the selection of one or more index terms to describe his material. Entering into cost are *training costs* to prepare people to use the language, *cost of dictionary preparation and maintenance,* and *cost of recovering from errors* in selecting terms, all in addition to the cost of the time actually spent indexing or preparing a query.

2.3   A SURVEY OF INDEX LANGUAGES

This discussion follows, in general, the approach taken by Frederick Jonker in his paper entitled, *The Descriptive Continuum, A 'Generalized' Theory of Indexing.*[10] The reader is cautioned that a continuum is not restricted to a single dimension, and any attempt to oversimplify the relationship among index languages can result in confusion, if not bafflement.

The languages to be described range from the hierarchical classification structure, which is a set of descriptors in which the relationship of every word to every other word is precisely defined, to the key word languages where far more freedom of vocabulary usage exists, but where word relationships are not necessarily defined. Then a group of *syntactic languages* is described in which the language user is able to assemble sets of descriptors into terms or phrases, using various syntactic relationships to create semantic concepts not defined in terms of individual descriptors. Following this discussion, in Section 2.4, we turn to a more formal, logical analysis of index languages.

2.3.1   Hierarchical Classification

This is probably the most widely used type of index language. It is based on the assumption that subjects of interest can each be divided into more specific subjects, a process repeated as often as necessary until a structure, or hierarchy, is created to cover the domain of subjects expected to be received by, or requested of, the library. Each subdivision, at each level, is given a single descriptor. There is nothing unique about a hierarchy. The same document set, or library, even in combination with the same group of users, can be structured in many different ways. Even different branches of the same hierarchy may be subdivided differently or to different depths. The principal value of this type of language is that when a user is unsure of his search descriptors, or an indexer of his index descriptors, it is easy for him to generalize or particularize from the point at which he started, and it is easy for him to learn the language in which he must phrase his message. Such a language structure is often illustrated by use of "tree" or "pigeonhole" analogies, as shown in Figure 2.2.

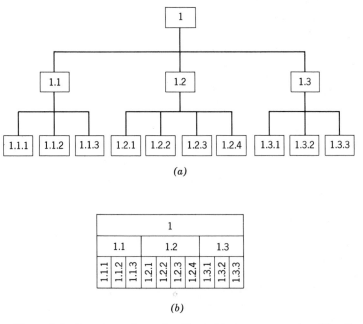

(a)

(b)

Figure 2.2   Representations of a hierarchical structure: (a) "Tree" representation of a hierarchical index structure. (b) "Pigeon hole" representation of the same structure.

The vocabulary of a hierarchical language is quite simple, consisting of a fixed* set of descriptors representing the allowable subjects.   There is usually no attempt to use mnemonic codes.   Instead, highly structured numeric or alpha-numeric codes are generally used.   Many libraries employing a hierarchical index language do not use more than one code number per document, although nothing in the language structure imposes this restriction.   When so used, there is no need for phrases, or syntactic relationship between descriptors, because there is never more than one descriptor in a record.   There is an interesting morphology, however, in that a descriptor at one level contains the symbols for all those generic to it, and this is the essence of a hierarchical language.   For example, in the Dewey Decimal Classification[2] we find that an artificial earth satellite is classified by the code 629.138 82.   This code contains within it, or implies the use of, the following additional descriptors which are higher in the hierarchy, hence more general:

600.	Technology (applied science)
620.	Engineering
629.	Other branches of engineering
629.13	Aeronautics
629.138	Uses of aircraft
629.138 8	Space flight (inertial navigation)

When we say "artificial earth satellite" in Dewey's language, we are also saying "aeronautics," and there is no way to avoid it.   The advantages and disadvantages of this situation we leave until the next section.

In Section 2.2.2 we stressed the importance of being able to change an index language to keep pace with changes in users' language usage. Expanding the vocabulary of a hierarchical language is relatively easy, but changing the meaning of an existing descriptor can be very difficult. Expansion can be achieved by extending descriptor codes to the right, and defining the next lower order set of meanings.   We might, for example, define 629.138 821 as "manned, artificial earth satellites," and 629.138 822 as "unmanned. . . ."   Alternatively, the subdivision could be by use, say, . . . 821 for earth reconnaissance, . . . 822 for space reconnaissance, . . . 823 for communications relay, . . . 824 for weapon carrying, and so forth.   An important point is to (try to) keep

* A language that never changes is difficult to conceive.   When we use the adjective *fixed* to apply to a vocabulary, we mean that the vocabulary is fixed at any given time but that it can be changed, usually by a specially designated authority, through a formal procedure.   The change procedure may be artificially tedious in order to discourage capricious changing.

the codes mutually exclusive   A reconnaissance satellite, for example, may be manned or umanned.   We should not, then, have as subdivisions of the code for artificial earth satellites

629.138 821	manned
822	unmanned
823	reconnaissance

because the third code does not exclude either of the first two.   It would be possible to have

629.138 821	Earth reconnaissance satellites
821 1	-manned
821 2	-unmanned
822	Space reconnaissance satellites
822 1	-manned
822 2	-unmanned

The difficulty with this approach is that there is no single descriptor covering the subject of manned satellites, which points out a basic defect in this class of languages, that there are some concepts which either are not able to be stated with a single descriptor, or are not able to be separated from another concept.   Yet one descriptor per document is all that is used in many systems.   However the structure is changed or twisted, the concepts we wish to define in our example have two facets: use of the vehicle and nature of its crew, and no subdivision of a higher level code can resolve this split in such a way that a single code could distinguish between manned and unmanned vehicles, regardless of usage, or between usages, regardless of whether or not manned.

The problem of changing the *meaning* of an already established descriptor is that this can affect the meaning of other descriptors.   If, for example, one were to modify the meaning of *aeronautics* in the Dewey Decimal System to include only flight based upon lift provided by the atmosphere, then *space flight* can no longer be a subordinate descriptor, and *aircraft* will have to be defined in such a way as to distinguish it from *space craft*.   Then, *space flight* and *space craft* would have to be reinserted somewhere else in the hierarchy, possibly necessitating a change in the meaning of some other descriptor.

In summary, hierarchical languages are rigid in the sense of being hard to change except by expansion at the bottom.   They are somewhat arbitrary in that the subsumption of one subject under another is fixed by the library, not by nature.   Finally, they are very valuable, their very weaknesses being convertible into strengths from another point of view.   Their rigidity makes them stable and makes it easier to train people to use them, but perhaps their most useful attribute is the ease with which a language user can state his subject more specifically or more generally by moving down or up the hierarchy. Even though subject subsumption may be arbitrary, the existence of a complete code structure assists the user to interpret it. Even if a searcher disagrees with the organization of the hierachy, he can study it and learn to cope with it.

In addition to the Dewey Decimal Classification system already mentioned, the hierarchical systems in most common use are the Library of Congress system and the Universal Decimal Classification (UDC), a modification of the Dewey system in wide international use.

2.3.2 Subject Headings

A subject heading language is one that makes use of a fixed* number of subject classes, just as does hierarchical classification, but does not usually adopt a special code for its terms, and generally is used in such a way as to permit more than one term to be assigned to the index of any given document. A subject heading language, however, has little if any structure or means of relating one term to another. This gives the designer a work-saving advantage. It is no longer necessary to create a structure into which all knowledge (or at least all that is expected at the designer's library) will fall. As a practical matter, subject headings tend to be made up to describe information received, not information expected to be received. The practical advantages of this feature can be enormous when an index language must be constructed from scratch, and little information is available on subject spread. The vocabulary of a subject heading language consists of natural language terms and phrases, but they are not made up of descriptors which are in themselves, elements of the vocabulary. If, for example, *data processing* were a subject heading, it does not follow that *data* and *processing,* individually, would be legal descriptors. Thus, although subject headings are composed of natural language words, these words need not be descriptors in the index language. Because the subject headings are not built up from index language descriptors, we may call them descriptors, regardless of the length or composition, as measured in another language.

As a document collection grows, it sometimes becomes necessary to enlarge the subject heading language. Adding new terms to cover subjects not previously covered poses no problem, for there is no resultant change in existing descriptors. However, subject headings are often split, creating a new term to cover the new subject, and changing the

* See footnote of Section 2.3.1.

meaning of the old term to exclude the subject area of the new term. Subject headings may also be subdivided to introduce some hierarchical structure into the language. As a general observation, subject headings have a tendency to increase their degree of structure over time, although no law governs this phenomenon. Because of their relative lack of structure, the subject headings are often listed for users in alphabetical order, and the existence of such a list is sometimes erroneously considered to be a necessary feature of the language. The order of listing of terms for language users has no particular bearing on the structure of the language. These two points—the tendency toward hierarchy and the habit of alphabetic listing—can be seen in comparing the old and new classification systems used by the Association for Computing Machinery for its publication *Computing Reviews*.[3]

Figure 2.3 shows the subject headings in use from the *Review's* inception in 1960 until the end of 1963. In 1964 a new classification was introduced which is shown in Figure 2.4. Note that Figure 2.3 has two levels of generality and that the terms are listed in alphabetical order by major heading. With the introduction of the new system came an additional level of generality and abandonment of alphabetic term listing. The new system could easily be called a hierarchical classification language, although it is somewhat lacking in depth.

Subject headings, then, represent simply a loosening of the structure of a hierarchical language. Their use makes initial language design easier since there is less to predict, and makes future changes easier to implement because no elaborate structure need be perturbed by such a change. Their lack of structure makes them more difficult to learn and use.

2.3.3 Key Word Systems

Both the languages described thus far share the characteristic that the number of subjects that can be described by them is fixed, and is equal to the number of defined terms. While a term in a hierarchy implies all terms above it, no variation or shading of the meaning of a term is possible. This is true even if the cataloging system permits use of more than one classification term per index record. Although the ACM does not do this, there is no reason why a document on the application of information theory (code number 5.6 in Figure 2.4) to linguistics (code 3.42) cannot be classified under both subjects. This technique is used by the Library of Congress which applies a set of subject headings as well as a hierarchical classification code to each document as shown in Figure 2.1. These terms do not modify

Administration and Operation of Computer Centers
GENERAL
ORGANIZATION

Analog Computers
GENERAL
APPLICATIONS
EQUIPMENT

Artificial Intelligence
GENERAL
PATTERN AND SPEECH RECOGNITION
SIMULATION OF HUMAN ACTIVITY

Automation and Process Control
GENERAL
COMMUNICATIONS SYSTEMS
INDUSTRIAL APPLICATIONS
THEORY

Business Data Processing
GENERAL
AUDITING
INSURANCE
INVENTORY
PAYROLL
PROGRAMMING LANGUAGES

Digital Computer Applications
GENERAL
AERONAUTICAL ENGINEERING AND SPACE
ASTRONOMY, ASTROPHYSICS, AND ASTRODYNAMICS
CHEMISTRY AND CHEMICAL ENGINEERING
ELECTRONICS AND ELECTRICAL ENGINEERING
HEALTH SCIENCES
LOGIC AND FUNDAMENTALS OF MATHEMATICS
MACHINE TRANSLATION AND LINGUISTICS
MECHANICAL ENGINEERING
NUMBER THEORY
PHYSICS
POWER ENGINEERING
SOCIAL SCIENCES
WEATHER AND METEOROLOGY
MISCELLANEOUS

Digital Computer Components and Circuits
GENERAL
STORAGE

Digital Computer Programming
GENERAL
ALGORITHMIC LANGUAGES
ASSEMBLY PROGRAMS
AUTOMATIC PROGRAMMING
SPECIFIC ALGORITHMIC LANGUAGES
STORAGE ALLOCATION
THEORY OF PROGRAMMING

Digital Computer Systems
GENERAL
GENERAL PURPOSE
REAL TIME CONTROL
PERIPHERAL EQUIPMENT

Education and Computers
GENERAL
DIGITAL
UNIVERSITY AND OTHER TEACHING USAGE
TECHNIQUES IN MACHINE TEACHING

History
GENERAL

Information Storage and Retrieval
GENERAL

Information Theory and Coding
GENERAL

Logic, Logical Design, and Switching Theory
GENERAL
FORMAL LOGIC
LOGICAL DESIGN AND SWITCHING CIRCUITS
THEORY OF AUTOMATA AND TURING MACHINES

Managerial Applications
GENERAL
MANAGEMENT SIMULATION AND GAMES
MATHEMATICAL METHODS

Mathematics
GENERAL
ANALYSIS

Numerical Mathematics
GENERAL
FINITE DIFFERENCES
FUNCTIONAL APPROXIMATION AND INTERPOLATION
INTEGRAL EQUATIONS
LINEAR SYSTEMS AND MATRICES
ORDINARY DIFFERENTIAL EQUATIONS
NUMERICAL INTEGRATION
PARTIAL DIFFERENTIAL EQUATIONS
TABLES AND SPECIFIC COMPUTATIONS
TEXTS

Standards
GENERAL
GLOSSARIES
TERMINOLOGY

Statistics and Probability
GENERAL
MONTE CARLO METHODS
PROGRAMMING
RANDOM NUMBER GENERATION

Technological Effects and Cybernetics
SOCIOLOGICAL EFFECTS

Figure 2.3 Subject headings used by the Association for Computing Machinery before 1964.[3]

1. GENERAL TOPICS AND EDUCATION
 1.0 General
 1.1 Texts; Handbooks
 1.2 History; Biographies
 1.3 Introductory and Survey Articles
 1.4 Glossaries
 1.5 Education
  1.50 General
  1.51 High School Courses and Programs
  1.52 University Courses and Programs
  1.53 Certification; Degrees; Diplomas
  1.59 Miscellaneous
 1.9 Miscellaneous

2. COMPUTING MILIEU
 2.0 General
 2.1 Philosophical and Social Implications
  2.10 General
  2.11 Economic and Sociological Effects
  2.12 The Public and Computers
  2.19 Miscellaneous
 2.2 Professional Aspects
 2.3 Legislation; Regulations
 2.4 Administration of Computing Centers
  2.40 General
  2.41 Administrative Policies
  2.42 Personnel Training
  2.43 Operating Procedures
  2.44 Equipment Evaluation
  2.45 Surveys of Computing Centers
  2.49 Miscellaneous
 2.9 Miscellaneous

3. APPLICATIONS
 3.1 NATURAL SCIENCES
  3.10 General
  3.11 Astronomy; Space
  3.12 Biology
  3.13 Chemistry
  3.14 Earth Sciences
  3.15 Mathematics; Number Theory
  3.16 Meteorology
  3.17 Physics; Nuclear Sciences
  3.19 Miscellaneous
 3.2 ENGINEERING
  3.20 General
  3.21 Aeronautical; Space
  3.22 Chemical
  3.23 Civil
  3.24 Electrical; Electronic
  3.25 Engineering Science
  3.26 Mechanical
  3.29 Miscellaneous

3.3 SOCIAL and BEHAVIORAL SCIENCES
 3.30 General
 3.31 Economics
 3.32 Education; Welfare
 3.33 Law
 3.34 Medicine; Health
 3.35 Political Science
 3.36 Psychology; Anthropology
 3.37 Sociology
 3.39 Miscellaneous
3.4 HUMANITIES
 3.40 General
 3.41 Art
 3.42 Language Translation and Linguistics
 3.43 Literature
 3.44 Music
 3.49 Miscellaneous
3.5 MANAGEMENT DATA PROCESSING
 3.50 General
 3.51 Education; Research
 3.52 Financial
 3.53 Government
 3.54 Manufacturing; Distribution
 3.55 Marketing; Merchandising
 3.56 Military
 3.57 Transportation; Communication
 3.59 Miscellaneous
3.6 ARTIFICIAL INTELLIGENCE
 3.60 General
 3.61 Induction and Hypothesis-formation
 3.62 Learning and Adaptive Systems
 3.63 Pattern Recognition
 3.64 Problem-solving
 3.65 Simulation of Natural Systems
 3.66 Theory of Heuristic Methods
 3.69 Miscellaneous
3.7 INFORMATION RETRIEVAL
 3.70 General
 3.71 Content Analysis
 3.72 Evaluation of Systems
 3.73 File Maintenance
 3.74 Searching
 3.75 Vocabulary
 3.79 Miscellaneous
3.8 REAL TIME SYSTEMS
 3.80 General
 3.81 Communications
 3.82 Industrial Process Control
 3.83 Telemetry; Missiles; Space
 3.89 Miscellaneous
3.9 Miscellaneous

Figure 2.4   Subject headings used by the Association for Computing Machinery since 1964.   (Source: Finerman and Revens,[3] *Communications of the ACM*.)

each other, however. LC merely says that a book is on subject A, and also on subject B, and also on subject C. Language systems

4. PROGRAMMING
  4.0 General
  4.1 Processors
    4.10 General
    4.11 Assemblers
    4.12 Compilers and Generators
    4.13 Interpreters
    4.19 Miscellaneous
  4.2 Programming Languages
    4.20 General
    4.21 Machine Oriented Languages
    4.22 Procedure and Problem Oriented Languages
    4.29 Miscellaneous
  4.3 Supervisory Systems
    4.30 General
    4.31 Basic Monitors
    4.32 Multiprogramming; Multiprocessing
    4.39 Miscellaneous
  4.4 Utility Programs
    4.40 General
    4.41 Input/Output
    4.42 Debugging
    4.43 Program Maintenance
    4.49 Miscellaneous
  4.9 Miscellaneous

5. MATHEMATICS OF COMPUTATION
  5.0 General
  5.1 NUMERICAL ANALYSIS
    5.10 General
    5.11 Error Analysis; Computer Arithmetic
    5.12 Function Evaluation
    5.13 Interpolation; Functional Approximation
    5.14 Linear Algebra
    5.15 Nonlinear and Functional Equations
    5.16 Numerical Integration and Differentiation
    5.17 Ordinary and Partial Differential Equations
    5.18 Integral Equations
    5.19 Miscellaneous
  5.2 METATHEORY
    5.20 General
    5.21 Formal Logic
    5.22 Automata; Turing Machines
    5.23 Mechanical and Algorithmic Languages
    5.24 Theory of Programming
    5.29 Miscellaneous
  5.3 COMBINATORIAL and DISCRETE MATHEMATICS
    5.30 General
    5.31 Sorting
    5.32 Graph Theory
    5.39 Miscellaneous

  5.4 MATHEMATICAL PROGRAMMING
    5.40 General
    5.41 Linear and Nonlinear Programming
    5.42 Dynamic Programming
    5.49 Miscellaneous
  5.5 Mathematical Statistics; Probability
  5.6 Information Theory
  5.9 Miscellaneous

6. DESIGN AND CONSTRUCTION
  6.0 General
  6.1 Logical Design; Switching Theory
  6.2 Computer Systems
    6.20 General
    6.21 General Purpose Computers
    6.22 Special Purpose Computers
    6.29 Miscellaneous
  6.3 Components and Circuits
    6.30 General
    6.31 Circuit Elements
    6.32 Arithmetic Units
    6.33 Control Units
    6.34 Storage Units
    6.35 Input/Output Equipment
    6.36 Auxiliary Equipment
    6.39 Miscellaneous
  6.9 Miscellaneous

7. ANALOG COMPUTERS
  7.0 General
  7.1 Applications
  7.2 Design; Construction
  7.3 Hybrid Systems
  7.4 Programming; Techniques
  7.9 Miscellaneous

Figure 2.4 (*Continued*)

so organized are often called "pre-coordinated" systems, in that whatever semantically meaningful descriptor combinations are allowed, have been made—the descriptors "coordinated" to form terms— by the language designers. We will generally avoid this usage because the descriptors that are coordinated into a term are not defined in the vocabulary of the language that results—hence are not truly descriptors. "Precoordinated" vocabularies, as we have said, leave gaps in their subject coverage and are slower to adapt to new subject matters. This is particularly true in libraries that must cover scientific literature wherein new concepts and terminology are constantly being introduced. To satisfy this need languages have been developed which permit their users to select several descriptors for an index, as many as are needed to describe a particular document. This family of languages is given many names but is most commonly called *coordinate* or *key word indexing*. A specific example of key word indexing is the Uniterm system, developed by Mortimer Taube et al.[16] Often we hear the word *descriptor* used to apply exclusively to a descriptor in this form of language.

These languages go part way toward allowing the use of concepts not specifically predefined, in that the vocabulary is large, consists of single words or short phrases, and encourages the use of many descriptors or terms per index to describe as many facets of the document as possible. Still, terms cannot be shown as modifying each other even if the indexer meant them to. *Brown* and *fox* are separate descriptors, and do not necessarily mean *brown fox*. Because there need be no structural relationship between terms, they can be added to or deleted from the vocabulary at will, making the language highly adaptive to subject matter changes.

One form of key word index language, which we call a *fixed vocabulary, key word language,* differs only slightly from the subject heading languages. The main differences are that key words are generally shorter than subject headings—usually a single word but possibly a short phrase—and the size of the total vocabulary, the number of possible terms which can be created, may be much larger than is common in subject heading languages. Like a subject heading language, the vocabulary is fixed. In such a language, if *information theory* and *linguistics* are both members of the vocabulary set, then a paper on information theory applied to linguistics would certainly be indexed by both descriptors. Significantly, however, the language has no way to tell us the connection between these descriptors. Literally, we must guess. Without a useful syntax, there is no difference between this language and a subject heading language, but the users of a language called a key word index will expect multiple descriptors, whereas users of a language called hierarchical classification will meekly make do without a complete description of documents in that language.

In spite of their lack of syntax key word languages do accomplish their purpose in being more adaptable to subject matter changes, and they do allow searchers to find documents more easily if the actual subject sought does not exactly coincide with a subject heading.   Note, in the ACM languages, that a search for anything concerned with *programming* could be quite tedious to request, while the same request requires only one word if a key word index is used.   Although there are headings that encompass *programming*, every computer application implies programming, although the word is not mentioned in all ACM headings, on *applications*.   We do wish to emphasize, however, that the difference between subject heading and key word languages is relatively slight and, what is even more important, that the commonly used phrases "precoordinated" and "uncoordinated" refer to descriptors, not terms, as we have defined them.   The pre-coordination is between individual words (descriptors) not between terms (combinations of descriptors).   *Terms* in any language described so far can be concatenated freely into phrases which do not modify each other, but there is a restriction on term composition, wherein descriptors do modify each other.

An example of a fixed key word system is found in use by the Defense-Documentation Center (formerly Armed Forces Technical Information Agency, or ASTIA).   Their language has a vocabulary of about 7000 terms and descriptors listed in the *ASTIA Thesaurus*,[22] and which are subject to occasional change.   DDC's index language, a sample of which is shown in Figure 2.5, also makes use of a subject heading system.   In this language, multiple subject headings, as well as multiple key words, may be applied to any index record.   The *ASTIA Thesaurus* defines some hierarchy among descriptors.   The National Library of Medicine[20] uses a similarly constructed language.

We made brief mention of the problem of the ambiguity, or uncertainty of meaning, caused by lack of a syntax for relating descriptors within terms.   It is for this reason that we cannot distinguish between a blind Venetian and a venetian blind, without going, as does DDC, to a second, more generically oriented language to explain context.   Here, we see the importance of recognizing the level of descriptor grouping to which syntax is applied, for if these descriptor pairs were subject headings there would be no confusion between them.   Associating descriptors together into semantic units which give a misleading idea of document content is called *false coordination*.

Sets of key word index terms provide greater flexibility of subject description than do precoordinated terms, but this is still not sufficient in some environments to be adequately descriptive of document subject matter.   Users of information sometimes want to search on the actual words that the author used, rather than having to use a set of predeter-

COMPUTERS
  (Computers & Data Systems)
  Includes:
    Calculating machines
  Generic to:
    ANALOG COMPUTERS
    ANALOG-DIGITAL COMPUTERS
    BOMBING COMPUTERS
    DIGITAL COMPUTERS
    DIGITAL DIFFERENTIAL ANALYZERS
    FIRE CONTROL COMPUTERS
    GUIDED MISSILE COMPUTERS
    IMPACT COMPUTERS
    NAVIGATION COMPUTERS
    PARALLAX COMPUTERS
    RADAR RANGE COMPUTERS
    SPECIAL PURPOSE COMPUTERS
    TORPEDO DATA COMPUTERS
  Also see:
    DATA PROCESSING SYSTEMS
    ELECTRONIC ACCOUNTING MACHINES
    PROGRAMMING(COMPUTERS)
    SIMULATION

Computing gun sights use GUN
  SIGHTS

CONCRETE
  (Structural Engineering)
  Generic to:
    REINFORCED CONCRETE
  Also see:
    CEMENTS

Concrete surfacing use PAVEMENTS

CONDENSATION
  (Physical & Physicochemical
    Concepts)
  (Change of state from gas or
    vapor to liquid or solid; also
    meteorological phenomenon, ex-
    cludes chemical reaction.)
  Also see:
    ATMOSPHERIC PRECIPITATION
    CLOUDS

CONDENSATION REACTIONS
  (Chemical Reactions)
  Includes:
    Reformatsky reactions
  Specific to:
    CHEMICAL REACTIONS
  Generic to:
    FRIEDEL-CRAFTS REACTIONS
    GRIGNARD REACTIONS
  Also see:
    DIENE SYNTHESIS
    GRIGNARD REACTIONS

CONDENSATION TRAILS
  (Meteorology & Climatology)
  Includes:
    Contrails
    Exhaust trails
    Vapor trails
  Also see:
    WAKE

Condensers(Electrical) use
  CAPACITORS

CONDENSERS(LIQUEFIERS)
  (Instrumentation)
  Generic to:
    REFRIGERANT CONDENSERS
    STEAM CONDENSERS

CONDIMENTS
  (Food)
  Includes:
    Pepper
    Seasonings
    Spices
  Specific to:
    FOOD

CONDITIONED REFLEX
  (Psychology & Psychometrics)
  Includes:
    Conditioned response
  Specific to:
    BEHAVIOR
    REFLEXES
  Also see:
    ADJUSTMENT(PSYCHOLOGY)
    LEARNING
    MOTOR REACTIONS

Conductivity(Electrical) use
  ELECTRICAL CONDUCTANCE

Conductivity(Thermal) use THERMAL
  CONDUCTIVITY

CONDUIT PLIERS
  (Industrial Equipment & Tools)
  Specific to:
    PLIERS
    SMALL TOOLS
  Also see:
    MAINTENANCE TOOLS
    SPLICING TOOLS

Conferences use SYMPOSIA

Confidence limits use STATISTICAL
  ANALYSIS

Figure 2.5   Sample from Defense Documentation Center Thesaurus.[22]

mined words, approximately synonymous to the desired words, but which
may not provide enough detail, and may be subject to misinterpretation.
In this case an approach can be used wherein the indexer is instructed
to select his index terms solely on the basis of importance in the context
of an individual document and not on the basis of their occurrence

on any approved vocabulary list or thesaurus. Except for word classes that might be excluded, such as conjunctions, prepositions, and numbers, the indexer is free to choose his own index vocabulary. Members of this family of index languages are called *free vocabulary* or *free key word languages*.

We have now discussed three language families which have in common the lack of a syntax for allowing terms to modify each other but which vary as to freedom of choice of terms, number of terms to use, and degree of definition of terms. In continuing our discussion of index languages we shall now turn our attention primarily toward syntax. The point was made at the beginning of this section that, although a language continuum might be said to exist, it does not follow that it is a one-dimensional continuum. The index language families to follow vary in both vocabulary and syntax.

2.3.4 Syntactic Languages.

The simplest family of syntaxes is that in which a fixed number of descriptors is required to make up a term, and the exact role of each descriptor in the term is specified in advance. Probably the simplest of these languages we may call *tagged descriptors*. Here, a descriptor has affixed to it another descriptor to describe the first. The role of the affix might be to classify the basic descriptor, denoting it as a proper name, an attribute, or an activity. It might be used to group together a set of descriptors all implied by one subject of the document. If the document were about an inventor *and* his product, descriptors of the person and the device might be separately tagged, to avoid confusion on retrieval.

A more advanced syntactic language is one in which the various descriptors modify one another, greatly enlarging the number of distinct statements that can be made in the language. One example of such a syntax is a computer instruction which is represented in the computer as a binary number, the first part typically specifying an operation and the second part an address, or the location, of the operand. Both the instruction and address descriptors are expressed by using the same vocabulary—numbers—but by assigning different meanings to differently positioned numbers a language of great flexibility is created. Similarly, use of numbers alone as descriptors on a purchase order can enable the creation of terms describing a list of items to be purchased. The different roles of the numbers might be: *quantity, style, color, unit price, total price*. The structure of such a language is illustrated in Figure 2.6. More appropriate to indexing, terms may consist of a key word

GADGET		CORP.		
ORDER		FORM		

Quantity	Style	Color	Unit Price	Price
3	104	6	10.12	30.36
12	347	58	9.00	108.00
			Total	138.36

Figure 2.6 A common form of artificial syntax.

descriptor and an additional descriptor for the subject context of the key word, so that we might say:

> *Tank, weapon*
> *Tank, petroleum*
> *Train, transportation*
> *Train, education*

This permits the use of context to resolve ambiguity in artificial languages, just as is done in natural languages. Without the prior definition of the syntactic role to be played by each descriptor, the reader may assume that *train,* appearing next to *education,* means take the interpretation of *train* implied by the general subject *education,* but he cannot be sure. With the definition of role, he is assured that he has made the assumption intended by the author of the term. This does not rule out ambiguity—homograph problems can still occur. For example, the descriptor pair *ship, transportation* may describe a vessel or an act of transporting. Ambiguities can be lessened by these means, however. Synonym problems also remain, for unless the vocabulary (not syntax) is restricted, *vessel* might be substituted for *ship,* compounding the search problem, yet adhering to the rule for term construction.

We may still consider ourselves within the same language family if we permit some variance in the number of descriptors of each type that may be present. A number of key words may be modified by a single subject descriptor, or a key word may be modified by more than one subject heading. The overriding consideration is that the role of any descriptor that does appear be precisely defined, and that each syntactic role have its own associated vocabulary. For example, we might use a term such as *train, coach; education* to denote two key words, both in the context of the same subject field.

The various roles played by descriptors in such languages may be called facets and, if so, we have described a language called *faceted indexing*[18] in which a variety of attributes, aspects, or facets of the subject are written into the index. The listing of title, author, and publisher on a library's index card is a form of faceted indexing. Here, it is position on the card that indicates the role of the facet. It could also be sequence, or relative position, as it is in the *tank* and *train* examples above. The term *faceted indexing* is more commonly used to describe methods of subject description than it is to describe document attribute indexing. There might be a code which identifies *steel* as a subject. But is this a special kind of steel? What aspect of steel is implied? Its manufacture? Its transportation? The raw materials used in its manufacture? These questions can be answered by appending modifiers to the subject term *steel* which might result in creation of an index term such as one of these:

> *steel, hardened, manufacture of*
> *steel, as a component, use in automobiles*

These resemble subject headings, but in a faceted language they are not made up in advance (not "precoordinated"). They are true terms constructed out of defined descriptors following a defined syntactic rule, such as: subject is followed by a restricting modifier, which is followed by a modifier descriptive of use or operation performed. Each facet may draw its descriptors from the same vocabulary. We might, for example, have the following terms:

> *glass, stained, design of*
> *textiles, glass, sale of*

Here, *glass* appears first as a basic subject, and then as a modifier. Where the vocabularies and roles are clearly defined, there would be no confusion caused by two uses of the same symbol.

In a faceted index term, then, each facet plays a specifically defined syntactic role, permitting the term to be readily parsed into its constituent descriptors. The descriptors, as do any descriptors that make up terms, have meaning themselves in the index language. It is possible to draw each descriptor from a different subset of the total vocabulary, which happens when one descriptor is verbal and another numeric.

Faceted indexing is not restricted to key word descriptors. Faceted hierarchical languages are possible also. For example, a single classification code could handle the first two descriptors in each of the "glass" examples above; that is, *stained glass* and *glass textiles* can each be defined by a single Dewey classification code.* The third facet, descriptive of process or action, could be described by another Dewey code or by a term from another classification language specifically designed for this purpose.

In natural language the parts of speech or elements of a sentence can be regarded as facets, each playing a different role in the composition of a vastly complicated syntactic unit—the sentence. Here, a combination of position and choice of vocabulary element is required to determine the role being played by individual words. The subject, verb, and object of a sentence are facets which are each representable only by limited grammatical forms. Prepositions and conjunctions are facets, playing special roles in sentence construction, but can occur in any major part of a sentence. There is a fundamental difference, however, between a natural language expression and one of the faceted expressions illustrated above. In the illustrated systems the precise role and relationships can be prescribed beforehand. In natural language we have no rigid set of rules which governs the relationship among words. We can have homographs and synonyms at the phrase level. There is not just one way to express a concept, and the same set of words can have different meanings depending upon the sentence that preceded them. Nonetheless, the descriptive power of natural language makes it sometimes advantageous for indexing use over the less ambiguous, but less descriptive, artificial languages.

One of the major reasons why natural language is not in common use as an index language is its difficulty of search. To tell if the last sentence contains the word *language* it is necessary to look at each word in sequence until either the term is found or the sentence ends. Searches of this length have not been an important difficulty of the other languages described thus far. The rise in popularity of *permuted indexing* has eased this situation, making limited natural language expressions easier

* 748.5 and 677.54, respectively.

to search. A permuted index resembles a concordance but, instead of giving only the location of word occurrence, it gives the surrounding context of each occurrence of each word, and is commonly known as key-word-in-context or KWIC indexing.[19] In practice the method is most often used with phrases, especially titles, selected out of the documents. The technique overcomes the problem of quickly determining the role of a word in a phrase, but this is done at the cost of memory or other space requirements. The sentence or phrase to be permuted is listed several times in alphabetical order by each word in the sentence (barring "common" words), retaining original word context. The sentence, "The black cat ran away." would be permuted as follows. First, reproduce the sentence once for each "noncommon" word:

$$\begin{array}{lllll} \text{The} & \textbf{black} & \text{cat} & \text{ran} & \text{away.} \\ \text{The} \quad \text{black} & \textbf{cat} & \text{ran} & \text{away.} \\ \text{The} \quad \text{black} \quad \text{cat} & \textbf{ran} & \text{away.} \\ \text{The} \quad \text{black} \quad \text{cat} \quad \text{ran} & \textbf{away.} \end{array}$$

Then, sort the sentences on the base word and rearrange as follows:

$$\begin{array}{llll} \text{The} \quad \text{black} \quad \text{cat} \quad \text{ran} & \textbf{away.} \\ \text{The} & \textbf{black} & \text{cat} \quad \text{ran} \quad \text{away.} \\ \text{The} \quad \text{black} & \textbf{cat} & \text{ran} \quad \text{away.} \\ \text{The} \quad \text{black} \quad \text{cat} & \textbf{ran} & \text{away.} \end{array}$$

The center, boldface column is used for searching. These lines would be merged with the permutations of other sentences providing a single list, or file, to be used for all searches. In this way any word in any sentence can be quickly located by an alphabetic search, and this permits use of natural language abstracts—index phrases—to be used as searchable records. The surrounding context can be used to resolve many problems of semantic ambiguity. The difficulty lies in the total number of characters needed for the simplest sentence, and the fact that no single approach to phrase selection, such as use of title, is guaranteed to be as descriptive as a subject heading or key word system *might have been*. The method shares with any key word system, with or without syntax, the lack of a built-in technique for generalizing or particularizing searches. Use of short, natural language phrases, we call *phrase indexing*. This should not be equated with KWIC indexing. KWIC is a technique that makes phrase indexing effective and economical.

Our final index language is the language of the document itself, the full, natural language. It is not feasible to use this language as an index without the aid of a computer because of the enormous volume of material to be searched or reorganized to permit searching at reasonable speeds. Exactly the same problem is faced as described for phrase indexing—that too many words have to be examined to find out if a given word occurs in the document. To permute in their entirety all documents in a library is not economically feasible today. If we assume that an average technical paper contains 5000 words, that half of these are common words, and that sentences average ten words in length, each document would generate 500 (sentences) $\times$ 10 (words per sentence) $\times$ 5 repetitions (one for each non common word) = 25,000 words of storage required *per document*.* A technique devised at the University of Pittsburgh[11] is the preparation of a concordance and the use of it to locate the search terms. The concordance is merely a resequencing of the document by which words are listed alphabetically and the locations of their occurrence in the original text are given. The search logic can be the same, then, as for a key word system, but full context is retained. It would be possible to search for documents containing the word *set* with the word *theory* to be found within two words in either direction. This would enable the recovery of the subject of *set theory* (or *theory of sets*) without recovering all documents mentioning both the words *set* and *theory*, in any context.

2.4 THE LOGIC OF INDEXING LANGUAGES

When we assign a descriptor to a document, we are making the statement that the document is a member of the set of documents described by that term. Similarly, when we admit a term to use in the vocabulary of an index language, we are assigning that term to a set of subjects, saying that all subjects in the set have the attribute that they are described by this term. In some languages, such as hierarchical classification, each set of subjects has only one descriptor, but more than one subject may share the same descriptor. In some a subject may belong to any number of descriptor sets. This tends to be true of the key word index languages. The convention of representing index terms as sets of elemental subjects, or sets of documents described, permits us to construct geometric analogies that are useful in studying index language structure. This method of approach permits a more uniform view of all index languages and tends to subordinate the differences among them.

To represent an index language geometrically we assume that every point or small region of a portion of a plane represents a subject. The

---

* The fact that some words are repeated in a sentence does not help. Each occurrence of each word generates a full repetition of its sentence.

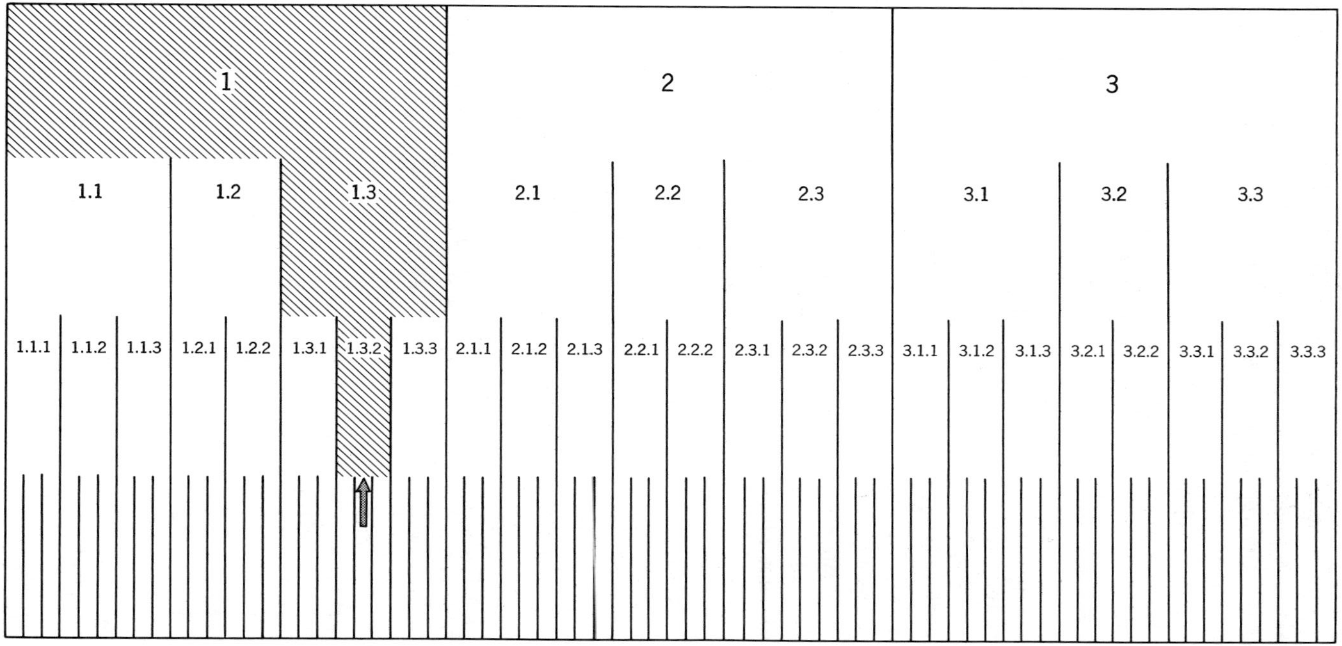

Figure 2.7 Hierarchical classification. In a hierarchical classification language, selection of any code or descriptor, such as 1.3.2 (arrow), places a lower bound on the region of subject space denoted and automatically selects all portions of the space above the bound, shown by the shaded area.

set of subjects represented by a term is then an area on this planar surface. The total portion of the surface considered, the complete set of subjects, is called *subject space*. In this conceptual framework an index language is a means of *partitioning subject space*.

A hierarchical language is representable by the configuration shown in Figure 2.7. This diagram is similar to that of Figure 2.2, but we have removed the dividing lines at top and bottom of the subject regions, and we can see how the selection of any single code (naming of a subdivision or pigeonhole) also implies the naming of all portions of the space in a direct line above the named region, but not below. The lateral subdivisions of the space are intended to be mutually exclusive, so that any stated subject falls cleanly in one and only one defined region.

A subject heading language is simpler but not so orderly. It is represented schematically in Figure 2.8 by a similar division of subject space into mutually exclusive regions, but with two differences. 1. No attempt is made to cover all of subject space, to have a descriptor for every possible subject. In the diagram, the shaded portions represent possible subjects that are not represented in the language. 2. While subdivision is possible, it is generally done only to a shallow and nonuniform extent.

Figure 2.9 illustrates the key word systems. The fixed-vocabulary key word systems, like subject heading languages, specify a partitioning of some, but not all, of subject space. Each rectangle in the nonshaded

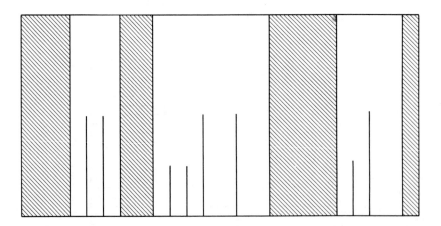

Figure 2.8 Subject headings. A subject heading language does not necessarily cover the entire space, makes no attempt at uniform "size" subdivisions, and may have a few levels of hierarchy. Shaded areas represent possible subjects not covered by this language.

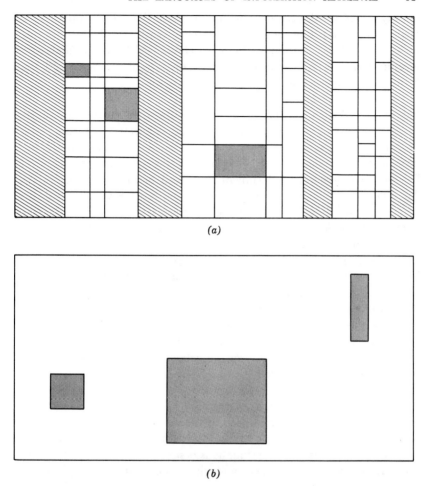

(a)

(b)

Figure 2.9 Key words. (a) Limited key words occupy predetermined areas of subject space. Not all the space need be covered by defined descriptors. (b) Free key word languages do not partition the space in advance of word use. Instead, because words can vary in meaning each time they are used, indexers are mapping out regions of subject space as they use words. In both illustrations the blacked-in areas represent a possible document description.

areas represents the set of subjects described by a key word. A free key word system shows no prior partitioning. Because neither the set of words (vocabulary) to be used nor the set of meanings of these words is specified in advance, the indexer is ruling out a region of subject space with each key word he uses and the extent of the region denoted by any given word may vary somewhat each time that word is used. Hence there is a risk of indexer and searcher ascribing different meanings to a term. This conforms with S. I. Hayakawa's[4] concept that word meanings are never fully determined in advance of utterance and that words never have exactly the same meaning twice.

To see clearly the difference between precoordinated languages and indexer-coordinated languages, we must realize that a region in subject space representing a concept need not be connected. It can consist of two or more small regions which do not overlap. However, a precoordinated language is one in which all the term regions that may be used to represent one document have been decided upon before use. An indexer-coordinated language permits the indexer to use small, disconnected "building blocks" to build a subject description out of a combination of predefined elements in a configuration that may never have been used before.

In the language structure illustrated in Figure 2.7, selection of a point in subject space exactly determines the region of subject space that will represent the document. In the language of Figure 2.9b, the indexer is free to select any set of regions he wants. The total region represented by this set (e.g., the set of three rectangles shown in black in the figure) need not have been predefined as a region, but its constituent elements (the individual blocks) have been predefined to some extent, although the exact coverage of subject space by a descriptor will vary with each use.

The languages which use facets or syntax are not so simple to represent geometrically. To attempt to do so, we introduce another representation, *Venn diagrams,* which graphically demonstrate certain logical relationships among sets. The technique is best explained by a simple example. In figure 2.10a the left-hand circle represents all people in the United States. The right-hand circle represents all men in the world. The intersection (darkly shaded area) represents people in the United States who are men. The lightly shaded areas, a and c, represent American non-men (women and children) and non-American men. If we introduce a third circle, married people, as shown in Figure 2.10b, we create the following regions: (a) Americans who are not men or married, (b) men who are not Americans and not married, (c) married people who are not American and not men (non-American, married women), (d) American married women, (e) American unmarried men, (f) non-American married men, (g) married American men. The region (a–b–d–e–f–g) represents all people who are Americans or men, regardless of marital status.

To represent an index with a Venn diagram we must define the area

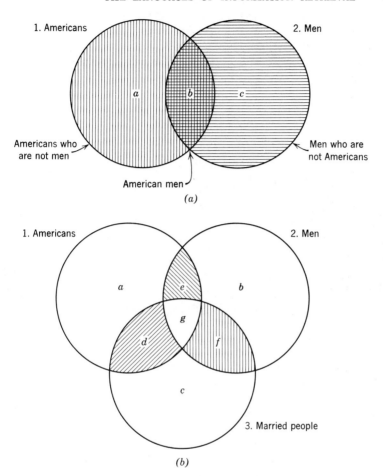

Figure 2.10 Venn diagrams. (*a*) The intersection of two sets or subjects. (*b*) The intersection of three sets or subjects.

we are to cover as the subject area that is, or could be, implied by the use of a term. Even though descriptors in a limited key word system may be so defined that no synonyms are permitted, any given subject may have more than one appropriate key word. We may, for example, represent *steel* and *manufacturing* as intersecting circles. The intersection cannot be equated to the natural language expression *manufacturing of steel,* but it includes this expression. The intersection covers all commonality of meaning between these words, including the use of steel in manufacturing something—say, steel tools used to manufacture wood products. In a key word language without syntax the intersection of

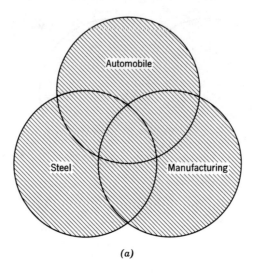

(a)

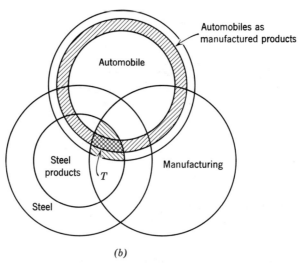

(b)

Figure 2.11 Key words and faceted index representations. (a) The union of three descriptors of a key
word index. Any point within the shaded area may be
within the subject of the document. (b) The faceted
index term, *manufacturing of steel automobiles,* is represented by the intersection of three terms. Only points
in the small shaded area are in the subject of the document.

steel, automobile, and *manufacturing* includes use of steel in manufacturing automobiles, use of automobiles in manufacturing steel, and manufacturing of steel for use in automobiles.

It is important to note that when an indexer writes down a set of key words he does not imply just the intersection of their subject areas. He is simply stating that the document is about A, is also about B, is also about C, and so on. A document could be about automobiles and about manufacturing. Both these words would be key words. The same key words would result if the document were about automobile manufacturing. In terms of a Venn diagram a key word index expresses the union of the terms stated. In Figure 2.10*a* the union of *American* and *men* is region a plus region b plus region c—it consists of anyone who is an American, a man, or both. The symbol for the union of subjects *a* and *b* is a $\cup$ b or $a + b$.

The faceted index term is represented by the *intersection* of its constituent descriptors. Figure 2.11*a* shows a Venn diagram representing the key word index implication of *steel, automobile,* and *manufacturing,* the union of these sets. Figure 2.11*b* shows a representation of the same descriptors if formed into a syntactic unit: *Manufacturing of steel automobiles.* We are not interested in the entire intersection of *steel* and *automobiles.* The syntax of the term implies a narrower use of *steel* (as a product) than would normally be assumed by its use in a key word index, and a narrower use of *automobile* (as a manufactured product). The representation of the term *manufacturing of steel automobiles* is the small, double-hatched area marked T, in Figure 2.11*b*. The reader can easily discern other meaningful subjects that could be formed out of the basic three descriptors and their implied roles. The logic of the Figure 2.11*b* applies to all forms of faceted or syntactic languages, from the simplest tagging of a key word up to a natural language. The reader must reason by analogy for the more complex languages, for diagrams cannot easily represent more complex sentences involving conditional statements or the use of general context, rather than a single adjective, to modify meaning. The reader must also be aware that although natural language offers the capability for great precision of description not all authors take advantage of it and not all natural language statements are necessarily small regions in subject space.

2.5   A COMPARATIVE ANALYSIS OF INDEX LANGUAGES

In Section 2.3 we stated that language structure is (at least) two-dimensional, varying in both syntax and vocabulary. In Section 2.2 we introduced four measures of language performance: expressiveness, ambiguity, compactness, and cost. In this section we compare the languages of Section 2.3 on these measures. Before proceeding, we wish to emphasize that probably the most important points that can be made about the parameters of language are that language can be a highly complex structure, not at all easy to measure or even study, and that hasty generalization based on small or restricted samples may be highly misleading. Language use is a manifestation of human behavior, the oversimplification of which is always hazardous.

So far in this chapter we have simply tacked the syntactic languages at the end of a one-dimensional continuum based on vocabulary variability. Let us now reconsider the two-dimensional aspect of language. In our progression of languages vocabulary ranged from a rigid set of mutually exclusive descriptors, as in hierarchical classification, to a freely variable, but more ambiguous, set of descriptors in a free key word language. Within the syntactic languages we also saw the phenomenon that the greater the freedom of choice of vocabulary, the more ambiguity there was in the language, and we found that syntax helps both to overcome this problem and to increase expressiveness.

We may apply a scale to both vocabulary and syntax to measure their variability, or freedom of choice by the user. A hierarchical classification language has no syntax to combine descriptors into terms. It has relatively little freedom of choice of descriptors in the sense that there will be only a few descriptors considered appropriate in classifying a document. A free key word language, although still having no syntax, offers a great freedom of choice of descriptors to express any single concept. The nonsyntactic languages, of course, offer no syntax variation. The simple syntactic languages, in which we might use two facets in an index term, offer a small amount of choice in organizing terms, and the languages with complex syntax, such as natural language, offer a wide choice, even with the same key vocabulary terms, in how to express a concept. A language that is highly variable will have less rigid rules of word meaning and syntactic construction. Indexers will have more freedom of expression, which opens the possibility both of greater expressiveness and greater ambiguity. A less variable language will have fewer word meanings allowed and fewer grammatical constructions. Although potentially less ambiguous, it will probably also be less expressive.

Figure 2.12 shows these language measures as axes of a graph. Distance away from the origin, in either case, represents increasing variability in word meanings or syntactic usage. Although we cannot make actual measurements on these scales, we have laid out the progression

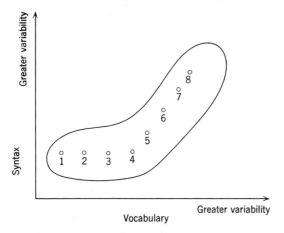

Figure 2.12   Useful range of languages: (1) hierarchical classification, (2) subject headings, (3) fixed key words, (4) free key words, (5) tagged descriptors, (6) faceted terms, (7) phrases, (8) natural language.

of languages described in Section 2.3.   The graph shows the nonsyntactic languages with increasing variability of vocabulary.   These languages are hierarchical classification, subject headings, and the key word systems.   Then the syntactic languages—tagged descriptors, faceted terms, phrases, and full, natural language are shown, with a great increase in syntax variability but little additional increase in vocabulary variability.   If we then draw a curve all around this line, we have very probably enclosed all the points in this plane representing useful languages, for it is difficult to conceive of a language with, say, a rich, variable vocabulary but no syntax at all or a complex syntax with only a small, rigid vocabulary.   We mean by this illustration only to exclude extreme language forms from consideration; we do not imply that a plotting board could be used to judge a language's performance.

We shall now consider each of the major languages previously described as measured on each of the four performance scales.   Clearly, "measure" must be interpreted broadly.   Our approach is to present a rating, showing only the rank ordering of languages on a measurement scale of each attribute.

2.5.1   Expressiveness

Although not strictly a logical requirement, hierarchical languages generally purport to cover all of subject space, even if only by use of

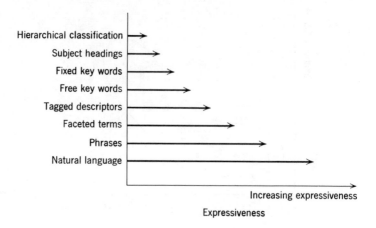

Figure 2.13   Relative language expressiveness.

the descriptor *other*.   Subject heading and fixed key word languages do not try for full coverage.   They concentrate only on those regions in which documents are expected to fall, their designers knowing that omissions can easily be rectified.   Free key word languages make no attempt to anticipate subject coverage but can accommodate any subject coverage requirement as it arises.   None of these languages, however, can necessarily provide the degree of precision or generality desired at any given time.   The syntactic languages have whatever subject coverage is defined for their vocabularies and then provide both for increasing the extent of coverage and for discriminating ability through combinations of descriptors.   There is no predefinition of the set of all possible terms, those syntactic units assembled by the indexer from descriptors.   This omission permits errors or poor expressions to be caused by improper association of otherwise proper descriptors; the problem of poor usage of language.   We see, then, that the syntactic languages, although offering more expressiveness, are also more prone to creating ambiguous terms.   Figure 2.13 illustrates the ordering of languages on the scale of expressiveness.

2.5.2   Ambiguity

By definition synonyms do not exist in a hierarchical language, and by convention they do not exist in subject heading or fixed key word languages.   In any of these languages near-synonyms are possible, since it is always a highly subjective matter whether or not two descriptors are synonyms.   Synonyms are controlled in these languages by use of

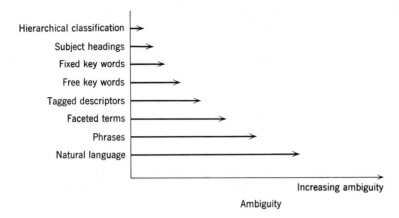

Figure 2.14   Relative potential ambiguity of languages.

dictionaries, with careful definition of terms in use.   A free key word language makes control of synonyms very difficult.   In syntactic languages there are more ways in which the same concept can be expressed by different symbols.   This is certainly true in natural language, but it is less of a problem in languages with a more rigid syntax.

There are some similarities in the conditions underlying the occurrence of homographs and synonyms.   The restricted vocabulary languages generally make the control of homographs easy, whereas a free vocabulary makes control almost impossible.   Use of syntax eases the problem sometimes, for the syntax enables the specification of context needed to resolve the homographs.   There can be full phrase or sentence homographs (see Section 2.2.4), but this is quite rare.

These forms of ambiguity are independent of each other.   One does not cause the other and one does not alleviate the other.   Their control is through the establishment and maintenance of authority, represented, in our usage, as a dictionary.   Hence the actual degree of ambiguity is as much a function of the dictionary as it is of the basic structure of the language.   Figure 2.14, then, shows an ordering of languages on this criterion, based not only on structure but on actual manner of use as well.

2.5.3   Compactness

There is successively less information per term in each language from hierarchical to free key words, because of the amount of information contained in the language structure from which the term was selected.

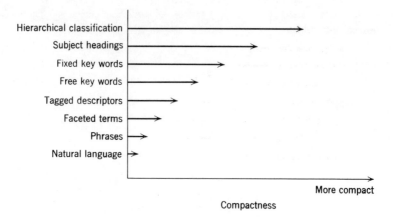

Figure 2.15   Relative language compactness.

In the syntactic languages, as syntax approaches the complexity and variability of natural language, the amount of information per term begins to increase. A term in these cases may be a natural language phrase or sentence, but the amount of space required to store an index term begins to increase in the syntactic languages, making them less compact. *The number of index terms* used in a record shows an exactly opposite behavior to that of information content. For example, whereas hierarchical languages usually use only one term, subject headings may use one to three or four terms; fixed key word languages, such as ASTIA's,[22] may use 5 to 10 descriptors, and free key word languages such as that devised by B. K. Dennis[1] of the General Electric Company may use as many as 10 to 20. Use of rigid syntax will reduce the number of terms selected, but, as syntax becomes more flexible, the length of terms will increase. This relationship suggests that *good indexing* calls for about the same amount of information (net length of index record), regardless of the language used to express it. The emphasis on good indexing arises because poor quality indexing shows wide fluctuation in number of terms used,[9] tending either toward a "shotgun" approach or one of oversimplifying the index. Relative measurements of compactness are illustrated in Figure 2.15.

2.5.4   Cost of Term Selection

This very crucial factor is among the most difficult to measure. Entering into a cost estimate are time required to index, training required for the indexers (which might be regarded as time expended before indexing), and risk (the cost or effect of indexing error). Based on these criteria, we feel that hierarchical classification is the most costly per term selected and that cost per term decreases as we move through the progression of nonsyntactic languages, rising again in the syntactic languages, as shown in Figure 2.16. Our reasoning is as follows. In hierarchical classification the indexer must not only find the appropriate branch of the classification structure, but must determine the appropriate level at which to stop. This requires a good understanding of both the document and the code structure. The problem is slightly simpler with subject headings because there are fewer levels to choose from, and, as we get to key words, the problem becomes closer to one of selecting important words on the basis of their grammatical roles or frequency of repetition rather than comprehension of the text. Also, nonhierarchical languages use more terms, with the very important result that the indexer can worry less about mistakes and about resolving uncertainties. With a key word language, he can select all terms which appear appropriate rather than try to pick the single best one. This not only speeds selection of individual terms but reduces risk or cost of error. Syntactic languages are not necessarily easier to use than hierarchical, but they often offer alternative ways to express essentially the same concept, again reducing the amount of time that must be spent to select a single, "right" approach.

Using these assumptions, we find that cost per term follows the same pattern as term length. This leads to the not-unexpected conclusion that more information requires more cost to provide it, and, because a fairly constant amount of information seems to be desired in an index,

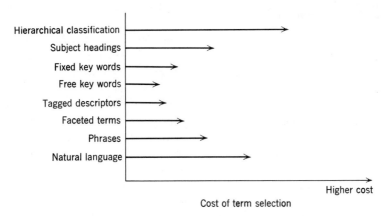

Figure 2.16   Relative cost per term of term selection.

the further conclusion may be drawn that the total cost of producing an index record will hold roughly constant over the various languages if all are employed with equal skill. This conclusion is to some extent supported by a study performed by Cleverdon[13] utilizing four different languages to index a set of documents. The costs in his experiment were controlled by limiting indexing time. Retrieval capabilities were found to be rather close, key words being rated somewhat higher than the hierarchical, subject heading, or faceted languages.

2.6   DICTIONARIES

When a language is complex enough to permit synonyms and homographs, the need for a dictionary, or language authority, to resolve these ambiguities is apparent. Even without these problems, a simple list of the "legal" descriptors in a language can be of help to the indexer or searcher in composing an index record or query. Such a list can also serve as a quality control device since it will contain the approved spelling of terms. We assign the name *dictionary* to all authority lists that specify the membership, spelling, usage, or meaning of the elements of a vocabulary. Included in our concept of dictionary are the usual meanings of *thesaurus, classification schedule, synonymy, glossary,* etc. Each of these can be considered a language authority and gives word meanings, in one form or another, and word relationships. Our reason for departing from standard terminology, as it has been previously, is to unify the meanings for the designers of a data processing system who will find relatively little difference of form or logic in the design and use of such files.

2.6.1   The Need for a Dictionary

Before examining dictionary functions in detail, let us define the context of this discussion. We are not discussing the science of lexicography, in general. The compilers and publishers of a dictionary of natural language for wide general use face problems and count on solutions not met in an information retrieval system. For example, a conventional lexicographer considers himself a historian or reporter, and must expend considerable cost and energy to survey actual language usages. He cannot, or will not, establish usage by decree, which would take much less effort. In his role as a reporter he need not try to "clean up" the language, to guard against dissimilar words merging their meanings, new words being created which mean the same as existing words, or the same word acquiring more than one meaning, but these are problems for the index language lexicographer, whose job it is to help his readers discriminate between terms and to reduce ambiguity in the languages. The index language lexicographer, then, cannot simply report on usage. He must guide or dictate usage. We are concerned with the role of a dictionary in an information retrieval system, assisting both indexers and library searchers in using and manipulating the library's index language. In particular, information retrieval systems have the following problems which require a dictionary-like tool, one which explains or defines word usage.

1. Synonyms and Homographs. One of the principal problems of language usage is that of discriminating between similar words or similar ideas. Confusion over word meanings can be resolved by appeal to an authority if all language users agree on the same authority.

2. Search for Appropriate Words. Regardless of whether synonyms and homographs exist in a language, a language user will often find himself in the situation in which he is unsure of the words to use to describe some concept. In this case he needs the same tool required to resolve synonym-homograph problems—a list of the vocabulary of the language and some definition of the meaning of each word. In other words, even if two words do not have exactly the same definition, as long as there is any possible commonality of meaning, there needs to be an explanation of the difference.

3. Record Authoritative Decisions on Usage. This differs only slightly from the first two problems. It refers to the need for, or utility of, a single, final authority, accessible to all system users, for all vocabulary usage rules and decisions. Since the index language is not normally the same as the natural language spoken by the system users there may be some difficulty when first learning the language until they fully understand that the retrieval system has its own language whose designers have the right to make their own rulings on word usage. Such problems can arise where inexperienced users insist on employing words in the sense normally used by them, perhaps the jargon of their profession, without recognizing that the library, as a different culture, may have a different jargon. A user, either indexer or searcher, can request that a dictionary change be made but, before a change is made, he must and can recognize the rulings currently in force. The dictionary, in perhaps its most important role, is a vehicle for communication among all language users.

4. Error Control. Among the most maddening problems of any data processing system is that of violation of input specifications, minor errors in the data to be processed. To a computer *McNamara* and *MacNamara, New York* and *NewYork, mathematics* and *mathmatics* are six *different* symbols. Unless great pains are taken, a computer program does not attempt to tell how alike the pairs are; it merely notes that they are not equal. A human reader can easily make these spelling errors, but he can immediately and easily notice the similarity in the word pairs and equate them. He may be a trifle irritated if a request for information on *NewYork* fails to recover anything because the library's *official* spelling is *New York*. Yet *NewYork* could as easily be a misspelling of *Newark* or *Newport* as *New York*. Even more likely to occur are confusions such as that between *Silver Spring*, Maryland, and *Silver Springs*, Florida, or *radium* and *radian*. The expense of a computer search of an index file makes it highly desirable to detect such errors as early in the program as possible, and to reject questions containing illegal words, words that definitely could not be found even if the search were to continue. The detection and rejection of words not in the approved vocabulary is another reason for needing a dictionary of the index language. We must be careful not to misconstrue a need for rigid control over input as implying that the dictionary is so rigid it cannot be changed. A word may be absent from the dictionary (hence rejected as an input term) either because it is a misspelling or because it is a genuinely new word in the language. In either case it should be brought to the attention of someone who is capable enough, and authorized, to decide which condition holds and who will either correct the spelling or take action to have the new word admitted to the approved vocabulary list.

2.6.2   The Role of a Dictionary

In listing the requirements of a dictionary, we have come close to specifying what it must look like or do. Yet, largely because of the semantic confusion about what a dictionary is (or what a thesaurus, etc., is), it is well to develop a formal definition, insofar as this is possible. The difficulty we shall experience in trying to define the word *dictionary* is akin to that a dictionary editor will have in defining *any* word.

The most critical point to consider is whether a dictionary can "define" words at all or the extent to which "meaning" can be conveyed from one person to another through written or spoken language rather than through perception of the thing denoted by the word. To begin this discussion, let us look at the problems of compiling a dictionary of a

natural language.   The following quotations are from S. I. Hayakawa;
all italics are his.

> It is an almost universal belief that every word has a correct meaning,
> that we learn these meanings principally from teachers and grammarians
> (except that most of the time we don't bother to, so that we ordinarily
> speak 'sloppy English'), and that dictionaries and grammars are the supreme
> authority in matters of meaning and usage.   Few people ask by what
> authority the writers of dictionaries and grammars say what they say.[5]
>
> *The writer of a dictionary is a historian, not a lawgiver.*[6]
>
> . . . one of the premises upon which modern linguistic thought is based:
> namely, that *no word ever has exactly the same meaning twice.*[7]
>
> To say dogmatically that we know what a word means *in advance of
> its utterance* is nonsense.   All we can know in advance is *approximately*
> what it will mean.[8]

If we accept Hayakawa's arguments, as we do, then we must accept
that a dictionary cannot be entirely self-contained, cannot define each
word of an entire vocabulary solely in terms of that vocabulary.   This
would appear to be completely at variance with our stated requirements
for a dictionary except for the word *approximately* in the last sentence
quoted from Hayakawa.   Unfortunately, although index languages and
their dictionaries have the appearance of great precision of definition,
mainly because of the imperious manner with which word meanings
are handed down, the expressiveness of such languages can suffer accordingly.   In return for rigid dictionary definitions which a computer can
use with a not too difficult interpretive program, we give up much expressiveness, and our precisely written definitions are only approximately
representative of the ideas they are supposed to convey.   We must accept, then, that we will accomplish no miracles in compiling a dictionary
to meet our previously stated requirements, especially that of serving
as an absolute authority.   The dictionary will unhesitatingly and with
great authority hand down decisions which are necessarily imprecise.
We are not going to get something for nothing.

Now we can go on to show some ways of constructing dictionaries
that meet our requirements, but which are all subject to the qualifying
remarks just concluded.

A dictionary that will prevent misuse of words is a virtual impossibility
but, as we described under the heading of *Error Control,* a dictionary
can be used to catch all attempts at using new words, and these words
can be referred to the lexical authority for his decision as to whether
they should be allowed to become vocabulary descriptors or be kept

out of the language. He can "define" the new word his own way and, by the two acts of ruling on admissibility and making a formal definition, he can exercise a degree of control over an index language that is impossible in the case of general use of natural language. The dictionary authority cannot prevent gross usage errors. If a searcher writes an erroneous descriptor which happens to be part of the language, it is enormously difficult to detect the error in most cases, dependent as it is on interpretation of context and recognition that some usages are prohibited in some contexts. For example, the word *London* is a reasonable descriptor in many index languages but, if used in the context of *U.S. Presidential Elections* in the 1930's, it could be an erroneous spelling of *Landon,* the Republican candidate in 1936. While a dictionary may not be able to change *London* to *Landon,* a more probable descriptor in this context, it may be able to reject *London* as being unrelated to the subject matter, and could easily suggest that an error has occurred by the simple device of not showing any connection between the word *London* and the subject of *U.S. elections.*

However tight the control of the lexical authority over the dictionary, he must recognize that languages change, and he must, like the lexicographer of natural language, yield to consistent pressure from language users for change in word meanings. A distinct advantage of index language lexicographers over their conventional brethren is the ready capability of an information retrieval system to keep records of itself, one such being the record of word use rates. Changes in these rates are indicative of language areas needing change. Perhaps words are falling into disuse and might be proscribed from the dictionary, or some words may be getting such heavy use that their definition should be narrowed by creating new words to describe portions of the subject originally described by the single term. Compare this latter situation with the discussion in Section 2.3.1 of expanding a hierarchic code.

Let us now review the kinds of definition that might be used. The word *definition* needs definition first. In our usage, *a definition simply gives the relationship between the word defined and another word or set of words, which need not be in the same language.* We may say that

> *red* is the quality in common among an American
> Beauty rose, a strawberry, the setting sun, and human blood.
> *ran* is the past tense of *run.*
> *plume* is the French term for the English word, *pen.*

Occasionally another relationship is stated in a dictionary and that is the location of some information pertaining to the word being defined, such as

New York: see page 16 (or disk 3, track 12)

The kinds of relationships usually expressed in a dictionary are

equality	*plume* (in French) = *pen* (in English) *ran* = the past tense of *run*
class inclusion:	*aeronautics* is a subdivision or subclass of *engineering*
class membership:	*New York* is an individual representative of the class, *city*
attribute:	*red* is an attribute of a *strawberry*
location:	*New York* (information about it) is on page 6 *Calculator:* see (the place where) *computer* (is defined)
conditional relation- ship, e.g., condi- tional equality:	*Lead:* 1. physics, a metal, atomic number 82. 2. nautical, a device used for measuring depth of water. 3. printing, a device for making space between lines of type.

A form of conditional relationship is a statistical relationship where no more tie between words is indicated than that they often occur together in the same document or sentence.

A tool which performs one or more of these definition services becomes an integral part of the language.

2.6.3   Types of Dictionary

The most commonly met dictionary in conventional usage is, of course, one which provides a natural language definition for each entry. Such a dictionary is very convenient to use because it gives ample opportunity for explanation of context, for examples of usage, and even for pictures of an object being defined. Thus, the lexicographer has a reasonable degree of latitude in drawing distinctions between words and contexts. This is not a particularly useful dictionary for a computer because of the difficulty of programmed interpretation of the text of the definition. It lacks one of the desirable attributes of an index language, stated in Section 2.2, that the language be comprehensible to a processor. The following list describes varieties of dictionaries that are in actual use, either in an information retrieval system or for general language use. We have included the latter both for the sake of completeness and because, even in a restricted vocabulary system, users will probably make use of dictionaries of the general language, by habit, to help resolve index language problems. We adopt the convention that the entry is the word being defined and the definition, regardless of whether or not the dictionary provides a "definition" in the usual sense, is whatever the dictionary tells about the entry. An argument, in our terminology, differs from an entry in that an argument is the word used for searching, and possibly will not be found in the dictionary.

1. The One-for-One Synonym Dictionary. Although not very common, this form of dictionary has the great advantage of simplicity and clearcut, unambiguous definitions. For each entry there is a one-term definition whose meaning is construed to be identical to that of the entry. More than one entry can have the same definition, permitting the accommodation of alternate spellings as well as different word forms. In a language that permits synonyms it is necessary to make some provision for relating a word to its synonyms. This may be done when the word has been used in an index record and is being entered into an index file, or when it is going to be used in a query. At one or both

Entry	Numeric code
Book	1 *
Calculator	2 ‡
Catalogue	3 *
Cataloguer	4
Computer	2 ‡
Descriptor	5 *
Document	1 *
Index	3 *
Indexer	4
Processor	2 ‡
Query	6 *
Search	6 *
Term	7 †
Word	5 *

Figure 2.17 One-for-one synonym dictionary.

* These pairings follow the usage of this book, that is, *book-document,* but the words paired are not generally used as exact synonyms.
† All vocabulary words must be in this list, whether or not there are synonyms.
‡ Any number of entries can be equated to the same value.

of these times each word must be converted into a form representative of all its synonyms to permit matching. The definition in this case can as well be a number as a natural language word. A number is more compact, hence more conservative of computer memory. A dictionary such as that described here was used by the U.S. Air Force.[21] A somewhat simplified form is illustrated in Figure 2.17.

2. *The Multiple-Relation Dictionary.* This name we give to a variety of dictionaries which, like the one-for-one synonym dictionary, have definitions composed of descriptors or terms, but may have more than one term in the definition; the definition terms may bear any of several relationships to the entry. The most common relationships are: synonymity, inclusion, subordination, and the conditional forms of these. A relationship of near equality is often used, more frequently expressed as "See also," instructing the reader to try all terms in the definition under this heading with the assumption that at least one of them is approximately equal to the entry in the context under consideration. Such a dictionary is the ASTIA Thesaurus illustrated in Figure 2.5. This dictionary form provides a human reader with the best features of both hierarchical classification and fixed key words. The language has structure, concepts can be expressed at various levels of generality, fine distinctions between subjects can be made; yet the language can easily be changed. It is most interesting to note that the flexibility derives almost entirely from one fact—that no code number is assigned to a "node" point of the hierarchy. Hence a change in the hierarchic structure does not produce a change in a string of related codes as is the case in a true hierarchical language. This is shown in Figure 2.18 where the code first used for analog computers (code 123.1) acquires a new, incompatible meaning as the dictionary is reorganized. This causes difficulties in searching previously indexed material.

3. *The Language-to-Language Dictionary.* Common in general language use, and becoming common in data processing, is a dictionary that provides a definition whose vocabulary is drawn from a different natural language than that of the entry. In form such dictionaries range from one-for-one synonymies to those having full text definitions, permitting phrases as well as words as entries. An interesting example is the dictionary developed by IBM for its Automatic Language Processor.[12] This machine has the feature that it will find the longest dictionary entry that will match a string of input words, thereby providing for idiomatic translation. For example, an input expression such as *il y a* ("There is," in French) would be translated, *as an expression,* into *there is* in English, and not word-by-word into *it* (or *he*) *there*

COMPUTERS   123

  Generic to

    ANALOG COMPUTERS   123.1
    DIGITAL COMPUTERS   123.2
    ELECTRICAL ACCOUNTING MACHINES   123.3
    ELECTRICAL CALCULATORS   123.4

  a. Portion of a possible entry and definition in a multiple-relation dictionary. In the column at right possible hierarchical codes are shown.

COMPUTERS   123

  Generic to

    ELECTRICAL AND ELECTROMECHANICAL CALCU-
      LATORS   123.1
    ELECTRONIC COMPUTERS   123.2

ELECTRONIC COMPUTERS   123.2

  Generic to

    ANALOG COMPUTERS   123.21
    DIGITAL COMPUTERS   123.22

ELECTRICAL AND ELECTROMECHANICAL CALCULATORS 123.1

  Generic to

    ELECTRICAL ACCOUNTING MACHINES   123.11
    ELECTRICAL CALCULATORS   123.12

  b. Example of how the definition in the first example might be revised to show an additional level of generality.

Figure 2.18   Changing an index language structure.

has. Naturally, the machine is built on the assumption that idioms will be entered into the dictionary in the first place. If the full expression cannot be matched with an existing entry, then small portions will be tried until the string is reduced to *il,* a common word almost certain to be an entry in any French dictionary. If an input word is found which has no match (e.g., a proper name) the machine will break it down letter by letter and either reproduce the original form of the word or transliterate, if appropriate.

4. Natural Language Definition.   We have already described this dictionary, at the beginning of this section, and have given the reasons against its use in a data processing system.

5. Thesaurus.   The thesaurus, invented by Peter Mark Roget,[14] groups words together according to the subject concept to which they are related.   It has two kinds of entries, the term or descriptor word, for which a location is given where the word appears again in context, and the concept word, the definition of which provides a contextual frame of reference in which the relationships of terms to the concept are explained.   Concepts are organized on a hierarchic basis.   The term *thesaurus* is sometimes used to describe what we have called a multiple-relation dictionary.   We have no quarrel with this usage for it corresponds to our definition of thesaurus if we recognize Roget's concepts as descriptors at a high generic level.

6. Classification Schedule.   A dictionary that gives natural language definitions for hierarchical classification codes is often called a classification schedule.   It differs in only one respect from a natural language dictionary.   The entries are numbers or subject titles, and, being members of the vocabulary of an index language, are in a different language than the definitions, which are natural language expressions.   There may be cross references in the definition, but rarely will a word or term used to define an entry be, in turn, an entry itself.   Thus, if a reader has difficulty understanding a definition, he will get little help from the schedule.   The first volume of the Dewey Decimal Classification is such a schedule, some sample entries from which appear in Section 2.3.1.

7. Location Tables.   To round out the review of dictionary types we include this one which provides no semantic information about an entry but in all other respects resembles a dictionary.   The "definition" here is a symbol giving the location of information about the entry.   An index to a book is an example.

2.6.4   A Dictionary Example

The Dewey Decimal Classification[2] (DDC) is one of the best known and, with the Library of Congress classification system, one of the most frequently used classifications in the United States.   A variant of it, the Universal Decimal Classification, is in common use in Europe.   We shall describe a *classification schedule* which, recall, is subsumed under our definition of *dictionary*.

Volume I of the DDC, subtitled "Tables," lists the vocabulary in numeric order. It includes a language translation of each descriptor into an English phrase or title. In a different typography from that of the titles are *scope notes*, natural language comments, not part of the translation of the meaning of the numeric descriptor, which assist the reader in selecting the most appropriate term. For example, descriptor code number 551.594 means *weather belts*, and has subordinated to it *Tropical, Subtropical, Temperate, Cold,* and *Polar* belts, codes 551.594 2–6. Each of these terms has an explanatory, or scope, note, such as

> *Tropical Belts*
>   No cool season; mean temperature of coldest month above 64.4° F
> *Subtropical Belts*
>   Arid or semiarid climate; mean temperature above 68° F for 4–11 months, 50°–68° F for 1–8 months

In yet another typography are the "see" references which direct the reader to other descriptors with similar or related meanings. We stress the typography because we have, in effect, three lists, or files, in one, each identified by the use of different type faces. In Chapter 5 we shall define these three facets of the definition as fields of information.

Volume II of the DDC is called the "Index." It contains an alphabetic listing of English language terms and gives the classification code or codes pertinent to that term. This permits a reader to locate the general subject area in which may be found some detailed subject, such as *epiglottis*. The code 611.22 is defined in a scope note in Volume I under the general heading, *Larynx,* as consisting of "laryngal cartilages, glottis, muscles of larynx." Starting with *epiglottis,* and being unfamiliar with anatomy, would leave the indexer or searcher with a formidable problem of locating the correct subject heading in the volume alone. Reference to the index, however, gives the following:

> *Epiglottis*
>
> | | |
> |---|---|
> | diseases medicine | 611.22 |
> | human anatomy | 616.22 |
> | human physiology | 612.78 |
> | surgical treatment | 617.533 |

Thus, although *epiglottis* is not a descriptor in the language, the translated title of a descriptor, nor even a word appearing in the title of a descriptor, its proper position in the hierarchy can still be determined. Returning to the ACM classification, we can see that the older form used the alphabetic index approach—the listing of terms in an order that makes it relatively easy to find a subject heading—and the new form uses the hierarchy approach—presenting headings in hierarchical order, but with order among highest level terms being completely arbitrary. There is nothing "natural" about either of these orders. Subjects could as well be ordered by frequency of use or by order of their occurrence in some special field (e.g., data on commodities could be indexed according to role in the basic industry-to-consumer chain of events, such as mining, raw-materials processing, manufacturing, distribution, retailing, consumer utilization of a product).

REFERENCES

1. Dennis, B. K., *High Speed Literature Searching on an IBM 704,* General Electric Co., Evendale, Ohio.
2. Dewey, Melvil, *Dewey Decimal Classification and Relative Index,* Forest Press, Lake Placid Club, Essex County, New York, 1959.
3. Finerman, Aron, and Lee Revens, "Revision of the Classification System," *Computing Reviews,* Association for Computing Machinery, **4,** 6 (1963), 309–311.
4. Hayakawa, S. I., *Language in Thought and Action,* Harcourt, Brace & World, New York, 1949, p. 61.
5. *Ibid.,* p. 54.
6. *Ibid.,* p. 55.
7. *Ibid.,* p. 60.
8. *Ibid.,* p. 61.
9. Jacoby, J., and V. Slamecka, *Indexer Consistency Under Minimal Conditions,* Documentation, Inc., Bethesda, Maryland, November 1962, p. 19.
10. Jonker, Frederick, *The Descriptive Continuum, A "Generalized" Theory of Indexing,* Documentation, Inc., Washington, D.C., 1957.
11. Kehl, William B., John F. Horty, Charles R. T. Bacon, and Davis S. Mitchell, "An Information Retrieval Language for Legal Studies," *Communications of the Association for Computing Machinery,* **4,** 9 (1961), 380–389.
12. King, Gilbert W., "Table Look-up Procedures in Languages Processing, Part 1, The Raw Text," *IBM Journal of Research and Development,* **5,** 2 (1961), 86–92.
13. Lancaster, F. W. and J. Mills, "Testing Indexes and Index Language Devices: The ASLIB Cranfield Project," *American Documentation,* **15,** 1 (1964), 4–13.
14. Roget, P. M., *Thesaurus of Words and Phrases,* Grosset & Dunlap, New York, 1947, Preface to First Edition.
15. Savage, T. R., H. C. Fallon, and M. E. Saxon, *ACSI-Matic Auto-Abstracting Project,* Interim Report, International Business Machines Corp., Yorktown Heights, New York, 1959.
16. Taube, Mortimer, C. D. Gull, and Irma S. Wachtel, "Unit Terms in Coordinate Indexing," *American Documentation,* **III,** 4 (1952), 213–218.
17. Thompson, Elizabeth H., Ed., *A.L.A. Glossary of Library Terms,* American Library Association, Chicago, 1943.

18. Vickery, B. C., *On Retrieval Systems Theory,* Butterworth & Co., London, 1961, p. 33.
19. ———, *General Information Manual, Keyword-in Context (KWIC) Indexing,* International Business Machines Corp., White Plains, New York, 1962.
20. ———, *Medical Subject Headings,* Third Edition, National Library of Medicine, Washington, D.C., 1963.
21. ———, *Programming Manual, Volume III, Unformatted File System,* International Business Machines Corp., Rockville, Maryland, 1961.
22. ———, *Thesaurus of ASTIA Descriptors,* Second Edition, Armed Forces Technical Information Agency, Arlington, Virginia, December 1962.

EXERCISES

1. Select a set of 10 words pertinent to your professional field or discipline. Look them up in a variety of dictionaries and other reference works such as: encyclopedias, thesauri, foreign language and technical dictionaries, old and new dictionaries. Compare the definitions and discuss the differences in light of the different aims of the dictionaries.
2. Select some short articles or papers and prepare indexes of them using subject headings or classification, key words (say, 10–20 of them per document), and a faceted language using a key word combined with a broad subject term to explain the key word's context. Exchange the indexes with a friend. Use the friend's indexes to try to reconstitute the gist of his original article. Discuss factors in the various index languages that contribute to success or failure.
3. As a class project, assemble a set of subject-related papers, articles, or abstracts. Examples are newspaper articles on France, sports, finance, the theater, and so on, or abstracts in a fairly narrow field taken from an abstracting journal. Devise an index language for this literature. Include, in the index record, an accession number, title, author, date, and source, and 5–10 subject terms. Select or design a language that seems appropriate to the material used. Index a portion of the documents. Note any problems encountered in the indexing process, such as ambiguity of index definition.
4. Devise a dictionary for the index language used in Exercise 3, being sure to index some documents before designing the dictionary to acquire some idea of what form of dictionary is needed. Assume the dictionary will be used as an error control device, on term spelling, as well as for term definitions. Index several more documents, and report whether the dictionary has been of help.

CHAPTER 3

The creation of index records

3.1 INTRODUCTION

A librarian or indexer looks at a document differently from a research worker or other library user. A user is seeking some information from a document about his subject, wanting to know what the author says about it. The librarian's job is to prepare for the queries of the users—to be concerned with subject matter mainly for the purpose of being able to guide a user to a document or to procure documents for the collection—not to pursue the subject matter for its own sake. The librarian is not a critic of content, but is an observer of user patterns, one who must anticipate what aspects of a document will prove interesting to, and may be requested by, the users.

In this chapter we shall consider the context of index records and some of the mechanics of preparing them. First, we shall concern ourselves with the content, or semantic aspect, of an index, and to the question of what concepts should be expressed in an index irrespective of the mode of expression used. Given an index language, we may ask how the indexer decides exactly what terms to use in the index of any given document. The literature is scarce on this topic. Most descriptions of index languages confine themselves to descriptions of logic and, perhaps, discussions of the "depth" of indexing (a point to be covered below), but avoid or give short shrift to any discussion which could answer for the indexer the question, "The word x is in the document. Shall I use it or its equivalent as a descriptor in the index?" This is another of those questions which have no universal answer. Rules for index content are, and must be, a matter of individual needs of individual systems.

Since an index record is a description of a document, it is, in a sense, a recoding or transformation of some aspects of the document it represents. Any discussion of indexing practice must include a discussion of some of the structural attributes of documents with which indexers must be concerned when performing indexing or cataloging functions.

We are concerned with these attributes both because knowledge of them helps in the design of information retrieval systems, and because of the increasing trend toward programmed analysis of language, including machine recognition of syntactic structure and of significant words in a text.

A document is a recorded representation of an idea or a physical entity. Examples are: this book, a photograph, a musical score, and a video tape recording of a man making a speech. We shall be primarily concerned here with written communication in natural language, but much of the material will be applicable to other forms of documentation. The receipt of a document by a library leads to the creation of an index or catalog record. The collection of index records is the key to information retrieval. The kind of record created determines what kind of search capability is needed, or is useful, and what quality of retrieval will be possible.

Most information retrieval systems in which mechanization plays an important role are restricted in that they tend to specialize in expository writing in monograph form, material characterized by the author's intent to inform his readers, and by his restricting himself to a single subject. The intent to inform is an important consideration in indexing documents since it allows the indexer to take material at its face value. Enciphered messages (when the reader does not have the key), inspirational writing and allegory, and opinion and propaganda have in common the attribute that the author may have used words in other than their most usually accepted senses. We shall largely restrict ourselves to what we wish technical publications were—straightforward attempts to impart information through written, natural language. When material to be indexed includes political writing, its meaning may be ambiguous because of the high propaganda content, and extra effort is needed to resolve the ambiguity.

The process of transforming an idea into a written document, be it a natural language monograph or an index record, is governed by certain rules, some prescriptive and some merely descriptive. Prescriptive rules govern behavior. They dictate what should and should not be done. They tell us to start a sentence with a capital letter, to indent the first line of a paragraph, to lead off a factual report with a summary of the report, not to split an infinitive, or not to use *ain't*. Descriptive rules tell what has already happened. They tell us that *a, and, to,* and *of* are among the few most frequently used words in the English language; that the words *imply* and *infer,* or *who* and *whom,* are becoming virtually synonymous, that the frequency distribution of words within a text can be described by a particular mathematical expression. Descriptive rules, however, do not force us to adhere to them while prescriptive rules may be enforced.

Together, these rules govern the structure of the documents with which we are concerned. We define *document structure* as consisting of *language* and *format,* again noting that we include both natural language texts and index records in our meaning of *document.* A language, in turn, has a *vocabulary* and a *syntax.* Vocabulary refers to the set of words or letter groups in use and the meanings assigned thereto. *Syntax* refers to the grouping of vocabulary words into larger units to expand the descriptive power of the vocabulary. *Format* is the positioning of word groups within the document. The format of an index record designed by the Library of Congress is illustrated in Figure 2.1. The placement of title, subject, call number, and so forth, are meticulously governed by prescriptive rules. The format of a natural language text will be less rigid, but there are still strong conventions governing the placement of titles, abstracts, indexes, and the like. These three elements of structure are governed by different rules which overlap to some extent, so that one is never absolutely certain which set of rules governs a given situation. For example, syntactic rules govern the positioning of modifiers with respect to the words they modify, but if the modifier and modified word are to be combined into one word (such as *fulfill*), we may reverse the usual word order and change the spelling. The spelling of this word is not normally considered to be an application of a syntactic rule. The grouping of elemental word combinations into larger phrases and sentences is governed by syntactic rules but, within the bounds of good usage, many variations are permitted. The usual newspaper convention of writing a name and title as: *Sen. Javits (R, N.Y.)* rather than *Republican Senator Javits of New York* is an example of the use of a prescriptive rule to limit the normally acceptable range of syntactic variations. Large publishing organizations codify their rules into what is called a *style manual.*

3.2   PRINCIPLES OF INDEX CONSTRUCTION

We have introduced three structural features of a document or index record: vocabulary, syntax, and format. The division of a document's structure into these elements is arbitrary. The number could possibly be expanded by considering, for example, morphology, or the structure of the vocabulary elements. Furthermore, the boundaries between the concepts are vague. Be that as it may, documents consist of strings of symbols, assembled, according to some set of rules, however incomplete or arbitrary, into meaningful words, phrases, and sentences. The indexer, whether a human or a computer, must comprehend the symbols of a source document and convey some of the meaning of the document's symbols to the index, usually in a different language. Formats and syntax are of no interest in themselves. They serve to help locate and interpret vocabulary terms. Special syntactic units denoting title, author, date, or other documents referred to are especially easy to locate, extract, and enter into an index record. This is because they are almost universally regarded as important for indexers, browsers, or careful readers, and are denoted by special tags, typography, or position on the printed page.

The composition of an index record varies widely, according to the library's role and resources. Our focus, here, is on the principles that govern index record design and particularly problems of index record subject content. Index structure is considered in greater detail in Chapters 5 and 6.

3.2.1   Types of Terms and Descriptors

The specific types of terms and descriptors that constitute an index record may be grouped into three classes: bibliographic, subject, and location. We must stress that any attribute whatever of a document that is of interest to the users of a library is a fit candidate for inclusion in the index of that library.

Bibliographic index terms are those concerning the document's title, author, publisher, date and place of publication, number of illustrations, and any other items which are descriptive of the document, more or less as a manufactured product. Items about the publication of the book are collectively called the *imprint*. Items about the book's physical construction, such as page count, are collectively called *collation*.

Subject terms, of course, tell what the book is about, in any or a combination of the index languages in use at the library.

Location terms provide a reference to another file. In the conventional card catalog, the call number is given, usually a combination of a classification term and another numbering system that produces a unique serial for each document. Other forms of location data are accession numbers (sequentially assigned serial numbers) or the computer address of another file.

Although catalogs usually contain all three types of terms, and often several terms in each class, some index files have as few as two terms per record. An example in ordinary library usage is a directory of the shelf arrangement of books, wherein the classification code is given and the number of the shelf on which books on that subject are stored.

Synonym dictionary entries, which may be interspersed with regular catalog records, may consist simply of two subject terms and the notation that they are equivalent within the language used by the library—in other words, "Subject X, see Subject Y."

Some terms of an index record can be searched for and some, for all practical purposes, cannot. For example, *date of publication* is a term that can be recovered from a Library of Congress catalog card. However, it is entirely unfeasible for use as a search term because placement of catalog cards is entirely random with respect to date. The choice of what terms are included in an index record sometimes seems to be a matter of tradition. In a typical catalog card, we may be given the place of publication, but not necessarily the nationality of the author, or his employment affiliation. In more specialized libraries such terms are more likely to be found, and we may encounter such term types as: *security classification, type of binding, reproduction process* used for art work, and moral judgments, all used as index terms.

Bibliographic data are usually straightforward, easily available, and inexpensive to provide. Location terms are a relatively trivial problem except in complex file systems which are considered in Chapter 8. The amount and type of subject terms is usually the most difficult question to resolve in the design of an information retrieval system, for they can be expensive to provide and expensive, in another way, to omit.

3.2.2 Point of View in Indexing

The most obvious index content rule would be, "Index all important topics." The fallacy of this statement, we hope, is apparent to the reader, for it simply transfers the problem of what to index into that of defining importance. We can describe the importance of a topic four ways:

1. Statistically, as a function of how often it is repeated.

2. By virtue of the author *saying* a topic is important through use of titles, subtitles, or the text, itself (e.g., "Now we come to the key point of this paper.")

3. By grammatical usage, even though not explicitly stated. For example, the sentence, "The airliner made use of radar to avoid the storm," clearly implies that *radar* is an important topic *to this sentence* while, "His radar-like eyes spotted the ship in the darkness," equally clearly implies that *radar* is not a topic of this sentence. In other words, if we judged the meaning of the sentence solely from the occurrence of the word *radar*, dissociated from its context, we would form a misleading impression of what the second sentence was about.

4. By specification of importance criteria by a user, such as, "I wish all references to drug names to be cited in the index, regardless of context in which used."

Unfortunately, real life examples do not always make the issue as clear cut as those above. As a matter of practical reality, the indexer is often faced with deciding whether an author has or has not labelled a topic as important, either by statement or by usage, or whether a subject in a document is or is not the same as that specifically called for by a library user. Even statistical significance measures pose a problem of determining a threshold between important and unimportant. Refer to Figure 3.1 and consider whether the sentences in the left-hand column meet the index selection criteria shown in the center column.

Whether or not the document excerpt matches the index criterion in any case, in this figure, is a function of the point of view of the reader. Point of view is generally recognized as one of the critical problems in satisfying user requirements in a library. The problem is more acute in hierarchical indexing because of the custom of using only one classification term per document. It is less severe in key word indexing where the indexer has the freedom to recognize how a topic will be viewed by different users, and to satisfy different groups of them by selecting descriptors representative of all important* points of view. Thus index logic enters into content determination by sometimes putting heavy reliance on the indexer in the matter of term selection and leaving to him the choice of what are important topics.

Point of view is a consideration, not only in deciding whether a document matches a stated user index criterion, but in deciding which index terms to use as well. Basically, this is the synonym-homograph problem again, wherein documents, sentences, words, or phrases can be equated to more than one index term (or match more than one index criterion) depending upon context, and it is up to the indexer to use his own judgment in selecting terms.

3.2.3   Indexing Breadth and Depth

Related to the questions of what to say in an index (subject matter) and how to say it (logic and language) are how many topics to index

---

* In using this word at this point we once again resort to approximation. We could not expect *all* points of view to be represented, and we must recognize the problems of determining what is important. Yet some selection decision must be made, and the result is usually an approximation of the "important" topics.

Sentence in document	Index criterion	Comment
1. The bill, having passed both houses of Congress, now goes to the President.	Activities of key government personnel.	Does this describe an actual activity of the President?
2. The radio worked perfectly during the entire trip.	Malfunctions of electronic equipment.	Is *no malfunction* a malfunction? The problem here is the wording of the index criterion, which probably should have been, "Reliability of electronic equipment."
3. I discussed the matter on June 22, 1964, at the White House with the President.	Enter into the index all personal names that appear in the document.	*President* is not a person's name. Yet, by naming an office, implying an activity of the incumbent, and giving the date, this statement clearly identifies a single individual, even though it does not name him.
4. We agreed to arrange for the export of three of our Model 14 machine tools as soon as an export license could be obtained.	Records of export of machine tools.	Did this export take place? What if the criterion had been worded, "Records of import . . . ?"

Figure 3.1 Examples of index criteria.

and how much to say about each. These we call the *breadth* and *depth* of indexing, denoting the extent of subject coverage, how many of the document's topics or users' points of view were selected for inclusion in the index, and how much information was given about each. Just as these two words have a common meaning, at one level of abstraction, in their conventional usage (both refer to a dimension), they are not truly distinct concepts in indexing. The difference between saying more about a selected topic and creating an additional topic may be purely a function of the number and role of facets in the index language. For example, we might be using a faceted index language which calls for descriptors of manufactured products to be linked to those of the product's composition and use. This might give us a term such as *ball bearing, steel, automotive,* to which could be appended *General Motors, Detroit,* by defining additional facets for *manufacturer* and *place of manufacture.* Use of such terms would normally justify calling this indexing in great depth, for we have named a product, its composition, its use, its manufacturer, and the location of its manufacturer, and we have denoted the role of each descriptor by its position in a predetermined sequence within a faceted index term.

What can we say about the breadth of indexing in this example? Have we covered only one subject, or five? If we say we covered five subjects, then we are not differentiating between facets and terms—between depth and breadth. We may say we have covered only one subject, *ball bearings,* but covered it in great depth. Then, if we were to strip away the connections between the facets, and make each one an independent key word, we would be decreasing the depth (saying less about the original subject, *ball bearings*) while increasing the breadth (increasing the number of topics indexed). Doing this would result in a net *loss* of information because we no longer have a specified connection among the words. The word *depth* is often used to refer to both these concepts.

We prefer to continue using both terms with the full understanding that they are not completely independent of each other. In our examples above, we could increase the breadth of the index two ways: by holding to the original, faceted language, but telling the indexers to select more products for inclusion in the index by lowering the threshold of importance for selection, and by selecting different kinds of descriptors, such as names of people, upon which to base a faceted term. In both cases, we increase the number of descriptors of an already defined type. If, on the other hand, we add a new facet, such as cost of a product, we are increasing the *depth* by adding a new kind of descriptor. We have also increased the breadth of the index. Thus, breadth can be increased or decreased independently of depth, but depth has some component of breadth in it, and a change in depth necessitates a change in breadth.

If we raise the question of what depth or breadth are desirable in an index, we run immediately into the many problems to be enumerated in Chapter 4 under the title "Retrieval System Performance." Breadth and depth of indexing certainly affect retrieval cost and effectiveness. We can measure the cost, but the value (positive or negative) of index breadth and depth are beyond calculation. They must be estimated and experimented with for each system.

3.2.4   Rules for Index Content

Once we accept the notion that universal indexing rules do not exist, we must consider how to devise rules to fit a particular situation. We are faced with a problem somewhat like that of the index language lexicographer in that we must ignore Hayakawa's warning (see Section 2.6), and try to anticipate the meaning of words before they have been uttered in an actual document. The index language authority has the severe disadvantage that he cannot affect an author's choice of words, nor does he get to rule directly on admissibility of words as they are used in indexing; he must teach his indexers what he wants before they index documents, and hope they will all carry out their instructions in a uniform manner. He is faced not only with point-of-view problems between indexers and various specialized user groups, he is faced with variations among indexers in their interpretation of the same documents and their reactions to training and supervisory control. Our aim here is not to stress the effect of variations among indexers. It should be obvious that if indexers cannot agree on word meanings nor on what constitutes a match between document content and index term definition, the result must be lower quality indexing and poorer responses to queries. What we do want to stress are the positive steps that can be taken by the designer of an index language to work towards indexer uniformity.

Two basic principles are involved. The first is that *uniformity of usage among indexers is more important than their adherence to rules of usage,* since the formal definition of word meanings and even syntax can be adjusted to actual usage far more easily than a language user group can be controlled in its usage. As examples of this form of adaptive control, consider the modern trend in English language lexicography toward accepting slang and "improper" usage rather than steadfastly and futilely bucking the trend as reflected in the critical vehemence[5] with which the 1961 revision of Webster's Unabridged Dictionary was met.[25] Similarly, in France, French language purists are protesting the Americanization of their tongue which, nonetheless, continues to advance.[8]

Our second principle is that *no complete set of index rules is possible.* As long as a reader can continue to find new thoughts being expressed in new contexts, he will continue to meet situations wherein he is unsure of the meanings. Recall, also that an indexer must try to understand the author's meaning as well as to predict how users of the index rules would have to provide for "proper" interpretations of all documents that a given library could possibly receive.

Making use of these principles requires heavy doses of tedious labor. Training courses are necessary, with many examples for students to work with, for many more rules can be demonstrated than can be described. Supervision is necessary in the form of checking of work to spot tendencies to deviate. Most critical of all, communication is required among indexers and between indexers and users, so that the former may understand how others are using the language. Communication is so important because it provides a voluntary means for aligning indexers with each other, and a forum by which an individual can try to covert the crowd (the other indexers) to his own ideas for handling new concepts.

Library indexing is a profession that calls for education and perception. It is difficult to tell a person so qualified that his best contribution will be made if he performs exactly the same as his fellows, even to making all the same mistakes. Yet, to a large extent, this is the case.

As to the second principle, even though a *complete* set of index rules can never be devised, there are ways by which the index language designer can help himself with the problem. He must, first, accept this principle so as not to be overwhelmed by the enormity of attempting to get a complete set of rules, and end up quitting far short of an attainable goal. Second, he must pick for himself some priority scheme, or importance-ordering, of subject categories, and concentrate on the more important areas, always working to keep the undefined subject areas restricted to ever lower priority subjects. Finally, the language designer must be in constant communication with its users, soliciting comments from them on difficult topics to index or queries to state, changing the language when necessary, and informing users of the changes. It is not unheard of for a set of indexing conventions, or scope notes (interpretations of index term usage rules), to exceed the formal definition part of a dictionary in length.

We must recognize that an index language is a "living" language—in practical, day-to-day use by a community of people. It will change as the community changes, which, in modern scientific libraries, is quite rapidly. The designer of such a language has a continuing responsibility to monitor and control its usage.

3.2.5 Examples of Indexing Rules

To demonstrate the variation in indexing rules that could occur even within the same index language we shall briefly describe a language, then show how the indexes actually produced can vary under different sets of rules. For each illustration we shall use the same document, the one reproduced in Figure 3.2.

Magnetic Disks

An indexed or "random access" memory of the magnetic disk type now is a feature of several electronic data processing systems. In such memories, every unit record is stored in its own addressable location. Thus the information need not be scanned and compared in order to find a particular record. All that is required is the address which uniquely locates the desired index record.

These memories store information on the surface of disks coated with magnetic material and rotating at extremely high speeds. Typically, such a disk will be from 2 to 4 feet in diameter and store the binary coded information in perhaps 100 concentric channels across the surface of the disk. In most cases several disks are stacked, one parallel to the other (as in "juke box" record players), but physically separated so that the magnetic reading and recording head can be physically moved from one disk to another and from one recording channel to another. The movement of the head is controlled by an addressing mechanism which determines, from the disk and channel identification supplied to it, the physical position to which the head must be moved.

Best known of these disk-type memories is the IBM Ramac disk unit which consists of 50 disks, each containing 100 channels with a capacity of 6000 bits, for a total capacity of 30 million bits or 5 million alphabetic characters. The time for the reading and recording head to move from a channel on one of the disks to a randomly located channel on another disk is approximately ½ second. Other, similar units are sold by RCA, Bryant, Telex, Laboratory for Electronics, Autonetics, and Aeronutronics. Although each approaches the problem of indexing in a slightly different manner, thereby providing different capacity and access rate characteristics, they are all fundamentally similar approaches to the mass data storage problem.

To illustrate the application of such a memory to the problems of information retrieval, experiments were conducted by J. J. Nolan [7] and F. E. Firth [8] of IBM. They thought of the Ramac disk file as separated into three sections. The first was a dictionary of the index terms used in the system, each with its respective address. The second section contained the coordinate index term records of their pertinent document serial numbers. The third section contained the bibliographical reference data in the form of document titles, each of which was addressable by the number found as the result of a coordinate index search in the second disk section.

During input, new entries were checked against the dictionary section for editing of new index terms. Then the document serial numbers were automatically entered under the appropriate index terms in section two and, as part of the same operation, the new titles were entered into the bibliography section. During search, the machine first determined the addresses of the index terms involved from section one; then it went directly to these addresses. Based on the logic of the request, it performed the necessary comparison operations. This resulted in matches which yielded addresses found in section three. Finally, the pertinent records in section three were printed out as a bibliography of titles which satisfied the request pattern.

Nolan compared continuous tape to the single-entry system of bookkeeping and the random access memory system to double-entry ledger accounts. In the IBM experiment conducted at the San Jose Research Laboratory in collaboration with the Technical Library there, the 305 Ramac was found to be mechanically sound for the purpose, but the reliability and completeness of any search, as with most other systems, were found to be wholly dependent on the quality of the human indexing and the effectiveness of the decision process for compatibility of index and search terms.

The disk type addressed access approach has a great deal of appeal, and certainly where usage is well defined it provides an extremely powerful approach to replacement of scanning by indexing. However, the problems in providing the item address so essential to the functioning of the unit must be recognized. Essentially, they all are a result of the fact that, since scanning in a disk memory is an almost impossibly expensive operation, any utilization must depend on an index of some form and therefore must have been anticipated by the organizer of the file. The methods for resolving this basic difficulty are many and are of varied utility, but none of them will succeed unless the activity is suitably restricted.

[7] J. J. Nolan, Principles of Information Storage and Retrieval Using a Large Scale Random Access Memory, IBM, San Jose, Calif., November 17, 1958.

[8] F. E. Firth, An Experiment in Literature Searching with the IBM 305 RAMAC, IBM, San Jose, Calif., November 17, 1958.

Figure 3.2   Sample document.   Source: Becker & Hayes. [2]

For an index language we shall start with the subject headings used by the Association for Computing Machinery (see Figure 2.4). We shall combine this vocabulary with a free key word system, and define a single syntactic relationship. This relationship will be a linking of a subject heading with a key word to imply that the key word was used in the context of the subject descriptor. The key word is not to be used in lieu of a subject heading, but to further define its meaning. A key word, then, shall represent some more specific concept than is able to be represented by a subject heading, and this includes names of people, places, organizations, or objects associated with the subject. We shall make the rule that all key words *must* have an associated subject descriptor but not vice versa. We shall assume that a query may specify either descriptor alone, or the complete term, or any combination of terms. Any number of terms may be used within the scope of these rules.

These rules fairly adequately describe an index language but give the prospective indexer or searcher no hint at all of how to use the language. How many terms will be used per index? What are the subjects stressed? Will all proper names mentioned in a document be in the index? If not, what are the selection criteria? Below are three sets of rules, each conceivably employable in some actual situation. We shall show how the document shown in Figure 3.2 would be indexed by each of these sets of rules.

1. For an engineering research library, subject emphasis is placed on progress in basic science, on specific engineering devices or techniques and their capabilities and limitations, and activities of technical personnel and laboratories, organizations, schools, and so on. To avoid excessive cataloging, only topics given major emphasis in a document should be indexed.

2. For an international trading company's library, emphasis is to be on commodities—their composition, manufacture, use, and sale,—and the manufacturers thereof. Topics should be indexed only if there is enough information in the document to provide a prospective importer/exporter with some specific information on composition, application, availability, cost, size, weight, or tariff data.

3. For an intelligence organization interested in the scientific capability of a foreign country, use the same basic rules as for the engineering laboratory except that, since this information is rather sparse, every proper name or equipment designation (e.g., model number) that appears in the document, in any context or with any relative importance, must be included in the index.

The indexes that resulted from the author applying these rules to the sample document are shown in Figure 3.3. Before looking at them,

Engineering laboratory	Trading company	Intelligence group
3.7 DISK	6.34 DISK	3.7 DISK
3.7 RAMAC	6.34 RAMAC	3.7 RAMAC
3.7 NOLAN, J. J.	6.34 IBM	3.7 NOLAN, J. J.
3.7 FIRTH, F. E.		3.7 FIRTH, F. E.
3.7 IBM, SAN JOSE RE- SEARCH LABORA- TORY		3.7 IBM, SAN JOSE RE- SEARCH LABORA- TORY
6.34 DISK		6.34 DISK
6.34 RAMAC		6.34 RAMAC
6.34 IBM		6.34 IBM
		6.34 RCA
		6.34 BRYANT
		6.34 TELEX
		6.34 LABORATORY FOR ELECTRONICS
		6.34 AUTONETICS
		6.34 AERONUTRONIC

Figure 3.3   Results of varying indexing rules.

it would prove a beneficial exercise for the reader to prepare the three indexes according to these rules and compare his results with the author's.   There is bound to be at least one discrepancy over three tries.   Probably the best way to grasp the nature of the variation among indexers is for the reader to try to explain each discrepancy in writing, taking, alternately, his own point of view and that of the author, and justifying each approach.

3.3   USE OF DOCUMENT STRUCTURE IN INDEXING

In this section we return to the three elements of a document's structure: vocabulary, syntax, and format, and consider how knowledge of these can aid indexing.

3.3.1   Vocabulary

The vocabulary of a document consists of the set of words, or word types,* used by an author.   When a given subject is to be discussed,

---

* A *word type* is a symbol, different from other word types, such as *the*.   A *word token* is an occurrence of a word.   In all but the shortest messages the number of word *tokens* far exceeds the number of word *types*, some words being repeated often.   The first sentence of this footnote contains 14 word tokens. Word types *a* and *word* occur twice each; hence, there are only 12 word *types*.

the vocabulary, or the set of word types, that can be used for effective communication is limited. Thus, a subject implies a set of words that is usually used in discussing it, and the set used in a document implies the subject discussed. A crude, but workable, index can be devised by simply listing each word of a document as a key word, and requiring the retriever to ask for all known forms, spellings, and synonyms of the words he uses as parts of his request. Roughly put, one of the techniques of automatic abstracting has been to ensure that the sentences selected from a document to form the abstract have heavy concentrations of the most often repeated, non-common words of the document.[20] The use of all word tokens of a document to constitute an index record fails to provide two things: *context*—the environment of a word as it was utilized that helps provide the sense of a word or *the particular meaning of a word or phrase out of several possible meanings,* and *concept*—the full significance created in the reader's mind by a phrase, sentence, or other syntactically governed word group. These terms are roughly analogous to Weaver's[22] *semantic* and *effective* or Hayakawa's[9] *informative* and *affective* aspects of communication. In all three cases, the former term (context, semantic, informative) can be interpreted as relating to the problem of distinguishing one "thing symbolized" from another, and the latter term (concept, effective, affective) as the image set up in a reader's mind when he perceives a set of symbols. For example, *OAS* can mean Organization of American States or *Organization de l'Armee Secrete.* Context can be used to differentiate between these meanings of the abbreviation. When the context indicates one of the meanings, the concept in the reader's mind will be an image of international cooperation or of terror. It is the author's view that the boundaries between the terms *context* and *concept,* as between *vocabulary* and *syntax,* are quite arbitrary. Consider the following example: "Smith is inclined against fascism and toward democracy." If we were to list the words of this sentence in alphabetical order, we could lose much of the context. If we selected a word entirely out of context, we could not tell, for example, which meaning of *inclined* was intended (*in favor of* or *tilted*). Even from the full listing, we cannot tell which belief Smith favored. It is reasonable, however, to infer from the alphabetically ordered word list: *against, and, democracy, fascism, inclined, is, Smith, toward* that the document discusses political beliefs, that Smith is somehow concerned, and that the meaning of inclined is *in favor of.*

Because we have defined vocabulary to deal with the selection of signs and referents or "things referred to" used by an author, we must include here a brief discussion of a special set of symbols—the punctuation marks. These are another example of the fine line between vocabulary and syntax. Punctuation marks, although they have meanings of their own, have meanings which are functional, which serve to define the context of some other symbols. The period, for example, is used to end a sentence which tells the reader that he should not necessarily treat the word before and the word after the period as syntactically related. The question mark tells the reader that information has not been conveyed about the subject of the sentence, but has been requested. The quotation marks serve a variety of purposes, some quite complex. In addition to denoting the precise words of a person, as restated between the marks, they can serve to modify the meaning of the word or phrase enclosed, usually by telling the reader not to apply the usual meaning to the word, but instead to look for some implied or allegorical meaning. The statement: "Mr. Jones 'stole the show,' " does not imply that Jones committed any crime nor that he was associated with any theatrical endeavor. The inner quotes tell us to put a different meaning on the enclosed words, and the resulting meaning of the sentence is that Mr. Jones dominated some proceeding in which he was involved. The use of quotes in this manner is an example of the use that can be made of the author's intent to communicate. He has taken the trouble to inform his readers that he has assigned an unusual meaning to a word, and they can take advantage of this, if the word is to be used in an index, by keeping words so noted apart from other occurrences of the word in which the conventional meaning was intended.

3.3.2 Syntax

Syntax is the set of rules governing placement of words relative to each other. As we have said before, the line of demarcation between syntactic rules and vocabulary rules is vague. Which tells us that the following sentence contains an error? "Everyone should remove their hat when entering the building." Have we selected the wrong symbol in using *their,* or should we say that a syntactic rule calls for agreement in number between pronouns and their antecedents?

Although selection of vocabulary terms to construct an index is a relatively simple technical problem, the use of syntax, especially in automatic indexing, can lead to difficulty. There have been successful programs that make use of syntax in interpreting vocabulary, but automatic syntactic analysis lags automatic word token analysis, *and use,* by a good bit. This is another example of the importance of the difference between the recognition of word types, or word functions, through syntactic analysis of sentences, and the use of the information in indexing. For example, to create a program which will recognize all persons' names or place names in a document, based upon syntactic analysis, would be desirable and useful in many libraries. But the capability to do this must not be confused with the end product of which this is a portion—the index of a document—for such information may not always be needed in an index or worth the cost. A large part of work in automatic indexing and information retrieval recognizes only one syntactic relationship, that of co-occurrence of words or index terms in the same document or document subdivision.

An indexer makes use of the document's syntax to determine the context that will help resolve ambiguities in word meanings. There is no point in describing the document's syntax in an index. Instead, he wishes to carry over its effect from the document to the index—to reproduce the contextual effect of word position in the index. A very simple example is this statement, "He did historical research _____ Michigan." If we fill in the blank with *at* we get one meaning, a general implication, through a usage common in the academic world, that work was done at the University of Michigan. If we fill in the blank with *on* we get the implication that Michigan was a subject, not a location, of research. If we use *in,* the implication is that the work was done within the state of Michigan. Regardless of the indexing system used, this distinction is an important one and must be manifested in the index. The manifestation in the index may not involve use of the same syntactic rules, but it must accomplish the objectives of differentiating between different meanings of the word *Michigan*.

3.3.3 Format

We are concerned here with the elements of format that contribute to understanding of the text, or to ease of indexing. Format is largely governed by prescriptive rules—those laid down by editors for their periodicals or by teachers for their students. The purpose is generally to ease understanding, to speed perusal, sometimes to attract reader interest. Adherence to a style on the part of authors of periodical publications sets up a form of communication or unwritten understanding with the habitual reader, which eliminates the need for some explanations and definitions. Lewis Jordan, News Editor of the *New York Times,* has stated,[12] "Most newspapers have developed distinctive characters, depending on the kind of reader to whom they appeal. A story of a stormy debate in the Security Council of the United Nations might be written one way in the New York Times and another in the New York Daily News." Rather than attempting to give a full discourse on writing style and layout, we shall just give some examples of format elements that are useful to an indexer trying to describe a document quickly and accurately.

1. Titles and Headlines. Titles and headlines are usually separated both spatially and typographically from the text. The form of separation almost universally follows standard rules for the publication or journal. The content of the title is more variable than are its position and typography, sometimes being under close editorial control and sometimes not. In journals where close control is maintained over titles, they can be profitably used directly in indexing. This is typical of professional journals where the title often constitutes a short abstract. It is not true in many popular journals, both technical and nontechnical, where titles are used to attract the reader, and may contain puns or other jokes calculated to catch the reader's eye. Consider the difference between the two titles of papers, published in professional journals, listed below. The difference in the understanding they convey of the content of the papers is quite large.

"On Keeping Up with Keeping Up," Jesse H. Shera, *UNESCO Library Bulletin,* Vol. XVI, No. 2, 1962*

"Message Route Control in a Large Teletype Network," Maurice Pollack, *Journal of the Association for Computing Machinery,* Vol. 11, No. 1, 1964.

2. Subtitles. Subtitles generally have less control exercised over them, and often require knowledge of prior titles or subtitles to understand them. However, the entire set of subtitles of a paper can serve as an abbreviated abstract for the paper. Subtitles can be content-oriented or functional. For example, the subtitle "Design of the Central Processor" is descriptive of the content, while "Statement of the Problem" or "Summary" are functional, describing the role of the paragraphs they introduce relative to the entire document, but telling nothing of the actual content of the paragraph. Format control over subtitles tends to be prescriptive, set by an editor, while the content tends to be relatively uncontrolled. Subtitles, like titles, are usually set apart physically from the text they accompany. Pollack's paper on message routing, which has so descriptive a title, has the following subtitle or section headings:

> *Introduction*
> *Routing Problem*
> *Methods of Solution*
> *Evaluation of Methods*
> *Final Comments*

* This paper carries the subtitle: "Recent Trends in Document Storage and Retrieval." The subtitle is used in the table of contents of the journal, but not in a list of titles that appears on the front cover.

which, unfortunately, add almost no descriptive information to the highly descriptive title.   On the other hand, Shera's paper has a very descriptive subtitle, and his section headings further delineate his subject matter. They are

> *New System for the Organization of Recorded Knowledge*
> *Main Groups of Systems*
> *Historical Evaluation*
> *Use of Marginal Punched Cards*
> *Use of Microphotography*
> *Aspect Systems*
> *Other Systems*
> *Use of Techniques of Automation*
> *Increase in the Production of Book Catalogs*
> *Use of Electronics*
> *Effect of the New Systems*
> *Benefits to Several Libraries*

Newspapers often summarize an article in headlines and sub-headlines. The headline in Figure 3.4 is from the New York Times of May 16, 1964, and gives an excellent summary of the subject matter and key names and places of the article.

The variation in descriptiveness of these subtitles demonstrates an important distinction, that of the difference between ability to recognize

LODGE BLOC PLANS
TO AID ROCKEFELLER
IN CALIFORNIA BID

———

Ambassador's Backers Are
Expected to Give Support
to the Governor Today

———

STOP-GOLDWATER MOVE

———

Envoy's Advocates Hope to
Win New Yorker's Votes
in Switch at Convention

New York Times
May 16, 1964

Figure 3.4   Example of a descriptive headline. © 1964 by the New York Times Company, reprinted by permission.

an element of structure and its use in an index. Knowledge of the prescriptive rules of format can help in the recognition of titles, abstracts, and so on, but mere recognition does not give us a good index, descriptive enough to be useful to help searchers find their material. Hence, teaching an indexer or computer program to recognize a structural element is not enough. It must be shown that the detected element makes an actual contribution to describing the document.

3. Summaries and Abstracts. Technical papers and reports often begin with a short abstract provided by the author. The preface or introduction to a book usually contains an abstract, although not necessarily clearly marked. Figure 3.5 shows the first page of a paper published in a typical professional journal.

When these are titled as such, and when the author has indeed summarized, they will be useful structural features for indexing purposes. When the author subtitles a paragraph *Summary* and proceeds to explain the organization of his material or justify its publication, the material is of little value in an index. Hence we lose the value of an easily recognizable format element, and its use in an index may have an adverse effect on the utility of the index as a retrieval tool. Many technical journals require a summary, but few exercise control over its content, except as to size. Newspapers, in particular, will tend to condense the sense of an entire article into the first paragraph,* thus satisfying the busy reader and assisting the indexer. A similar technique is sometimes used in technical papers and sometimes within structural subdivisions of a document, an example of the latter being the paragraph sentence which introduces or summarizes a paragraph.†

4. Headings. Headings are highly *pro forma* structural features that are often used in communications among members of an organization. Headings can include the name of the message originator and addressee; security classification, if appropriate; date; routing; priority or precedence; a subject code; or other, relatively simple items that always appear in the same position in a message. They are often found in

---

* "The way to begin a news story is . . . to summarize the story, beginning usually with the climactic event or with a statement of the meaning of the event. Newspaper men call the opening paragraph or paragraphs of their story the lead. They lavish great care upon it because they know they are competing for the reader's time."[13]

† William Strunk, Jr.,[21] discusses the organization of paragraphs and suggests the use of a sentence at the beginning of a paragraph to introduce the new topic which is the subject of the paragraph. Phyllis Baxendale[1] discusses the use of this concept, here called the "topic sentence," as an aid to automatic document indexing and points out that her experimentation showed that a topic sentence was used 92 per cent of the time in her experimental body of data.

Computer techniques, now employed by management in the planning, scheduling and control of projects, generally rely on the formulation of project "networks" as input to the computer programs.

This paper discusses a computer procedure for improving the input by obtaining networks with certain minimal properties.

With this improvement in input, the overall efficiency in using existing programs can be increased.

Computer construction of minimal project networks

by Bernard Dimsdale

PERT[1,2], LESS[3], CPM[4,5] and other techniques applied to the planning, scheduling and control of projects involve the construction of project representations called *networks* which pictorialize the relationships among the component activities of the particular project under consideration.

For example, in fabricating a structure the activities may involve: building forms, erecting steel, pouring concrete, procuring materials and equipment, etc. Whether "pouring concrete" is a single activity which occurs just once, or a single activity which is repeated as construction proceeds, or a complex of component activities involving ordering sand, delivery, cement mixing, etc. depends on the specific nature of the project at hand and is of no interest here. The point is that project planning involves specifying the component activities of the project, whatever they may be, and specifying the order in which they occur.

Once the list of activities is obtained and the order in which they are to occur has been specified, an *activity* network may be drawn in which the *nodes* designate *activities* and the *branches* (arrows) connecting nodes indicate that the activity represented by initial node precedes the activity represented by terminal node.

To illustrate, assume that a project involves activities *A*, *B*, *C* and *D*, and suppose that *A* must precede both *C* and *D* and that *B* must precede *D*. Figure 1 shows the corresponding activity network and a table containing the same information.

IBM Systems Journal
Vol. 2, March 1963

Figure 3.5　A technical paper with a short abstract.

<table>
<tr><td colspan="4">NAVAL MESSAGE (SHORT FORM)
OPNAV FORM 2110-29 (10-58)
Reorder from FPSO Cog. "I" Stock Points</td><td colspan="3">SECURITY CLASSIFICATION
UNCLASSIFIED</td></tr>
</table>

DRAFTED BY		PRECEDENCE IMMEDIATE	DATE/TIME GROUP 11Ø4Ø3Z	MESSAGE NR. 31

FROM:

    FLEAWEACEN WASHDC

TO:

    ALL SHIPS COPYING THIS BROADCAST

INFO:

    COMEASTSEAFRON / FLEWEAFAC NORVA / FLT HURRICANE FCSTFAC MIAMI/

    UNCLAS

    11Ø4ØØZ GALE WARNING. BETWEEN FORTY TWO AND FORTY FIVE NORTH FROM

    THIRTY FIVE WEST TO EUROPEAN COAST. WIND WESTERLY TWENTY FIVE TO

    THIRTY FIVE KNOTS

    WR NR3365   WU/JN

RELEASE	TOR 11/Ø417Z	TOD	CWO *Jn*	WO	DATE 11 OCT 63

1	2	3	4	5	6	7	8	9	10	11	12	13	14	15	16	17	18	19	20	21	22	23	24	DATE/TIME GROUP
I	I	A	I		I	I	I	I	I		I		I										I	11Ø4Ø3Z

SECURITY CLASSIFICATION
    UNCLASSIFIED

Figure 3.6 Example of a message using controlled headings. Source: Radioman 3 & 2, U. S. Navy, Bureau of Naval Personnel, Navpers 10228-D, Washington, D. C., 1964.

telegrams and dispatches, whether military or civil, or in interoffice memoranda in business organizations. They tend not to be found in technical papers or news articles (except for the dateline in the latter). Items appear in headings because they are often used, and their presentation in a highly controlled manner makes it easy for all users or readers to find them. Figure 3.6 shows the headings of a typical military dispatch.

The advantages of controlled headings to an indexer are that they are often used as search terms, hence are important to include in the index, and they are easy to locate and interpret. Only rarely, however, is subject matter described in a heading. When it is, it is generally in the form of a classification code affixed by the author who is not the person best qualified to decide upon the subject classification that each library should use.

5. Tagging. Tagging is a primitive syntactic technique that uses characters not otherwise used, a special positional relationship, or both to identify or modify a word. Capitalization is a form of it; the use of a specially formed character, usually to indicate that the word in which it appears is a name or the beginning of a sentence. In situations in which the documents are printed solely for entry into an information retrieval system, tagging may be used more elaborately, explicitly identifying all names and places, with unique characters or codes. Another more common but more ambiguous form of tagging is represented by our previous example of Senator Javits (R., N.Y.), the unusual string of characters following the name being an excellent means by which a computer could be able to recognize that a name has preceded the string. The characters of the string are not special; they have many other uses. It is the combination of the letter and punctuation pattern and the position which is unusual enough to be a recognition device.

Not new as a tool, but new as a formal procedure, is citation indexing—the use of chains of document references to describe a subject-related set of documents. Citation indexing uses one of the most common, and easiest to identify, structural elements of a document, its reference citations, as a means of associating a group of works assumed to be on much the same subject because of frequent cross referencing by the authors. This is described later as an indexing technique. If the author of a paper in which we are interested makes a reference to a paper he has used, it is likely that we will also be interested in this source and the sources of this source. Reference citations are relatively easy for indexers to identify. They appear in footnotes, special reference sections at the end of chapters, or in bibliographies at the end of books. The format of a citation follows a rigid rule imposed by a journal or publisher, hence is constant throughout any given document.

This list of format elements is not complete, but is sufficient to define the nature of format as an indexing aid. The advantage of format use in indexing is that the elements are relatively easy to recognize by manual or automatic techniques. Therefore, they offer an economical, fast approach to indexing. The difficulty that arises in the use of format lies in the facts that the content of a structural element is not uniformly useful in describing document content, and not all documents in a library have the same format or format elements.

3.4 STATISTICAL SELECTION OF INDEX TERMS

The application of computers to indexing of documents has led to a number of different studies which are centered upon use of various statistical attributes of a text to select appropriate index descriptors, terms, and phrases. In this section we shall examine some of the variables used in statistical language analysis, consider the relationship of "common" words to significant words, and, finally, present a theory of word significance.

The concepts developed in this section are intended to apply to machine indexing. Although they may be of interest to the human indexer in that they present a completely different approach to significance, they could not practically be incorporated in rules given to an indexer as the basis for his selection of significant terms.

3.4.1 The Basic Variables

The most commonly used variables in statistical analysis of written language are letter frequency,* letter group frequency (letter pairs, triples, quadruples, etc., also called digrams, trigrams, tetragrams, etc.), word frequency, and word size. The first two, analyzing as they do symbols that make up words, are of less interest in information retrieval than are the full word statistics. Word size is of limited interest, although, as we shall see, there is an interesting statistical relationship between word size and frequency of use. The frequency of occurrence of words in a text is the most important statistical measure that has been used in automatic processing of natural language for information retrieval purposes. Before examining the role of word frequency analysis in information retrieval, let us briefly consider some of the basic distributions of the variables named above.

Letter frequency is the best known of these variables, probably through popularization by Edgar Allan Poe in *The Gold Bug*.[18] The letter frequencies shown in Figure 3.7 are taken from several different sources, as noted in the table, and represent measures of the frequency of occurrence of letters in written English. Some variation can be noted, but not much, which is unfortunate, because if they were very different we might be able to use the differences in telling which type of documents were used in compiling each list, a capability we would like to have in information retrieval. Digram and trigram frequencies, samples of which are shown in Figure 3.8, are important in cryptanalysis, a highly specialized form of language translation. They offer modest assistance in information retrieval for they can assist in error detection and in recognition of certain types of classes of words. We might, for example, want to recognize word groups such as: all nouns, Russian place names, or chemical compounds. The occurrence of such letter groups as:

* In linguistics more interest might be shown in *phoneme* frequency than in letter frequency. Phonemes are speech units. In natural language there is not a one-for-one correspondence between phonemes and written letters.

. . . OVICH, . . . LAND, or OXY . . . can assist in recognizing the word type even if the full word is not in the dictionary. The International Morse Code shows a sensitivity to letter frequency in that it uses shorter codes for more frequent letters (apparently as measured in English). Compare the codes in Figure 3.9, written in order of increasing length or transmission time, with the table of letters, in order of decreasing frequency of use.

One of the earliest users of word frequency analysis was G. P. Zipf,[23] who attempted to prove that users of natural language select words

(a)	(b)	(c)
E	E	E
T	A	T
A	O	A
O	I	O
N	D	N
I	H	R
S	N	I
R	R	S
H	S	H
L	T	D
D	U	L
C	Y	F
U	C	C
P	F	M
F	G	U
M	L	G
W	M	Y
Y	W	P
B	B	W
G	K	B
V	P	V
K	Q	K
Q	X	X
X	Z*	J
J		Q
Z		Z

Figure 3.7 Letters in order of frequency of appearance in written English. Source: (a) H. F. Gaines†; (b) E. A. Poe[18]; (c) F. Pratt[19]. *Poe's list omits J and V. † From *Cryptanalysis: A Study of Ciphers and Their Solutions,* by Helen Fouche Gaines, copyright 1956, by Dover Publications, Inc., published by Dover Publications, Inc., New York 14, N.Y.[6]

Digrams		Trigrams	
TH	RO	THE	HIS
IN	LI	ING	RES
ER	RI	AND	ILL
RE	IO	ION	ARE
AN	LE	ENT	CON
HE	ND	FOR	NCE
AR	MA	TIO	ALL
EN	SE	ERE	EVE
TI	AL	HER	ITH
TE	IC	ATE	TED
AT	FO	VER	AIN
ON	IL	TER	EST
HA	NE	THA	MAN
OU	LA	ATI	RED
IT	TA	HAT	THI
ES	EL	ERS	IVE
ST	ME		
OR	EC		
NT	IS		
HI	DI		
EA	SI		
VE	CA		
CO	UN		
DE	UT		
RA	NC		

Figure 3.8 Digrams and trigrams in order of frequency of appearance in written English. Source: *Cryptanalysis: A Study of Ciphers and Their Solutions*, by Helen Fouche Gaines, copyright 1956, by Dover Publications, Inc., published by Dover Publications, Inc., New York 14, N.Y.[7]

under a constraint (descriptive rule under our terminology) which is that the word frequencies, if taken from a large enough sample, fall into a distinct pattern. Zipf plotted the *frequency* of occurrence of each word in a document against the *rank* of that word on a frequency-ordered list* and derived the expression $f = kr^{-1}$ where f is frequency, r rank, and k a constant. The general shape of the curve represented by this relationship is shown by the heavy line in Figure 3.11. Mandelbrot[16] improved on this somewhat, stating the relationship as $f = kr^{-B}$

---

* That is, the most frequent word is rank 1, the second most frequent is rank 2, and so on.

	Letter	Morse representation	Letter rank by frequency
1.	E	.	1
2.	T	-	2
3.	I	. .	6
4.	A	. -	3
5.	N	- .	5
6.	M	- -	16
7.	S	. . .	7
8.	R	. - .	8
9.	D	- . .	11
10.	U	. . -	13
11.	W	. - -	17
12.	G	- - .	20
13.	K	- . -	22
14.	O	- - -	4
15.	H	. . . .	9
16.	L	. - . .	10
17.	F	. . - .	15
18.	B	- . . .	19
19.	V	. . . -	21
20.	C	- . - .	12
21.	P	. - - .	14
22.	X	- . . -	24
23.	Z	- - . .	26
24.	Y	- . - -	18
25.	Q	- - . -	23
26.	J	. - - -	25

Figure 3.9 International Morse Code listed in order of increasing character length. Source: *Cryptanalysis: A Study of Ciphers and Their Solutions,* by Helen Fouche Gaines, copyright 1956, by Dover Publications, Inc., published by Dover Publications, Inc., New York 14, N.Y.[7]

where B is "near" unity, but can vary somewhat with the text. In an unpublished research project, the author has discovered values of B well below unity, but the languages used for the study were heavily constrained both in vocabulary and syntax, and perhaps were not deserving of the name natural language.* The hypothesis was drawn that

* In one case "telegraphic" style was used—short, terse sentences using a rather stereotyped vocabulary—and in the other only descriptors from a key word index of the documents were used. Values of B derived were about 0.8 and 0.5, respectively.

THE	3	OR	2	WHEN	4	ONLY	4
OF	2	HER	3	WHAT	4	ANY	3
AND	3	HAD	3	YOUR	4	THEN	4
TO	2	AT	2	MORE	4	ABOUT	5
A	1	FROM	4	WOULD	5	THOSE	5
IN	2	THIS	4	THEM	4	CAN	3
THAT	4	MY	2	SOME	4	MADE	4
IS	2	THEY	4	THAN	4	WELL	4
I	1	ALL	3	MAY	3	OLD	3
IT	2	THEIR	5	UPON	4	MUST	4
FOR	3	AN	2	ITS	3	US	2
AS	2	SHE	3	OUT	3	SAID	4
WITH	4	HAS	3	INTO	4	TIME	4
WAS	3	WERE	4	OUR	3	EVEN	4
HIS	3	ME	2	THESE	5	NEW	3
HE	2	BEEN	4	MAN	3	COULD	5
BE	2	HIM	3	UP	2	VERY	4
NOT	3	ONE	3	DO	2	MUCH	4
BY	2	SO	2	LIKE	4	OWN	3
BUT	3	IF	2	SHALL	5	MOST	4
HAVE	4	WILL	4	GREAT	5	MIGHT	5
YOU	3	THERE	5	NOW	3	FIRST	5
WHICH	5	WHO	3	SUCH	4	AFTER	5
ARE	3	NO	2	SHOULD	6	YET	3
ON	2	WE	2	OTHER	5	TWO	3

Number of 1's	2	0	0	0
2's	10	9	2	1
3's	9	8	6	7
4's	3	6	11	11
5's	1	2	5	6
6's	0	0	1	0
Total Characters in column	65	76	97	97
Average Characters in column	2.64	3.04	3.88	3.88

Figure 3.10 List of most common English words and their length. Source: *Cryptanalysis: A Study of Ciphers and Their Solutions,* by Helen Fouche Gaines, copyright 1956, by Dover Publications, Inc., published by Dover Publications, Inc., New York 14, N.Y.[T]

B is a measure of the author's style, which includes such factors as terseness, richness of vocabulary, and length of document. If this were the case, $B = 1.0$ denotes natural language, conventionally used, and decreasing values of B indicate increasingly constrained language. Herdan[10] also discusses a numeric measure of style in his treatment of statistical language analysis, a treatment far more comprehensive than is possible here.

The analysis of word *length*, like letter or n-gram analysis, is of only peripheral value in the present development of this science. It is interesting, however, to note the correspondence between word length and word frequency in conventional usage. Figure 3.10 shows a list of the most frequent words taken from a sample of 242,432 English words. Note the increase in average word length as we go from the first column (highest frequency) to the third and fourth columns, and note also the relative unimportance of most of these words to subject determination. The suggestion arises that word length might be used to tell important from unimportant words, and do so at a very low cost—simply that of counting the letters. A more thorough analysis of word length distribution is found in the work of Herdan.[11] With the introduction of the importance of words and the possibility of assessing this quality by statistical means, we are at an appropriate point to introduce the general subject of significant words and their recognition by statistical techniques.

3.4.2   Common Words and Significant Words

In a paper published in 1958 H. P. Luhn[15] proposed a way of measuring word significance by use of word frequencies, a step in his overall aim of preparing an abstract of a document automatically. He noted, first, that the most frequent words are "too common to have the type of significance being sought . . . " and could be eliminated from consideration by use of a common word list or by use of a "high frequency cut-off through statistical methods. . . ." A similar, low-frequency cut-off, he said, could be established to remove infrequent words. This appears intuitively reasonable, for in a large paper or book the occurrence of a word just once or twice does not appear to endow it with much significance. Luhn presented a diagram similar to that shown in Figure 3.11 to show the frequency-rank curve truncated at either end. He then proposed that a curve, somewhat as shown by the dotted line, could be superimposed and would represent the significance of a word as a function of its rank. This method of determining significance was used in a program that went on to weight sentences of the input docu-

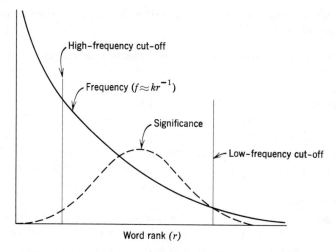

Word rank (r)

Figure 3.11   Relationship of word significance to frequency, after Luhn.[15]

ment and to select those with the best concentration of significant words for inclusion in the abstract.

Reasonable as this argument may seem, we must take a very careful look at it, for it has increasing importance in modern information retrieval research. What is significance? Luhn did not define it. Standard dictionaries tend to stress importance or news value in its definition, neither precise enough concepts upon which to base a formal statistical measure. We shall, however, make some use of this approach later. In statistics, when testing a hypothesis, significance is defined in terms of a number differing from an expected value; that is, divergence from the expected is significant. In either case, we want to know when a word either conveys enough news or differs sufficiently from the expected to justify its selection as a descriptor in an index record designed to tell how this document differs from other documents. Before we attempt a formal definition of significance, let us consider two related concepts— sampling word usage to arrive at a "true" distribution of words in a given language, and the definition of a "common" word.

Cherry[4] makes this comment on the sampling problem:

> How can samples be taken, sufficiently scattered as regards subject matter and sufficiently lengthy, to be considered truly representative of "conversational English"? The difficulty has been underlined by Berry[3] who remarks upon the results of a statistical count of 25,000 words of telephone conversa-

tion which showed the word "mudguard" to be one of the more frequently used words in English!

To show how annoying this measurement problem can be, in Britain, where this sample was taken and from where Cherry wrote, the word *mudguard* means what *fender* means in the United States. It was only necessary for one of the parties monitored by Berry to have been an automobile garage or automotive insurance company for the word to have shown up with the high frequency found so distressing by Cherry and Berry, yet both feel that this event somehow invalidates the sample. *If we cannot find a true distribution of word frequencies, then we must accept that we cannot rely upon deviation from true frequency to provide a measure of significance.*

Although no one has yet devised a way to tell the expected frequency with which the words that intuitively seem subject-laden will occur in randomly selected samples of English text, estimates of occurrence rates of some words have been made, and these seem to be consistent over many independent samples. A few such samples are shown in Figure 3.10. These words are often designated "common" or "noninformation-bearing". They appear to fail to be significant by both our definitions: they tell no news, and they occur at a predictable rate. Still, we cannot dismiss these words so lightly. We must test whether "common" words indeed lack significance or importance just because they were expected. Consider, for example, the use of letter frequency tables in cryptanalysis. Is it insignificant to have determined which letter of a cipher represents the letter *e* because *e* is such a high-frequency letter? Would it be more valuable to know the cipher representation of *x, y,* and *z* or of *e, t,* and *a*? We must assume that the latter group is of greater importance in breaking a cipher *because* they are more common. Perhaps the analogous point in regard to common words is that the high-frequency, expected words may be significant or information-bearing because they did not fail to appear. In pursuit of this point, we shall consider two possible uses of common word frequencies. The first is a summary of an actual research project in which rather common words were used to determine authorship of disputed documents. The second is a hypothetical, multi-language processor that may find common words the most useful.

Mosteller and Wallace[17] performed a study which made use of word frequencies to resolve the disputed authorship of some of the *Federalist Papers.** While the statistical techniques they employed are beyond

---

* The *Federalist Papers* were a series of essays written by Alexander Hamilton, James Madison, and John Jay in support of the adoption of the Constitution by the states, and are credited with a strong influence in its final ratification.

Word	Hamilton rate	Madison rate
upon	3.24	.23
also	.32	.67
an	5.95	4.58
by	7.32	11.43
of	64.51	57.89
on	3.38	7.75
there	3.20	1.33
this	7.77	6.00
to	40.79	35.21
although	.06	.17
both	.52	1.04
enough	.25	.10
while	.21	.07
whilst	.08	.42
always	.58	.20
though	.91	.51
commonly	.17	.05
consequently	.10	.42
considerable(ly)	.37	.17
according	.17	.54
apt	.27	.08
direction	.17	.08
innovation(s)	.06	.15
language	.08	.18
vigor(ous)	.18	.08
kind	.69	.17
matter(s)	.36	.09
particularly	.15	.37
probability	.27	.09
work(s)	.13	.27

Figure 3.12 Discriminator words used in authorship problem. Source: Mosteller and Wallace.[17]

the level of this book, a look at the word list used for final discrimination between possible authors, and the frequencies associated therewith is enlightening. The word list is shown in Figure 3.12. It can be seen

Since the papers were published anonymously, the precise authorship has been lost in some cases. Note: The purposes of the Mosteller and Wallace study were to demonstrate certain statistical techniques as well as to solve the authorship problem.

"by"			"to"			"upon"		
Number of occurrences	H	M	Number of occurrences	H	M	Rate of occurrence (per 1000)	H	M
1–2	2		20–24		3	0 (exactly)	0	41
3–4	7		25–29	2	5	0–1	1	7
5–6	12	5	30–34	6	19	1–2	10	2
7–8	18	7	35–39	14	12	2–3	11	
9–10	4	8	40–44	15	9	3–4	11	
11–12	5	16	45–49	8	2	4–5	10	
13–14		6	50–54	2		5–6	3	
15–16		5	55–59	1		6–7	1	
17–18		3				7–8	1	
	48	50		48	50		48	50

Figure 3.13 Frequencies of selected indicator words in authorship problem. The frequency of occurrence of words within a class interval in 48 known Hamilton and 50 known Madison papers. Source: Mosteller and Wallace.[17]

that most of the words in column one fall in the loosely defined category of commonly occurring and noninformation bearing words. The second and third columns show the mean occurrence rate in papers of known Hamilton and Madison authorship, respectively, Jay not being involved in the authorship dispute. Note, particularly, the rates for *while* and *whilst*, words meaning essentially the same thing, one being heavily favored by one author and one by the other. Figure 3.13 shows the raw frequencies with which the words *by, to,* and *upon* appear in documents.

The conclusion of the authors was that all the papers that were in dispute were written by Madison, although there is a variation from paper to paper in the degree of certainty of this statement. The importance of the study to the topic under discussion here, common words, is that some rather common words proved to be quite significant for the purpose of this study. Because only 30 words were used in the final analysis, and they performed the required discrimination between authors, they can hardly be denied to have conveyed the information sought. The information sought, of course, was an index term—the name of the author.

For the second example of the uncommonality of common words let us hypothesize a processor which is to be fed documents in any of a variety of languages. These are to be translated into English, and the first step must be to determine the language of the document in order to select the appropriate dictionary for use in the translation process. There are a number of ways of determining this.   Let us consider two:

1. Count letter frequencies in the text and compare the table of frequencies with tables of "standard" letter frequencies for each language, selecting the dictionary corresponding to the table which best fits the computed table.

2. Count word frequencies.   Select the most frequent ten words and search lists of common words separately maintained for each language under consideration.   The lists would be restricted to articles, pronouns, prepositions, and conjunctions, and need not be longer than 10 to 20 words each.   Choose the language in whose word-group there is the greatest number of "hits."

Either method could be used with many variations, but our point here is not to produce an efficient program so much as an infallible selection scheme.   What is the possibility that method 2 can fail?   Let us consider the lists of common words in Figure 3.14 selected from the four parts of speech given above.   These words are not necessarily the most frequently used in these languages but they are very common. There are no symbols in common to any two lists, although if enough languages and words in them were represented duplication of symbols would occur (e.g., *y* in French and Spanish; *il* in French and Italian; or *also* in English and German).   For the lists we have shown an English text, say, of a thousand words, would certainly produce in its ten most frequent words matches for most of the words presented here in the English column but would be very unlikely to match any word in either

English	French	German
a	à	aber
an	de	auf
and	des	der
at	et	ein
but	il	er
for	la	es
of	les	ist
or	pour	sie
the	un	über
to	une	und

Figure 3.14   Frequently occurring words in different languages.

Frequency	Term	Frequency	Term	Frequency	Term
40	the	3	attack	2	chase
18	Cuba	3	Bahamas	2	commandos
15	to	3	error	2	exiles
13	of	3	fired	2	government
9	a	3	Migs	2	force
8	that	3	out	2	had
7	and	3	Ruzek	2	he
7	it	3	shots	2	hit
6	in	3	situation	2	last
6	on	3	they	2	off
6	said	3	were	2	or
6	was	3	yesterday	2	planes
5	Floridian	2	after	2	raids
5	incident	2	American	2	recurrence
4	an	2	as	2	reported
4	by	2	avoid	2	run
4	delivered	2	both	2	shipping
4	for	2	bow	2	this
4	State Dept.	2	Buchanan, Jerry	2	Thursday
4	United States	2	Caribbean	2	warning
4	vessel	2	charge	2	with

Figure 3.15 Word frequency list from a newspaper article. Source: "Cuba's Apology to U.S. Closes Ship Attack Case", *The Washington Post,* April 3, 1963.

remaining column. Figure 3.15 shows the high frequency portion of a word frequency list for an article in the *Washington Post* of April 3, 1963, which is reproduced in Figure 3.16. What is the probability that this method will select the wrong language? It appears to be virtually zero. This statement is not subject to mathematical proof, for we cannot prove the commonality of the words. An experimental test of this hypothesis can, however, be repeated as often as desired, using texts from many different languages, and varying the standard lists. For the purposes of this discussion we regard the method as proven.

If the most common words selected to be "noninformation-bearing" conjunctions, prepositions, pronouns, and articles can discriminate so well, are they insignificant or lacking in importance? Or are they, for a processor in the situation we have postulated here, the most significant words of all, the ones that contribute to the key decision—selection of

Cuba's Apology to U.S. Closes Ship Attack Case

Cuba delivered a full apology to the United States yesterday for the attack on the American cargo ship Floridian last Thursday and the State Department said it considered the incident closed.

The unusually blunt admission of error by Communist Cuba, plus a declaration "to avoid a recurrence of the incident," was delivered by Czech Ambassador Miloslav Ruzek to Robert A. Hurwitch, deputy director of the State Department's Cuban task force.

This acknowledgment, it should be noted, follows the United States announcement on Saturday of a crackdown on Cuban exiles' hit-run attacks on Castro Cuba.

Ruzek told reporters after he delivered the Cuban message, that: "The Cuban government also notes the seriousness of the situation and requests a stop to this kind of thing (hit-run raids) lest the situation get out of hand."

Error Is Claimed

After Soviet-built Migs fired warning shots near the Floridian 25 miles off the Cuban coast, the Cuban government first said its planes "probably fired in error."

The State Department said Cuba stated yesterday "that the pilots of its two Mig aircraft had arrived at the erroneous conclusion that the Floridian was an enemy vessel." Cuba said "it had no wish to interfere with U. S. or other inetrnational shipping in the Caribbean," the State Department continued, "that it regrets the incident of March 28, and that it is undertaking to adopt all possible measures to avoid a recurrence of the incident."

Ruzek quoted the Cuban note as saying the Cuban planes were in pursuit of another unidentified vessel when they "overflew" the Floridian "and before identification they fired some warning shots across the bow." Members of the Floridian's crew, however, reported Thursday that the Migs made several deliberate shooting passes, off both the bow and stern of the vessel.

As the clouded Caribbean situation now stands for the record, both the United States and Cuba are committed to try to forestall incidents that might spiral into major conflict.

16 Exiles Jailed

In Nassau, Bahamas, 16 Cuban exile commandos who set out last week on a raiding mission against Cuba were sent to jail yesterday for seven days pending investigation by British colonial authorities.

They were charged with possessing firearms without license in Bahamas waters.

A 17th raider, Jerry Buchanan, an American from Miami, pleaded guilty to an illegal entry charge.

Police Prosecutor Wilton Boyd said Buchanan was released in $70 bond and his case was adjourned on condition that he leave the Bahamas by Friday.

A second boat belonging to the commando group, the Escambray Front anti-Communist Cuban army, meanwhile was reported prowling along Cuba's coast looking for Russian vessels to attack or to contact underground forces, presumably to deliver arms.

Figure 3.16 From *The Washington Post,* April 3, 1963.

a dictionary? Referring to Luhn's diagram, Figure 3.11, it appears that the peak of significance comes, in this situation, near the left edge of the graph.

We have now shown how common words can be used to determine authorship in a case where true identity of the author was the most significant information sought. We have shown how common words can be used to determine the language in which a document was written, so that it becomes possible to select a dictionary and proceed to translate the document. A theory of common and significant words must be able to account for these examples. Such a theory is offered in the next section.

3.4.3   A Theory of World Significance

The hypothesis offered here is that word significance is indeed a function of frequency of occurrence, but also of the extent to which this frequency is predictable. If a reader knows that certain words will occur with high frequency in a given document or set of documents, then these words are not necessarily the most significant to him. The most significant are the highest frequency words that deviate from predicted frequency. *Words are significant as subject descriptors, then, in proportion to the difference between their actual and expected frequencies.**

Let us consider some examples. In the "universal" translator of the last section, no prior knowledge was presumed about the documents, and we found (intuitively) that we could use the most frequent words for our major decision.

In Selective Dissemination of Information (SDI)[24] a subscriber is permitted to define his subjects of interest, and to receive notices of publication of papers on these subjects. This is, in effect, a clipping service tailored to individual requirements. Suppose we subscribe to this service and request material on the subject of **computer programming.** In the United States we generally expect publications to be in English, and there is not normally a provision in SDI for either specifying or excluding a natural language. Hence the most frequent words in the documents we receive will be the usual words listed in Figure 3.10. Immediately beyond (lower frequency) then we should not be surprised to find such terms as **compile, code, register, loop, flow chart, memory, input, output, storage,**

---

* A high-frequency word that was not expected to be so is significant. The absence of a word (low-frequency) that was expected with high frequency does not produce an important index term but may be important in subject classification.

load, relocate, and so on, but even they are not significant to a person who is a programmer and who knows he is to receive only papers on programming; that is, it is predictable that they will be high-frequency words. What might be significant to the programmer are such words as information retrieval, multiprogramming, cross-correlation, or any other term tending to indicate the programming specialty or application of the author.

At the University of Pittsburgh[14] an information retrieval system was developed that permits a user to search virtually the entire text of a document for the presence of a single word. It is possible to search for the word red in a document, and to retrieve all documents containing it. More realistically, although the system was designed for searching legal material, a search could be instituted for any reference to a given name or commodity—for J. P. Morgan or for centrifugal sump pumps. The poser of such a request is saying, in effect, "Regardless of any other words in the document, and regardless of anyone else's idea of importance of subject, I am defining a document to be of interest to me if it contains the word _____." Such a statement essentially shifts the peak of Luhn's significance curve over the required word wherever it appears in the frequency distribution, even if at the bottom of the list.

In these three examples (the translator, SDI, and the full-text search) we have shown plausibly how the significance curve can peak anywhere from the high- to the low-frequency end of the distribution. In each case the peak was positioned when the interested party, the searcher of information, stated the frequencies he expected, assumed them without stating them explicitly, or indicated no interest in the frequency of words in the distribution. This is illustrated graphically in Figure 3.17. Here in Case I the shaded portion of the graph illustrates the set of words that would have been significant had there been no prior knowledge or prediction of word frequency. These are the highest frequency words of the document. In Case II we assume the language and major subject to be "known"; that is, we assume we have predicted approximately the set of words and frequencies shown in the shaded area by excluding "common" words. Because we have predicted them, the significance of these words is near zero. Those words we did not predict but which occurred often (the unshaded area immediately to the right of the shaded area) become the highly significant ones, and the curve of significance is essentially Luhn's curve as shown in Figure 3.11. In Case III we assume only one important word, probably one specified as the only descriptor in a query. The sharp peak, then, represents the significance of this single word.

With this as a background, we can come to a final resolution of what

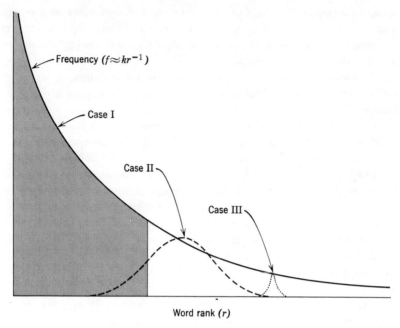

Figure 3.17 Relationship of word significance to frequency, significance not fixed.

we feel is a definition of word significance in the context of information retrieval and document classification, or indexing.

There are two commonly used definitions of significance: that which is new or important and that which differentiates one subject category or interest from another. Given a hierarchical classification system, a system user may assign different significance to each level of the hierarchy used to define his subject. For example, he may attach no importance to the fact that a document is about **science** or, within that, about **engineering,** because these are the only general subjects of interest to him (hence he expects them each time). Perhaps because a computer engineer is interested in both electrical and mechanical design problems, he may indicate slight significance to whether a document is about **electrical engineering** or **mechanical engineering** and then show increasing significance if, say, an electrical engineering document covers **servomechanisms.** Generally, though, an information user does not consider the arrival of a document on his own subject specialty to be significant. It is far too common an occurrence. To this person the significant information in a document is what is said about that subject, the words "below" those that discriminate his subject from others. Different subjects, at different levels, may be selected by different users. In this sense the news and discrimination definitions of significance are compatible.

Significance, then, is not inherent. It is a relative measure. The assignment of significance may be visualized as occurring in three parts. First, the interrogator of a file of information assigns a set of low significance measures to the set of words which he expects to occur often, but in which he has no special interest, so long as they do occur as predicted. Thus the high-frequency words are the "common" words. The assignment of low significance to these high-frequency words is generally done implicitly. Second, the interrogator names the set of words to which he assigns top significance in the discriminating sense— the words which best describe his subject. These words define his general area of interest, and he wishes to exclude from consideration any documents whose frequency distributions differ from the expected at this region of the distribution. Finally, although this is also usually stated only implicitly, his real interest lies in what he can find out about the subject defined in step two. What is significant in the news sense is what follows after the first two criteria of word distribution have been met.

We feel that this approach resolves the ambiguity over the meaning of word significance—basically that arising over the concepts *important* or *new* on one hand and *expected* on the other. What is *most* significant is what is *new* or unexpected about the general subject that was expected.

REFERENCES

1. Baxendale, Phyllis, "Machine-Made Index for Technical Literature, an Experiment," *IBM Journal of Research and Development,* **2**, 4 (1958), 354–361.
2. Becker, Joseph, and Robert M. Hayes, *Information Storage and Retrieval: Tools, Elements, Theories,* John Wiley & Sons, New York, 1963, p. 179.
3. Berry, J., "Some Statistical Aspects of Conversational Speech," *Communications Theory,* Willis Jackson, Ed., Butterworths Scientific Publications, London, 1953, p. 393.
4. Cherry, C., *On Human Communication,* The MIT Press, Cambridge, Massachusetts, 1959, p. 107.
5. DuShane, G., "Say It Ain't So!" *Science,* **134**, 3489 (1961).
6. Gaines, H. F., *Cryptanalysis,* Dover Publications, New York, 1956, p. 218.
7. *Ibid.,* pp. 226–227.
8. Giniger, Henry, " 'Franglais' Invasion Stirs Paris," *New York Times,* April 5, 1964, p. 1.
9. Hayakawa, S. I., *Language in Thought and Action,* Harcourt, Brace & World, New York, 1949, p. 82.

10. Herdan, G., *Language as Choice and Chance,* P. Noordhoff N. V., Groningen, 1956, p. 32.
11. *Ibid.,* Chapter 5.
12. Jordan, Lewis, *News, How It Is Written and Edited,* The New York Times, New York, 1960, p. 5. Copyrighted 1960 by The New York Times and reprinted with permission.
13. *Ibid.,* p. 9.
14. Kehl, William B., John F. Horty, Charles R. T. Bacon, and Davis S. Mitchell, "An Information Retrieval Language for Legal Studies," *Communications of the ACM,* 4, 9 (1961), 380–389.
15. Luhn, H. P., "The Automatic Creation of Literature Abstracts," *IBM Journal of Research and Development,* 2, 4 (1958), 159–165.
16. Mandelbrot, B., "An Informational Theory of the Statistical Structure of Language," *Communication Theory,* Willis Jackson, Ed., Butterworths Scientific Publications, London, 1953, pp. 486–502.
17. Mosteller, Frederick and David L. Wallace, "Inference in an Authorship Problem," *J. Amer. Statistical Assoc.,* 53, 302 (1963), 275–309.
18. Poe, Edgar Allan, "The Gold Bug," *Tales,* Dodd, Mead, New York, 1952.
19. Pratt, Fletcher, *Secret and Urgent,* Blue Ribbon Books, Garden City, New York, 1942, p. 252.
20. Savage, T. R., H. C. Fallon, and M. E. Saxon, *ACSI-Matic Auto-Abstracting Project,* Interim Report, International Business Machines Corp., Yorktown Heights, New York, 1959.
21. Strunk, William, Jr., and E. B. White, *The Elements of Style,* The Macmillan Co., New York, 1959, p. 11.
22. Shannon, Claude E., and Warren Weaver, *The Mathematical Theory of Communication,* The University of Illinois Press, Urbana, Illinois, 1959, p. 95.
23. Zipf, G. K., *Human Behavior and the Principle of Least Effort,* Addison-Wesley Publishing Co., Cambridge, Massachusetts, 1949, pp. 19–55.
24. ———, *General Information Manual: Selective Dissemination of Information,* Brochure E20-8092, International Business Machines Corp., White Plains, New York, 1962.
25. ———, *Webster's Third New International Dictionary,* G. & C. Merriam Co., Springfield, Massachusetts, 1964.

EXERCISES

1. Using any of the sets of rules in this chapter (Section 3.2.5), index several documents and compare results of someone else's attempt to do the same. For each discrepancy, justify both points of view. Discuss how the rules could be improved to improve indexer consistency.
2. Select several technical books in your own field. Search several libraries using different index systems for them. (Try, for example, the school library and the nearest city library or an industrial library.) Compare and discuss any differences, with particular attention to breadth and depth of indexing, point of view and consistency among catalogers.
3. Work in groups of two or more people. Select a set of three or four

documents of mutual interest on the same general subject. These can be news articles, technical papers or abstracts. Decide on an index language. Each person should prepare a set of index rules to be utilized by another in indexing each document.

   a. Compare the resulting indexes.

   b. Critique the index language used, in detail.

   c. Try the experiment again, with a different person using the rules and compare the remarks made by each indexer in the critique.

4. Read the coverage of the same news event in several different newspapers. Try for papers of widely differing outlook and appeal. Compare their structural features. Can anything about the papers' attitude toward the story be inferred from the differing treatments? Discuss. Compare the articles on the basis of breadth and depth and point of view.

5. Make a list of the adjectives used in each story used in the previous exercise. Compare the lists and discuss the significance of the differences in regard to what they tell about the authors. Repeat for verbs and nouns.

6. Devise a procedure for determining the part of speech of words as they occur in natural language text. Write the rules explicitly. Do not make use of word lists (e.g., do not use a rule such as "*Be* is a verb."). You can make use of length (e.g., two-letter words are more likely to be prepositions than anything else), prefixes, and suffixes (e.g.,-*ing* usually indicates a participle). It is sufficient to identify word groups as: nouns or pronouns, verbs (all forms), conjunctions or prepositions, and modifiers. Context may be used; for example, a preposition rarely follows another preposition.

7. Select some sentences from a book or newspaper and demonstrate how the meaning can be changed by changing "unimportant" words, such as prepositions (see the Michigan example in Section 3.3.2) or punctuation.

8. Write a definition of a "common" or "noninformation-bearing" word (other than by listing all of them). Apply the rule to a news article. Does it remove all "common" words? Does it remove any "important" ones? Discuss your results.

CHAPTER 4

Retrieval of index records

4.1 INTRODUCTION

In Chapter 1 we showed that an information retrieval system requires its users to make known their information needs to it. We shall now consider the related problems of formulating a statement of information needs and the use of this statement to control a search of index files in order eventually to retrieve the desired information. This statement is commonly called a *query* because its author is asking a question or asking for information.

The elements of the retrieval process, as we shall study them in this chapter, are (a) the composition, or formulation, of the query, (b) the matching of the query against records in the library's files and the determination of the relevance of the records to the query, (c) the actual retrieval of information contained in files, (d) the evaluation of the retrieval process, and (e) development of strategies for using resources available to accomplish the searcher's objective.

One of the terms whose meaning is disputed among practitioners of information retrieval is *information retrieval,* itself. In the vast majority of libraries, if we want the answer to a specific question, a search of the index file produces a document reference, and the library's work is done when the book is produced. To the research worker looking for a single fact, his work is just beginning, for now he must look through all the books given him for the one fact. He is liable to complain about the quality of the library's service, feeling that, in response to his specific question, he did not get the *information* he wanted directly, but instead got a pile of books. In recognition that this problem exists, we find that such terms as *document retrieval, fact retrieval, data retrieval,* and *information recovery* are variously used to describe retrieval of books in answer to a question (document retrieval) or retrieval of the information sought, directly (the latter three terms). In the definition we shall use, information retrieval means the retrieval of information, or

106

symbols, from a file, and is independent of the nature or form of the information retrieved or the use to be made of it. If a searcher queries a file and retrieves a list of call numbers of books which he must then retrieve from another file or store, we consider this information retrieval, just as we do the physical retrieval of the books themselves, or retrieval of the ultimately sought facts from these books. The only difference between a file search that results in retrieval of a call number and one that retrieves, say, an author's name, is that the former, although it is information in every sense, has little utility unless used to search another file, the set of hard copy documents. The number of searches required, before a system user finally gets the information he is actually seeking, is a factor entering into system cost and effectiveness but not, we feel, into the definition of the term. However, to relate the term *information retrieval* to general usage, we can make the following definitions and comments: *

Data retrieval: The retrieval of a string of symbols in response to a query.

Fact retrieval: Usually the same as data retrieval, but what is a fact is, of course, highly subjective. A term to be avoided in careful discussion.

Document retrieval: Frequently a two-step operation, involving retrieval of a datum or "fact" (such as a call number), then a very large symbol string, the document.

Information retrieval: A term, in our usage, generic to all the above.

4.2   PRINCIPLES OF RETRIEVAL

To retrieve an item of information from a file, it is necessary to state what is wanted, in what records and files this will be found, and, what is sometimes a separate statement, how to tell when the information has been found. Then there must be a comparison of information needs with information stored and, finally, physical recovery of the information. The query conveys the statement of required information to the files. In matching the query against the stored information in the file, there may be two separate operations, one to determine whether the stored record contains the type of information specified by the query, and then, possibly, one to measure its degree of relevance to the query. The latter operation, far more often, is combined with the matching operation. In this section, we cover the mechanics of this process.

* The author is indebted to Dr. Robert M. Hayes who suggested this approach in a personal communication. Some slight changes have been made for which the author is entirely responsible.

4.2.1   Selection of Information

An index record, representing as it does a set of document attributes, may derive its interest to the searcher from the presence of any of these attributes.   This leads us to a careful delineation of the difference between *matching* and *selecting*.   In *matching,* we compare words or terms contained in a query with corresponding terms contained in an index record.   In doing this we: (*1*) compare the query with the index, (*2*) compute a measure of the relationship between query and index record, and (*3*) decide whether the index satisfies the query.   Matching does not include selecting.   *Selecting* means *taking information from a record.*   The human searcher of a card catalog selects his information from a card without much conscious effort, but a computer must be explicitly programmed to select something.   Hence, to a programmer of retrieval systems, the difference between matching and selecting is important because he must perform specific, separate functions to handle the two separate operations.

The user of a card catalog may vary his mode of selecting terms.   For example, if he enters with a full bibliographic citation (for example, *title, author, publisher,* and *date*), he is likely to select only the call number from the catalog card.   However, if the search is only on subject, the searcher is probably going to copy out the full citation as well as the call number because he plans to establish a relevance threshold when he has seen several index cards.   Index records, such as cards in a catalog, can also be used by varying the selection rules to verify spelling of an author's name, determine authorship of a book known only by title, determine year of birth of an author, or to collect many other items of information.   In a programmed system it is necessary to state, either as part of the query or as part of the program, the index terms that are to be retrieved.   The cause of confusion between matching and selecting often comes because although the search terms may vary, the *selected* terms often constitute the entire record (e.g., a catalog card), and final selection of individual terms from this record is then done by the requestor without much conscious thought.

4.2.2   Query Formulation

The query is the communication form by which a user interrogates a library or store of information.   Authors create documents and transmit them to libraries where they are encoded (indexed) after a scheme usually designed with the probable users' interests in mind.   The library distributes the documents to users at the appropriate time and according to appropriate matches of stated user interest with the content or other attributes of the document and with stated relevance criteria. In this sense it is like a communications switching center, or post office, where a large number of messages are routed through a central point, and where the messages are filed, encoded, assigned a priority, and retransmitted to the addressees or to other communication centers for retransmission. The principal difference between one of these systems and an information retrieval system, viewed as a communication system, is that in a retrieval system, the author, or message originator, does not determine the ultimate addressee. At best, he writes to a class of potential readers whose interest and extent of knowledge he must presume. At the library it is necessary for the user to define his interests in order to receive his messages. The user's interest statement is not necessarily given in the same terms as the author's implied interest statement. Any attribute of a book can potentially attract a reader. Thus an additional step is introduced into the communication process, that of the potential recipient defining his own "address" in terms of the attributes of documents he wishes to receive. The process of encoding the user's interest statement, or "address," is the *query formulation process*. The coded statement is the *query*. The process of formulation and the resultant query are analogous to the process of indexing and the resultant index record.

The query, like the document and the index, is a message written in a language and subject to the rules of usage of that language. Like the index, the query is usually written in a highly stylized, restrictive language designed more to reduce ambiguity than to permit a wide range of expression. This is a strength from the point of view of permitting mechanization of index searching, but it is also a weakness in that it makes it more difficult for users to communicate with the library.

A special problem of the query language is its expressiveness. Ideally, the query language should permit the requestor to express all the information he has about the object of the search. This ideal is probably not fully attainable, except in a full text index system, but is an important consideration in design. The query language design is very much a function of index design, for if a fact or concept cannot be stated in the index, there is no point to being able to state it in a query. For example, if the index language permits use of only six digits in a Dewey classification code, there is no point to permitting more in the query language. Hence, the requirement for query language expressiveness must be interpreted relative to the index language.

Query language vocabulary must be compatible with that of the index. Hence, the vocabulary is restricted to that of the index system or to a vocabulary that can be translated (or re-encoded) at the library into that of the index. For the purposes of this discussion, we shall assume the usual situation, that the vocabularies of the index and the queries are the same. This requirement can be advantageous to the searcher since it permits him to consult a catalog, glossary, or thesaurus, and, by ascertaining how his subject was indexed, determine how to phrase his query. In this way a mathematician, for example, can quickly discover that the subject of number theory can be described in a query by one number: 512.81 in the Dewey Decimal System. However, the opposite situation is also common—the user cannot readily discover a code or index term which, to his satisfaction, describes his subject. It is this situation that necessitates the next structural element of a query language, that of syntax.

The combining of basic index descriptors into terms using tags, modifiers, or facets follows the same rules for the query as for the index being queried. This means of combining basic vocabulary elements needs no further discussion. A special feature of the query is the combining of terms to make a more meaningful phrase or total query. In other words, it is the connecting link between terms that is of most interest now.

The terms comprising an index record are actually connected by unstated symbols; that is, a document is about *A,* also about *B,* also *C,* also *D.* The use of the word *and* was consciously avoided here because of the confusion between the common meaning of the term and its meaning as a logical operator. For example, "Tom and Bob went to the ball game" means "Tom went to the ball game. Bob went to the same game." A symbolic means of representing these and other, more complex, logical relationships exists and is called *Boolean algebra.*[2] In Boolean usage, "Tom and Bob" means "that which is in common to both Tom and Bob." We shall use the following notation:

The *conjunction* or *intersection* of two terms is represented by the symbols $\cdot$ or $\cap$, as $A \cdot B$ or $A \cap B^*$. It means the subject area in common to subjects A and B. In a query it means that both A and B must be present in an index (must occur in a common index record).

The *disjunction* or *union* of two terms is represented by the symbols $+$ or $\cup$, as $A + B$ or $A \cup B$. It means the broader subject defined by either term A or term B. It *includes* the intersection but is not limited thereto (see the discussion of Venn diagrams in Section 2.4). In a

---

* Just as in algebraic notation, the sign may be omitted if no confusion results. Thus, AB or $A(B \cup C)$ both imply that A is to be conjoined or intersected with the expression that follows.

query, $A \cup B$ asks for either term to be present, or both, but does not require both.

The *complement* of a term, often represented as $\sim A$ or $\overline{A}$, implies that the term should not be present in an index; that is, if a query calls for $A \cap (\sim B)$ (A and not B) then A is required to be present and B is required to be absent in any index record selected.

The use of the operator *not* can be deceiving. If the expression $\sim A$, in which A is an index term, appears in a query, then A cannot appear in any context at all in the index of a selected record. Often, what the requestor wants is to exclude a particular term only in a limited context. For example, a question in a key word language about American imports of automobiles from countries other than Canada should not exclude the word **Canada** altogether, for a document may discuss export of automobiles from Great Britain to both Canada and the United States. When context is explicitly stated, as in a faceted index, the use of *not* has more validity. Thus we may search for **gas** $\cap$ ($\sim$ **fuel**) to find documents on gases in contexts other than that of fuel. Some special symbol would be required here to show that this is a pair of descriptors in a faceted term, not a pair of independent terms. Another use of *not* is to reverse the meaning of a relationship statement which constitutes a query term; for example, $\sim$ (date = 1965) states that the date descriptor of an index shall be anything other than 1965.

The query need not describe all terms of the index, only those pertinent to the particular search at hand. Because there are so many ways by which an indexer can express subject concepts, either the query must encompass all of them or multiple queries are necessary. The alternative is that information may be missed in the index search process. In using a card catalog or in scanning shelves of books, we commonly employ a complex strategy called *browsing*. We enter this process with a general idea of the subject of the search or even with a few very specific descriptors—perhaps title or author. If we find just what we want on the basis of the original "query," the procedure ends. If not, we are likely to begin to search for alternate spellings, variants of subject heading cards, or different classifications under which our subject may have been classified. The routine of trial and error proceeds so smoothly and informally that we may not recognize its basic nature. The process of matching an original query against an index file, evaluating the results obtained, and modifying the search on the basis of the previous outcome and our knowledge both of the subject and the index, is a very complex one which cannot be easily duplicated in automatic systems. The principal result of this difficulty is to force the requestor to think out his query variations before he submits his question the first time. Much of the need for a syntax arises out of the anticipation of concepts and concept variations far more complex than can be expressed by a single word or list of words. Although there is no fixed syntax for all queries, the tendency for automatic systems is to adopt a very formal one to ease the problem of machine interpretation. A typical syntax might consist of the stated or implied connectives between query terms and the relationships desired between the value of the query term and the index term. For example, the syntax might consist of the following elements:

1. The connector between query terms can be *and* or *or*.

2. The relationship of the query term to index term can be that the query term is *equal to, unequal to, greater than, or less than* the index term.

3. If the index term is composed of a set of facets, then the same combinatorial rules for facets apply to the query, the symbol ∩ being implied between the facets of the term.

Such a syntax would be appropriate to a system composed of key words with one or more additional facets per index term. Were the index pure classification, the query syntax could be somewhat simpler. Where the index is the full text of the document, it may require a query syntax as complex as natural language itself. Indeed, one possibility is that a query to a natural language index would be an essay on the desired subject, rather than a connected list of key words.

Figure 4.1 shows how some sample queries, whose natural language expression is given first, might be expressed in various query languages.

4.2.3   Query Translation

Query syntax, while providing much flexibility for the retriever, still constrains him to write down exactly what he wants searched on, and the precise search alternatives. Within reasonable limits, the retriever can enter his own hierarchy—he can ask for **Lemons ∪ Limes** or for **Citrus Fruit**. A problem may arise, however, when the retriever either does not know the hierarchy or it is too long to write down. Consider a search for the topic, **Airports in the United States**. The key word **United States** might be used, but the searcher may realize that this term need not have been mentioned in the text or the index of a document about a particular airport, say, in Milwaukee. He might wish to ask, as an alternative possibility, for any mention of any specific state. This, however, would be an extensive list. Similar problems arise when a large number of synonyms is available to express a single concept and the

Desired information	Query language	Query	Comment
1. Use of information retrieval in business management.	Dewey decimal	651.5	Definition of this term is, "Information storage and retrieval systems in business. Including filing, indexing, preservation, destruction of business correspondence, reports, minutes, other special material."
2. Use of information retrieval in business management.	ACM subject headings	$3.7 \cdot (3.52 + 3.54 + 3.55 + 3.57)$	See Figure (2.4) for explanation of codes.
3. Use of information retrieved in business management.	Key words	*Information retrieval · management · (business + industry)*	
4. Joint British-French efforts in aircraft production.	Key words	*(Great Britain + Britain + England + United Kingdom)· (France) · (Aircraft + airplane + airliner) · (production + manufacture + design).*	A synonym dictionary would reduce the complexity of this query.
5. Computer programming language studies published after 1964.	ACM subject headings	$4.2 \cdot (\text{date} > 1964)$	See Figure (2.4) for explanation of code. Assumption is made that *date* refers to the document date.
6. Computer programming language studies published after 1964.	ACM subject headings	$4.2 \cdot (\sim (\text{date} \leq 1964))$	Illustrates a needless but valid use of operator.

Figure 4.1 Sample queries.

requestor is required to outguess the authors or indexers in making up his query. This section is devoted to methods, beyond query syntax, that can be used to improve communication between the requestor and the communication center.

Index searching or table look-up operations in general imply a common language between the search terms or arguments and the terms stored in the records. One cannot, for example, locate the American expression, aluminum, in a file if the search descriptor is the European usage, aluminium. When it cannot be guaranteed that all authors, indexers, and requestors will use a common language, either some means of translation must be used or excessive errors will result. This is one of the prime functions of a dictionary, as defined in Section 2.6.

Although use of a query translation function imposes a burden on a system for translation time and for dictionary building, it can be a great asset to requestors and indexers in that it allows them to use words with which they are familiar and comfortable. It is especially useful when fixed-vocabulary languages are used and when compact codes are used to represent natural language words in computer-stored records. Rather than require system users to memorize long lists of codes, natural language terms can be used for all man-machine communication, and translation programs employed to convert word forms.

Whatever the method, the essence of query translation is to communicate the stated information requirement of a retriever to the index. Note that this is not the same as communicating the retriever's mental concept. Presumably the translation of idea to symbols has been done when a query is first formulated. If the query is in the language (vocabulary and syntax) of the index, further translation is unnecessary. It may be inconvenient or impossible to use identical languages for queries and indexes. This is particularly true of a very large, widely diversified library having a high rate of input, and where a highly compact index notation may be an economic necessity. When this is the case, the query must be translated into index language for the index has already been formed and stored, making translation in the opposite direction expensive. When it is not the case, as in full text indexing, the translation can proceed in either direction. In general, because both indexes and queries usually have restricted vocabularies and highly restrictive syntaxes, query translation is far simpler than is natural language translation. For example, a requestor can direct the dictionary to translate any query term into all synonyms simultaneously, without, himself, knowing the synonyms; that is, A is replaced by $A_1 \cup A_2 \cup \ldots \cup A_n$ where each A_i is a synonym of A. This rather simple technique is quite useful in index searching but would hardly do in the usual language translation situation.   It serves well to illustrate how query translation differs from natural language translation.*

4.2.4   Searching and Matching

An information retrieval system compares queries with indexes and then selects or retrieves the appropriate information from the indexes that match the queries.   In terms of the communication center analogy, we have discussed the nature of the incoming messages and a special kind of message called a query, sent by a prospective message recipient to ensure that he gets the messages he wants.   Let us now consider the operation of the center—the process by which incoming documents are switched on to the appropriate outgoing channels by means of a query.

The essential process of index searching is table look-up, taking a query term as an input and searching an index file for occurrences of this term.   In an automatic retrieval system, there will usually be more to a query than a single search term.   Hence, index searching must include some logical analysis or computation on the records being tested in the look-up process to see if the appropriate combination of query terms has been found in the index.   There are two common organizations of index data, the choice of which affects the process but not the essential logic.   See Figure 4.2.   In one method, the index of a document is the basic record, and each of these is stored in the order in which received.   To search such a file, each record must be separately examined to see if it satisfies the query.   In the second method, each record of the file, called an *inverted file,* contains one index term and the accession or call numbers of all documents in whose index records that term occurs.   To find all documents mentioning **cat** by this system, it is only necessary to search the index file for the record containing **cat** and, from this record, retrieve all the accession numbers.   If two subjects are required (**cat** and **dog**, for example), then two records must be retrieved, their reference sets intersected, and the results used to satisfy the query.

In simple table look-up operations we have a single argument, and enter a table looking for an exact correspondence between the argument

---

* The AN/GSQ-16 Language Translator built for the U.S. Air Force[14] gives alternative meanings of words when it cannot tell which of several possibilities should be used in translating a given text.   Resolution is later done by an editor.   In a query, there is no particular reason for trying to narrow the choice to a single synonym; in fact, the multiple translation is an advantage in that it covers all choices that might have been made by the indexer or author.

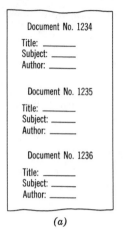

(a)

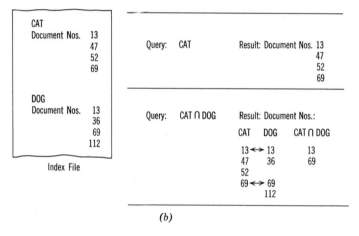

(b)

Figure 4.2 Basic index search logic: (a) Document-order file, searched in full for each query. Each record is tested for presence of the query terms before the next record is considered. (b) Term-order file, the required terms are searched for and their containing document references are retrieved.

and a term stored in the file, or the first table entry greater than, or smaller than, the query term. In using a query to interrogate an index file in either of the two sequences illustrated in Figure 4.2, we actually perform a set of look-up operations and then evaluate a function of the results of the individual searches. Let us consider in detail how this is done with just one of the file types—the index record file in document order.

Each term of the query is used as a search term independently on each index record. When all query terms have been tested for presence in a given index record, we have a set of functional values—yeas and nays—one for each query term, denoting whether or not that term was present in the form required. The index record is selected or rejected on the basis of an evaluation of the set of indicators* for all query terms. The evaluation consists of "computing" a function of this set, the function being defined by the syntax of the query, and arriving at a yes-no decision as to selection or rejection of the record. Assume, for example, that a query asks for the presence of: **oranges, lemons,** or **limes** in **Florida** or **California** which can be represented symbolically as $(A \cup B \cup C) (D \cup E)$. As a match function, the expression is evaluated by assigning values to the term symbols, zero if absent, one if present in any given index record, then performing the indicated Boolean operations. If the final value is one (implying that the values of both $(A \cup B \cup C)$ and $(D \cup E)$ are one†), then the index record is accepted. If zero (either of the two major terms is zero), then the index record is rejected.

The match function can be more complex than that illustrated above. For example, in the preceding paragraph, we really asked for any of three fruits *in* **Florida** or **California.** The "in" would probably imply the use of a modifier tag with the key word. If this were the case, we should have to request: **(Florida** $\cup$ **California)** $\cap$ **(in),** making the total query in symbolic form: $(A \cup B \cup C) (D \cup E) (F)$. However, complex, the matching operation is representable as a Boolean function where the individual terms may, in turn, be representative of other functional relationship statements. Thus, we may have the symbol A meaning that: $G > 2$ or $(23.5 - G)^2 \leq 100$. Then the requirement, $((23.5\text{-}G)^2 \leq 100) \cup B$ might be written $A \cup B$, and means that either the arithmetic restriction on G must hold or the term B must be present.

The matching process, then, consists of *testing* or evaluating a stated match function to determine whether the terms present in the index record fulfill the requirements of the query. *Searching* we define to be the process of acquiring records to be matched, and is mainly concerned with the sequence in which records are matched.

---

* There are faster ways to do this, taking advantage of a term's role in the Boolean expression, but there are no significant logical differences.

† $1 \cup 1 = 1, 1 \cup 0 = 1, 0 \cup 0 = 0, 1 \cap 1 = 1, 1 \cap 0 = 0, 0 \cap 0 = 0$.

4.2.5   Relevance

The match function is not necessarily a binary decision function which draws a clear distinction between those index records that do and those that do not match the query.   Such a measure we call the *relevance* of the index to the query.*   A decision function is required to accept or reject indexes on the basis of their relevance.   This function can take many forms.   It can be a simple, fixed threshold whereby all documents whose indexes bear a relevance of measure greater than x are selected.   It can be a relative threshold whereby the y per cent most relevant records are selected.   A completely different approach is to require the decision to be made by the requestor who could be shown a list of all indexes with relevance greater than some moderate level, and be required to make his own decision as to which documents he would actually like to select.   This is essentially the decision function used in the browsing process.   That is, in browsing, the searcher does not fix a relevance measure in advance.   He formulates a query, retrieves some records, such as catalog cards, and only after he has seen the results of his search does he make a relevance decision.

A *decision function* is a formalization of the relevance requirements. Where relevance measures are not used, a decision function and a match function may be the same.   Where there are relevance measures, these functions may be quite different.   A match function, for example, may be $A \cup B \cup C$.   However, if each index term in the record has appended to it a measure of the relevance of that term to the document being described, a searcher can take advantage of this additional information. He may, for example, impose an added requirement for the search, such as requiring that the sums of the relevance measures of any index terms that match the query terms be at least N.   An index record might contain none of these terms.   Then it has no relevance.   The record may contain all three terms, but the relevance weights may not add to N, and the record would be rejected in a search as being lacking in relevance.

A number of programmed relevance measuring techniques are possible, and we may classify them into three, nonexclusive categories:

1. Those in which the index record contains a measure of the importance, relevance, or applicability of each index term to the document

---

* We re-emphasize—we *define* relevance as a measure of the extent to which an index matches a query.   Others use the term to mean the extent to which the retrieved information satisfies the original need.   This is a related, but not identical, concept.

it describes.   The measure can be applied by the indexer or by a machine utilizing a variety of statistical techniques.

2. Those in which similar measures are applied to the terms of a query by the requestor who would have to provide a decision basis as well.   He might, as in our example, submit a query consisting of the union of a set of terms, each with its own importance factor, and a decision function that calls for summing the weights of the query terms matched by index terms and selecting any indexes that score greater than x points.

3. Those that provide a nonquantitative statement of the relevance of one document to another.   An example is citation indexing[9] in which the indexer uses the author's reference citations to create a list of terms that tell a searcher where else relevant information may be found, once an initial index has been recovered.   The citation, by author A of a work of author B, is deemed to establish the relevance of B's work to A's work.

The first two methods have had relatively little success in the practical world unless, as Becker and Hayes[1] point out, we accept an indexer-selected key word as having an implicit relevance measure associated with it by the very fact that it appears in the index.   This is the basis, in fact, of citation indexing.   Becker and Hayes further state that a refinement of the relevance scale to more than two values (a two-valued scale being *word present* or *word absent*) is no change in concept. Although we agree this is no change in concept, it is nonetheless true that indexer-assigned relevance or importance measures increase the problem of nonuniform indexing if the scale were widened; that is, the more points on the relevance scale, the less likely it would be that indexers and requestors will agree on the appropriate value.

The statistical relevance measures have fared slightly better, probably because of the tendency (or, at least people's *belief* in the tendency) for computers to be more consistent than people, even if they cannot yet be as perceptive.   Stiles' association factor[13] for computing the relevance of one word to another across many documents is one example.

Stiles's technique works as follows.   First, using each query term as a base, prepare a list of index terms which have been used "often" together with that query term throughout the library's collection of indexes.   Membership in this list is determined by applying the following formula to compute an association factor for each term in the index file with respect to the query term:

$$a = \log_{10} \frac{(fN - AB - N/2)^2 N}{AB(N - A)(N - B)}, \tag{4.1}$$

where A is the number of documents indexed by the query term, B, the number indexed by the other term (whose relevance is being computed), f, the number of documents indexed by both terms, and N, the total number of documents in the library. A cut-off value of 1.0 was established, term pairs having an association factor less than unity being considered not significantly related.

When the first step has been performed for each query term, resulting in identification of a set of closely related index terms for each member of the set of query terms, step 2 is performed, which consists of selecting those terms appearing in the association lists of more than a specified number of query terms; that is, index terms relevant to more than n query terms. The selected words are called *first generation terms*.

The third step is to start with each first generation term and repeat steps 1 and 2, producing thereby a list of *second generation terms*.

Fourth, compute an association factor for the relation of each term to each other term in an expanded query consisting of the original request terms, plus all first and second generation terms. The average of these factors, for any base term, is used as a relevance weight for the term, so that the expanded query can have its constituent terms ordered by relevance or importance of the term to the query. Terms with many interconnections within the expanded query will have a high relevance; terms with few connections a low relevance.

Finally, for each document index searched, the sum of the weights of terms which match terms in the expanded query is computed and used to measure the relevance of the document to the original query.

Another example of relevance measuring is Luhn's idea[10] of using an assumed relationship between word importance and word frequency, within one document, as discussed in Section 3.4.

Citation indexing makes use of clustering, as does Stiles, but on the document level.* It is more a term selection technique than it is a relevance measure. It benefits heavily from using the judgments of the author, himself, in rating the importance of other words. The technique is quite useful in research or in any situation in which an exhaustive search is desired. As a means of narrowing a search, to pinpoint a precise topic in a large collection, the method is less useful.

4.3   RETRIEVAL PLANNING

Whenever a requestor has an opportunity to use more than one query to achieve his goal he is faced with a classic decision-making problem

* In the paper by M. M. Kessler,[8] it is proposed that only citations which appear several times in a group of cross-referenced documents be selected as citation index terms. We have generally used the expression in a broader sense.

of determining the best strategy to use to reach his objective. Use of more than one query can mean that the requestor asks a question, gets his response, and retreats to his desk to ponder the output. He then has the opportunity to return to the library and ask a new question. It can also mean use of intermediate output techniques which provide a searcher with information on the progress of a search at one or more points before retrieval of the information ultimately sought. Retrieval of data from a dictionary for use in formulating a query to an index file is an example.

Although most libraries welcome users back to improve the net quality of the service, there is a tendency not to use browsing, or intermediate searching, as an integral part of searching when an automatic retrieval system is available. Our point of reference in this section is when there is more than one query possible, leaving the requestor to work out the best path to his ultimate result. Should he try for the best possible result on the first try or should he make the first query one that will give him the best information on how to ask the next question? Which method will give the best results, the soonest? Although no universal answer exists, it should be clear that perfection is rarely achieved in one try,* and that some consideration should be given to the basis on which the first query will be modified if it is unsatisfactory. For that matter, how can we tell when a query has worked satisfactorily? A paltry number of relevant documents scattered among irrelevant ones may indicate that the library does not have much on the subject rather than that the retrieval system has performed badly. This introduces another aspect of retrieval planning, how to determine whether a query *can* be improved.

To use mathematical techniques to determine an optimum plan (an optimum use of resources—queries) would require a capability to measure the quality of a query response (relevance) and probably some measure of the content of the file or the distribution of relevant material. The former, as we have said, is rare and the latter may be postulated as nonexistent, the lack being the reason for having an automatic searching system in the first place. If information on the distribution of material relevant to a given query were present, this information, itself, would be contained in one of the system files, which file would have to be searched to be able to find the distribution data. If it is to be searched, then there is a need for information on the distribution of relevant material in *this* file. And so on. There is always some missing informa-

---

* It sometimes appears that every requestor believes (1) that he is best qualified to formulate his own query in index language, and (2) that his formulation is the best possible description of his subject. One actual try with a system that does not provide intermediate outputs is usually enough to shake his faith.

tion. We feel, then, that a query plan must be based on imperfect information, which is usual in situations calling for the employment of strategy. In fact, the requestor is often better off if he realizes the extent of his ignorance, and plans to bracket his target,* knowing that this is almost certain to require several tries, but being sure that each try provides some positive assistance on planning the next move. One approach is to formulate a query considered reasonably likely to achieve the desired results, to the best of the searcher's knowledge, but whose main purpose is to detect patterns in the response. Such patterns may point to query terms which are best dropped in the next try, or to terms not used in the query which might recover new, pertinent information. The next query, regardless of the apparent success of the first, might then be aimed at generalizing the first—broadening the subject definition to see what was missed the first time. The third, and all subsequent, queries would then be aimed at trying to get the best response by cutting back on the response to the second query.

4.3.1　Query Enhancement

We define *query enhancement* to mean any procedure by which a query is changed for the purpose of improving the results of anticipated results of the query, other than a change solely to achieve language compatibility. The enhancement process, like relevance, seldom used in practice today, would normally be guided by the requestor. This would take the form of instructions added to a query on how the query is to be modified.

The simplest form of query enhancement is one in which a query term is to be replaced with a set of alternative terms. The requestor programs the replacement, and expects the query to find the information needed to modify itself. The most common example of enhancement by replacement is the use of a universal match, or mask, character. This is a

---

* The allusion to artillery is quite pertinent. The U.S. Army requires of its artillery observers (who control gunfire by observing the impact point of projectiles, and recommending the adjustment required to hit the target) that they use a bracketing technique, getting closer to the target each time by first achieving a bracket (one volley in front of and one behind the target), then halving the distance between impact points of these salvos. This process is repeated until the remaining distance is less than the lethal range of the explosive in the projectiles. It is also interesting and pertinent that when the first volley falls very wide of the target, the observer cannot tell whether it is long or short in range, and his first adjustment is to narrow the angle subtended at his eye by the target and the impact point, solely for the purpose of being able to detect the direction of range error on the next volley.

symbol which is defined to be equal to any other symbol in a match operation, or, equivalently, masks out the symbol being tested, removing it from consideration. Suppose it is desired to search for works by an author whose name is either Smith or Smythe, but the searcher is uncertain which. If the character # will match any other character, then the search term Sm#th# will find all Smiths and Smythes. The use of # is an implied instruction to the match program to translate Sm#th# into all terms found in the index file with the attribute of having either five or six letters, Sm in positions one and two, th in positions four and five, and any letters in positions three and six.*

Equally common in searching is uncertainty of letter *position*. For example, the name McIntyre has variants: MacIntyre, McIntire, and MacIntire. The major problem here is that, if the Mac form is used, all the remaining letter positions are shifted to the right from the Mc form, and the universal match character is of little value. A solution is to write the query term in a manner such as this:

Letter Position	Required Letter
1	M
$M + 1$	$A \cup C$
$A + 1$	C
$C + 1$	I
$C + 2$	N
$C + 3$	T
$C + 4$	$I \cup Y$
$C + 5$	R
$C + 6$	E

The notation $A + 1$ means one position to the right of the occurrence of A. If A has not occurred, the statement can be ignored. Thus the second position of the name $(M + 1)$ can either be A or C. If A, then the next position is C. In either case C is followed by INT(Y ∪ I)RE.

If we had a synonym dictionary which included generic or sub-class relationships, a requestor could submit a query such as this: "Search on combatant ships or any particular type of combatant ship." The requestor need not be able to name all classes of men-at-war, so long as he has confidence in his dictionary. If the dictionary includes the relationship *member of* or *example of* (implying an identifiable individual rather than a subset), the query could demand, "Search on battleship or any particular battleship, by name," or "Search on USS Missouri or any other ship of the same type, or the type in general." In neither case need the

* See exercise 1 at the end of this chapter.

query author, himself, know the missing information. The SMART Automatic Document Retrieval System,[11] produced at Harvard University, has such a capability.

A more advanced form of query enhancement is one that would make use of an analysis of results of one query to affect the next, with the object being to achieve the desired results by means of a series of queries. Such techniques would be useful in any case where requestors were not familiar with file content either because of size, diversity of data, or diversity of the library users. As in relevance measuring, one of the most effective ways to determine whether a query needs to be modified is to let the requestor see what was retrieved and let him decide if it needs to be changed. This is, of course, the process of browsing, which can be considerably enhanced if the requestor has a high-speed computer or other device to do his searches for him and quickly present him with the results. It is not necessary that the entire query be carried out before any attempt is made at analysis. Analysis of pertinent dictionary records is often an excellent basis for query modification. The index records, even if they are not detailed, may provide enough information to permit detection of major errors (e.g., spelling) and to suggest alternative approaches. They may well point out where a query term should be changed because it is a homograph of another term in common use in the library, or they may indicate an author, publisher, or institution as a likely source of more information on a topic.

Some possible automatic techniques include counting the number of records retrieved and taking action depending upon the sum. One possibility is for the requestor to include in his query the number of documents he wants, expects, or is willing to take.* Various actions could be taken depending on whether the number of retrieved documents is too few, about right, or too many. Some examples of such actions are the following:

1. If less than a specified number of document references are retrieved in response to a query, generalize the logic and try again. Logic can be generalized by changing all (or some) intersection connectors, $\cap$, to union connectors, $\cup$. Similarly, if too much is retrieved the first time, $\cup$'s can be changed to $\cap$'s. Although this method substitutes an essentially random process for relevance measuring, it is fast and logically simple.

2. If a hierarchical classification is involved, the system can be in-

---

* A common fallacy in information retrieval is the assumption that a searcher wants all pertinent documents. He sometimes may, and is more likely to in a research environment, but often he has not the time to read them anyway, and would gladly settle for a limited-volume cross section.

structed to go up the hierarchy, one level at a time, each time insufficient material is returned.   The system cannot be directed to go down quite so readily, for the query must specify, at each branch point, which path or paths are to be taken.

3. If key words are used, measure the relevance of each document to the query (a possible way—count the number of query terms present in the index record, use this as the relevance factor), and select the top $P\%$ of the documents as measured by this factor.   Then, varying the threshold value, P, gives a control over the number of documents that will be retrieved in subsequent tries.

We note that replacing a term by its class name does not, in itself, accomplish generalizing a search.   The class term must be replaced by the union of itself and all its membership, and this process may need repeating down one or more additional levels.   To give a simple geographic example, generalizing up from **France** may give **Europe,** but there may be many documents about European countries that do not use the word **Europe.**   Here, the class term should be replaced by its membership to yield: **Europe ∪ France ∪ Germany ∪ Switzerland ∪ Italy,** etc.

The major difficulty with automatic query modification is that the requestor may not know the "semantic direction" that the computer will take.   Such a problem arises when a dictionary entry has more than one synonym, each representing a different subject context, as the word *motor* has quite different implications in psychology and in mechanics.   Choice of one synonym sets a "direction" toward that subject. Hence, while the requestor may be assured his query is being generalized, or made more specific, he would not really be sure it is being improved. To insure improvement, he needs to know direction.   This implies a good prior knowledge of the file to give him foreknowledge of the possible directions, with requestor control of direction of change, or the use of intermediate outputs to inform him and to let him select the path at each node.   The latter method is no longer automatic modification, so let us return to the former.

If the dictionary is constructed to show subject classification of entries as well as relationship to each other, then the requestor can, by use of the classification term, specify the direction the program is to take in expanding the query.   For example, if a Dewey decimal code is annexed to each term in a dictionary, an entry might be as follows:

	Motors
629.134 35	*Airplane*
621.313	*Electrical Engineering*
621.25	*Hydraulic Power*
629.25	*Motor Vehicle Engineering*

The terms here are classes, each of which may have its own set of related terms when the keyword appears as an entry. Each class has a subject code associated with it to permit a requestor to choose the path to follow through the network of interconnected terms in finding synonyms or other replacement terms for the input term **Motors**. Regardless of dictionary organization, if there is a term-order index file (Figure 4.2) then the program, with or without direction from the requestor, can try various combinations of replacements of original with dictionary terms. It can test each combination against the term file and compute the number of document references that would be retrieved. This will provide a *quantitative* measure which can be used by the program or requestor, or both, to select the best adjustment of the original request.

Query enhancement can make use of logic changes as well as the word replacement techniques already mentioned. The basis upon which a decision is made to change the query is not affected by the enhancement technique and vice versa.

In several of the examples of this section, we made use of a count of the number of documents retrieved to be used in determining how to ask the next query. We do not intend to suggest that retrieval results should be measured solely in terms of this number, nor are these methods offered as proven techniques of query enhancement. However, these examples, based on the statistic, number of documents retrieved, do illustrate the concept of retriever control of query response through programmed analysis of results, and programmed iteration of the query. Any use of query enhancement that does not include a relevance measure is a hazardous substitution of quantitative analysis for qualitative analysis.

4.3.2 Intermediate Output

Intermediate outputs are messages returned by an information retrieval system to a searcher that are used to assist him in carrying out his search or improving his query. In one form, these can be progress reports, such as descriptions of what is happening at any phase of a search. The number of records retrieved or expected to be retrieved from a given file by a given query is an example. Alternatively, intermediate outputs can consist of information extracted from files and used as a basis for the formulation or improvement of a later query.

In the last section we gave as an example of automatic query enhancement use of a count of the number of index records or call numbers recovered from a file ordered on index term. In this usage, the number of call numbers that would fulfill the query is recovered before any actual documents are retrieved and could be used as the basis of a decision on whether the search for the documents should proceed or the query should be restated. A dictionary, used to retrieve synonyms of proposed query terms, provides another form of intermediate output. Here, the searcher makes one query solely for the purpose of finding the best set of terms to be used in a subsequent query.

Operationally, the intermediate outputs in both these examples would be presented to the searcher who, himself, uses the information to modify his original query or to help formulate his query. Because the analysis of the retrieved data would be performed by a man, not a computer program, more sophisticated pattern analysis can be expected to be used than would be possible in a fully automatic mode. L. B. Doyle[5] proposed essentially such a technique, in which dictionary words would be displayed on a television-like screen, with word connections shown by lines of various widths to indicate various relationships between the words. The result would be a network of words, rather than a linear list, as in a conventional dictionary. The searcher would follow any path or paths he desired through the network to find the set of words and word relationships most suited to his interests.

Some other forms of intermediate output for use by the searcher in improving the quality of his search are the following:

1. Retrieval of the index records of documents that meet his search criteria and perusal of these before retrieving the documents themselves. In this way, the index record serves as something of an abstract and tells the reader more about the document it represents than he would know from the simple knowledge that it met his search criteria. He may observe patterns in the responses that show defects in his query or he may discover some terms that he failed to use, and the use of which may improve his yield. Use of the index record for this purpose relieves him of having to read large quantities of text to make this determination.

2. Various record counts, such as those proposed for use in automatic query enhancement, could be made and presented to the searcher for use in the same way that a program would use it. Depending on file design, such figures can be arrived at with relatively little expense. The advantage of presenting them is that the searcher can make a rapid evaluation of the query without all contingencies having had to be planned for in the program, and he can take action accordingly.

3. Index records can be retrieved but, rather than being presented to the searcher, they can be analyzed statistically and these results presented to the searcher for use as above. Such an analysis might tell how often query terms occur together in a query, giving a kind of measure

of the usefulness of each term, relevance measures if they are present in the index records, data distributions, frequency distributions of other terms in index records (e.g., in the retrieved records the term T_1 occurred N_1 times, T_2 N_2 times, etc.)   The SMART System[12] incorporates some of these techniques, as options for the user.   The system has the full text of the document available, and is able to compile a number of statistical, semantic, and syntactical attributes of documents for use in query improvement.

4.4   RETRIEVAL SYSTEM PERFORMANCE

Evaluating, or in any way measuring, the performance of an information retrieval system is a very difficult thing, mostly because both the criteria for measurement and the very boundaries of the system are hazily defined.   Libraries are rarely operated for profit.   Hence the relative simplicity of a measure based on return on investment is not applicable.   The purpose of a library is almost always to help a group of people external to the library to do a "better" job, where "better" can have such meanings as "faster," "cheaper," "more likely to be right," or "less likely to be surprised."   The situation hardly exists where it is possible to study the performance of a group of library users, such as an engineering staff, under a variety of controlled conditions, to determine the true effect of the library on their work.

When evaluating any system, there must be a careful delineation of what the system is, what components of it we wish to measure, and what relationships of the components are to be selected for measurement to other components or to the system as a whole.   When we measure performance in information retrieval, do we include, as factors to be measured, patron skill in using the system, or the librarians' skill in selecting documents for storage, or the extent to which knowledge is available in a subject?   Is it meaningful to evaluate a system but ignore these questions?   Would this not be like evaluating an airplane on flight characteristics, alone, without considering whether pilots could be trained to fly it, or airports built to handle it?   On the other hand, libraries are needed, and systems must be designed.   Is it necessary to go to the length of a study of the entire culture to design an information retrieval system?

There are no simple resolutions of these problems.   There is a tendency to oversimplify a system when designing an evaluation technique. The ease with which these oversimplifications can be detected by a critical observer does not make void the concept of simplifying what cannot be measured in full.   On the other hand, there is no particular merit in oversimplification, *per se*. An evaluation measure must have some meaningful relationship to the system it measures, and it must be able to be applied to several systems to provide a comparison among them. Finally, there is the problem of *predicting* performance, as opposed to measuring it *after occurrence*. Prediction is a useful design aid. *Post hoc* measurement is history—of value on the next project, and perhaps for quality control but not of value in the design of the system being measured. It is probably more important to understand the performance of a measure, in this regard, than it is to have a "perfect" measure, for to be fooled by a measure is worse than to be left by it with some uncertainty.

Another aspect of the evaluation problem is in the choice between quantitative and qualitative evaluation factors. Quantitative factors are part of the oversimplification trend—the selection of measures having to do with the cost or time required to perform some operation (answer an average query, say), or the number of documents or queries handled per unit time, or the percentage of prospective patrons who actually use the library's services. These can be valuable in comparing systems that perform with essentially the same quality, but *we take it as an axiom that the primary measure of performance of an information retrieval system must cover the quality of service provided to the user group*. Time and money constraints may be imposed by the users, in which case trade-offs become necessary between quality and cost, or quality and speed, but, quality of service is the goal at which to aim.

If we differentiate quality from speed then we are saying that, independent of the time required to perform a search, there are problems of how well the search was performed or could be performed. It is to these problems that we shall principally address ourselves in this chapter. The reader will find no summation which prescribes the method of evaluating systems. The method used in any specific instance needs to be as carefully tailored to the specific problem as was the design of the system to be evaluated. Just so, the term *quality* will not be further defined, and should be taken to mean, roughly, *absence of error*. The reason why quality of performance is hard to define is that most systems are concerned only with absence of some kinds of error, or relative quality, given that some error-inducing influence is present in the system.

4.4.1 Retrieval Errors

The matching process is essentially one of testing the hypothesis, "This index record fulfills the requirements of the query," for each index record in the file. As in any hypothesis testing, errors are possible. We shall follow statistical terminology[7] and define:

> *Type I Error:* A false rejection of the hypothesis—the index actually *does* fulfill the query, but it is erroneously *not selected.* This is sometimes called a *blank sort,* the failure of a record to be selected when it should have been.

> *Type II Error:* A false acceptance—the index *does not* fulfill the query but it *is accepted.* This is also known as a *false drop.**

In the sense used here, "fulfill" a query means "be relevant to" the query, where the relevance is determined by a match of the index with a query other than the query used to retrieve the documents; that is, an index would not have been retrieved if it had not fulfilled the query according to the stated match function of the query. The determination that it actually did not match must be made by an observer other than the retrieval device, usually an irate user of the system who, when checking the response to his query, finds he disagrees with the match process on some of the documents retrieved, implying that he is mentally using different criteria than were stated in the query. The difference between evaluations is what is called *error.* The reader is warned to note carefully that the "errors" we shall be discussing here are mere differences of opinion among matching mechanisms, human or inanimate, and that differences exist among mechanical systems on how they would treat the same query just as several human readers would have differences of opinion on how relevant they consider a given document to a given query.

4.4.2   Causes of Retrieval Errors

Because we recognize retrieval errors to be largely attributable to communication failures among components of an information retrieval system, *error* is probably not a truly accurate term for this phenomenon. Because it is in common use we shall continue to use it, but we must emphasize that the word is not to be considered synonymous with *mistake.* Retrieval errors can arise through indexing error, query formulation error, syntax restrictions in either query or index, or vocabulary restrictions in either query or index. Let us consider these causes in greater detail.

* Both the terms *blank sort* and *false drop* are derived from punched card processing. In the former case, when a deck of cards is sorted so that all cards containing a given descriptor would fall into a specified "pocket," and no card does fall, we have a "blank sort." Should an undesired card end up in the pocket, we have a "false drop."

1. Coding Errors. The most obvious errors are simple transcription mistakes, such as digit inversion, misspelling of a term, or omission of a required term (such as author) in the indexing process. Such errors are not really attributable to the retrieval system, but good system design may help to reduce or at least to detect them by properly designed data forms, training programs, and machine editing of input data.

2. Syntax Deficiency. Probably the most frequent errors that are attributable to the system are those induced by the primitive syntax of the index or query language. For example, the co-occurrence of two key words in an index does not imply that they were used in connection with the same subject in the document (see the discussion of false coordination in Section 2.3.3). If the entirety of a document were "Smith bought a washing machine from a Communist country, and the agitator does not work," there is no implication whatever that Smith is a Communist agitator, yet few key word systems could avoid retrieval of this message in a search for **Communist agitators**. A similar sort of difficulty can arise in a query containing a phrase such as **baseball ∩ New York**. In natural language this can mean baseball *in* New York (City), or baseball *by* (the) New York (Yankees), or both. These illustrations bring out the full significance of the use of a limited syntax in indexing and querying, as opposed to the full syntax of natural language. Natural language has many ambiguities, but also has many redundancies to overcome them. In machine processing, we tend to use unambiguous, nonredundant syntaxes to simplify (or even make possible) programming the interpretation of the language. This simplification is a benefit gained, as usual, at a cost. The cost is retrieval error due to the inadequacy of the syntax. The phrase **baseball ∩ New York** is not ambiguous *in query language* because the interpretation *in* or *by* New York is not expressible in query language. The ambiguity is created when an attempt is made to translate the phrase into the more expressive natural language.

3. Vocabulary Deficiency. A bit more subtle is the error problem caused by the inability of the index or query vocabulary to describe a concept. This will arise particularly in systems using fixed vocabulary (whether key words or classification). An obvious example of such a deficiency is a classification system lacking a code for a new concept. For example, how would one classify "nuclear propulsion systems for interplanetary travel" using the 1870 version of Dewey's classification scheme? For the indexer, this problem can be resolved by inventing a new code, usually a new division of an existing one. The retriever, however, who might be a specialist in the new subject, must guess under what existing class the indexer filed the document, or under what class a new, subordinate class was created. The problem can also arise in key word systems—especially fixed vocabulary systems. At what point in time do acronyms such as *radar, sonar,* or *laser* enter the approved vocabulary list, and how can we retrieve the early works on these subjects written when the presently acceptable key word was not yet admissible as an index term? By definition of a key word index, some words appearing in the document must be omitted from the index. This limits the ability of the index to describe the document, and the retriever, knowing the limits and difficulties of indexing, is restrained from a single precise description of his subject by the fear that the indexers will have expressed his subject some other way.

4. Search Logic. In a programmed retrieval system there are likely to be restrictions imposed by the program on the logic of a query. Examples include the following:

a. Systems which permit *and* logic only, that is, which restrict the query to a string of key words or subject terms *all* of which must be in any index selected. This would result either in overrejection or in the retriever relaxing his search criteria beyond what he really wants. The former causes Type I errors; the latter, Type II.

b. Systems which cannot accommodate inequality searching on numeric terms. Consider how a literature search for all material on a given subject published after (or before) July, 1959, would have to be coded without use of an inequality symbol.

c. Free key word systems which do not automatically equate words (either in the index or in the query) to their synonyms, requiring the searcher to put all synonyms in his query or, failing this, to risk error.

Each such logic restriction simply means that some questions cannot be formulated in the language. Hence a less descriptive question is used, resulting in poor retrieval.

4.4.3 Effects of Retrieval Errors

System errors affect both individual users and the system itself. The effect on the user is often ignored as being a problem external to the library, even though service to the user is the reason for the library's existence. However, the measurement of effectiveness of engineers, research chemists, students, or intelligence officers is not a part of library science, and this leaves the library dependent upon what users *say* they need as a basis for improvement.   What is the true effect of poor quality library performance on an individual user is probably impossible to measure, especially in light of our previous comment that quality is usually a relative measure.   We could possibly estimate the effect of completely denying information to a user, but are quite hampered when trying to tell the difference between giving him all available information, or only 80 per cent of it, or responding to a query in 10 minutes or in 24 hours.   What we can say is that user performance is bound to suffer if library performance is poor.

The effects of retrieval errors on the retrieval system, itself, are indirect.   They are manifested by a change of behavior pattern by system users.   Retrieval systems exist where, in spite of the fact that documents are subject indexed, they are almost always searched solely on the basis of call number.   This could mean that users have come to lack any confidence whatever in subject retrieval and will request only copies of known documents, of known relevance.   Although there is nothing inherently wrong in a library operation of this type, it implies something of a waste to perform indexing that is rarely used and may mean that the users are forced to do without valuable information.   The situation can result from either error type or a combination.   (There is no reason to assume that the occurrence of one error type in processing a given query precludes the occurrence of the other type also.)   A reaction such as the change in usage patterns is not instantaneous and may take years to occur.   Unfortunately, over this period many of the user personnel will change and new people will be introduced by their colleagues to the library as a system which can be interrogated one way only—by call number.   Thus the situation can arise where users simply do not think in terms of subject retrieval, do not even know it is possible in their library.   To these people the system operates without error.   This leads to the conclusion that system retrieval errors, if not controlled by system operators—the librarians—will result in a use pattern that avoids errors by degrading the expected performance.   Long term operation at a degraded level will eliminate any demand for error-free operation in the original sense, an adaptive feature not at all desirable, but preventable, just as muscles are prevented from atrophying by repeated exercise.

4.4.4   Performance Requirements

Any discussion of the measurement of system performance must begin with a discussion of what performance is wanted by the system's users and its operators (the latter being presumed concerned with costs, the former with error-free retrieval within reasonable time constraints). We have shown in the last section how sustained poor performance can result in no demand for quality performance. Hence, we must postulate a third interest in performance—those concerned with total system operation: total cost (cost of system operation as well as cost of system inadequacy) and total error evaluation (retrieval errors and errors in work of the users caused by retrieval errors).

Let us first consider the retriever's point of view of performance requirements, and let us start with, say, a high school student, working on a homework assignment in history, who needs the assistance of a library to provide some key facts. As likely as not, this student will accept any authoritative statement on his subject. Hence he may head for an encyclopedia in the reference section of his library or he may locate any historical volume that the card catalog indicates will cover his subject. Such a user prefers a high Type I error rate; that is, he is unconcerned with the number of pertinent documents he misses so long as he gets at least one. Any Type II error is an irritation. This user would waste too high a percentage of his time discarding erroneous or unneeded information.

At the opposite extreme, consider an intelligence officer preparing plans for an amphibious landing on a hostile shore. Every fact about the climate, oceanography, and topography of the proposed landing area, the disposition of enemy forces, their state of training, armament, and morale, and the attitudes and personalities of the residents of the area may affect the success of the operation. This researcher, then, cannot afford to miss anything. He will not tolerate any Type I errors in his searching. He may have to tolerate a high rate of Type II error to gain this assurance.

Most retrieval system users fall between these extremes but the extreme cases do exist. They serve to illustrate the subjective nature of performance standards—that we must always ask, "What performance is desired?" before attempting any evaluation. Indeed, even this is often difficult to accomplish, for polling library users about the nature of the service they wish, and their feelings about the service they have can lead to some peculiar results, frequently requiring an advanced gamesman* to interpret them. Consider, for example, a group of users who need all facts (or think they do), hence cannot tolerate Type I errors. When polling their opinions on a proposed new system that would make a more careful selection for them and reduce the amount of extraneous

---

* The reference here is to gamesmanship or one-upmanship as defined by Stephen Potter[11] in his series of tongue-in-cheek books on the subject. Gamesmanship may well rank ahead of mathematics as a fundamental study for systems analysts.

reading without reducing the amount of pertinent material they would receive, often it is found that they will reject any such suggestion. This is not because they do not need such service. It is because they do not trust the hypothetical system to do the job as advertised. Similarly, any admission by the systems analyst or pollster about the errors that the system will make often results in the proposed system being scornfully rejected. People who do not hide the fact that they themselves make mistakes are sometimes unable to cope with the concept of a constant, predictable per cent of error in a mechanical system. The reasoning (or lack of it) here, seems to be that human errors are so unpredictable, in nature and frequency, that it is safe to plan on perfect performance and learn to shrug one's shoulders when the inevitable errors show up. When a fixed percentage of error is predictable, an additional burden is placed upon the human user of the system to expect this and plan his work around it. This is simply too difficult. The designer of an information retrieval system is faced with two major problems relative to system performance: finding users' requirements and interpreting the responses he gets when he asks what is wanted, these being clouded by honest inability to state requirements* and the unfortunate tendency of some people to try to outguess the designer on the nature of the system that will ultimately be created.

4.4.5   Error Measurement

Here we face two problems: Who decides what is an error? How can we measure the number of pertinent documents *not* retrieved? Just as different users have different performance standards, they will use different criteria in evaluating the relevance of a document to their queries. The response to the same query will be rated differently by different recipients, even though they all represent the same discipline and degree of mastery of it. In any attempt to measure system error, over time for a large number of users, statistical sampling techniques must be used.

Measurement of Type II errors can then be achieved, for any group of users, by polling them on their reaction to sets of documents retrieved

---

* The users of any system, be it library, supermarket, or computer can be expected to have valuable ideas on how the system can be improved or redesigned. In polling them, however, a system designer must recognize that they will not necessarily be creative or articulate in describing the mechanics of the improvement, and may not be able to visualize how they will react to a radically new idea. C. P. Bourne[3] comments, on this point that, "This may be somewhat like asking a person in the early 1900's what features and performance he would like to have in an automobile."

in response to their queries, to find the number of irrelevant documents retrieved.

Measurement of Type I errors poses the problem of finding the number of relevant documents *not retrieved* by the query. How do we establish relevancy except by the query, which presumably has already failed to retrieve a certain set of documents? This can also be handled by a form of sampling, but one even more subject to individual variation. The queries to be tested for Type I error can be run and the responses evaluated just as in Type II error measurement. Then these queries can be generalized, rerun, and the new responses evaluated. The second run of a generalized query should produce all of the first documents plus some new ones. Of these new ones, some are relevant *to the first query,* and some are not. The number of documents that are relevant to the first run serves as a measure of Type I error for that query. The validity of the measure depends, of course, upon the ways in which the query was generalized. At least two aspects of generalization must be considered—the "direction," or subject path chosen, and the "distance" or extent of generalization. The latter can be handled by increasing the extent of generalization slowly (simple if hierarchical classification is the index scheme), and successively rerunning the query until no new relevant documents (to the first query) are obtained. The direction of generalization, like the determination of relevance, is highly subjective. This procedure is quite elaborate, yet may be as important to measuring the performance of a system as the simpler, oftener tried measurement of Type II error.

4.4.6   Cost Measurement

The procedures involved in measuring the costs of indexing and retrieval belong to another domain than information retrieval—they differ little from any other form of work measurement.* The aspect of cost measurement that is of interest to information retrieval is the recognition of hidden costs, such as those in the following examples.

In Section 4.43 we gave an illustration of a library whose subject indexing was inadequate and led to a use pattern that avoided subject searches. In this library, even though catalogers are busily at work affixing classification numbers to documents, it is the users who actually do the useful work of associating a document with a subject class. The

* In a paper on cost analysis Bourne and Ford[4] state, "For the most part, these techniques are not new or novel—they might even be considered standard industrial engineering tools—however, they have generally not been applied to the analysis or evaluation of proposed or actual information systems."

retriever finds out through references or recommendations of his colleagues what documents he might have an interest in, and he requests these by number. The indexing work done by the library's appointed indexers contributes little to the process of matching user needs with document content.

If a system had a high Type II error rate, it would force the retriever to scan his material, essentially performing another search on a limited set of documents, to select the truly relevant ones.

If a system had a high Type I error rate, the result could be low quality work on the part of the system users who are dependent on the system for information.

All three of these examples point out hidden costs in the operation of an information retrieval system, costs which would not normally be considered in budget planning for the library because they are borne not by the library but by its users. There are the costs of duplicate indexing (the retriever must repeat the search-selection process after a formal retrieval operation has resulted in too much retrieved data), and inadequate indexing (the retriever fails to find all the information he needs to perform his own function satisfactorily). In any organization heavily dependent on a library to keep its people abreast of a current, rapidly changing situation these hidden costs could dominate all other cost considerations. A drug company forced into an expensive experiment or the failure of an intelligence group to prevent an attack by detecting an enemy capability are examples. Note that in any situation in which time is an important factor degradation of the quality of the work done by retrievers is the almost inevitable result, regardless of the type of errors made by the system. This is an almost impossible parameter to measure.

4.4.7   Usage Rate

The usage rate of an information retrieval system is often used as a measure of performance, as is the number of document references retrieved in response to queries. There seems to be some useful information in the number or proportion of members of an organization who use the library facilities, especially if this is unusually high or low. However, except for vague indications—low usage implies something wrong, high usage implies something right—we cannot convert query or response rate into a direct measure of efficiency or quality of performance. Indeed, high usage could result from excellence of service which attracts more users, or from such poor performance that users must ask many questions to get the answer to one. Low usage could result from such good service as to obviate repetitive queries, or from user apathy caused by poor performance.

4.4.8 Retrieval and Acquisition

One reason for the difficulty of measuring retrieval system performance is its heavy dependence on the library's acquisition policy. Recalling our definition of an information system as a communication system, with the library as a switching center, we must realize that we cannot assess the quality of the total operation solely in terms of the switching operation. If the library does not receive the "correct" set of documents, it cannot serve its users well. Remember that a library is not like a post office or telegraph office whose functions are to deliver messages to addressees clearly identified within the message. The library receives "messages" and also receives, from the potential addressees, descriptions of the attributes of the messages they wish to receive. If messages bearing these attributes are not present in the library, the library's retrieval capability should not be blamed, although its acquisition policy might be.

We might classify documents which are relevant to a given query as follows:

a. Present in the library and retrieved
b. Present in the library
c. Not present in the library but existent elsewhere
d. Nonexistent

The set of documents which is in class b but not a is due to Type I retrieval error. The difference between b and c is due to acquisition policy. Discussion of "cause" of the existence of set d would put us in the realm of philosophy, but it is important to recognize the existence of d because library users may want to know whether or not material exists elsewhere, and some libraries maintain catalogs, called *union catalogs,* of material stored in other libraries. The closer the library's acquisition policy matches known user interests, the smaller is set c. The better the retrieval system, the closer does set a approximate set b.

The user of a library will not normally care whether system deficiencies are due to the indexing and retrieval system or to acquisition policy. His interest is in the information. A procedure for translating user interest into acquisition is as important to the library as is retrieval, but there is another side to this coin which introduces another reason for the difficulty of measuring system performance. Users must conscientiously report their fields of interest and their degree of satisfaction with library services in order that the library may develop an acquisition policy. Failure by users to report interests, or failure to recognize that a library must serve *all* its users and must distribute its funds and energies accordingly, can result in the unhappy situation of an otherwise efficient library providing its users with the wrong services.

4.4.9   Value Measurement

Cost and value of a commodity or service are not measures of the same thing.   Cost can be expressed in terms of money, time, manpower, or a combination.   Hall[6] lists three concepts of value: market value, value-in-use, and imputed value.   The notion of market value of an index record is usually meaningless, since index records are relatively rarely sold on a profit-making basis, although there are firms engaged in just this business.   For the type of libraries we have been considering, however, market value has no meaning.   Hence, when a library invests funds in producing an index record, it does not recover this investment by resale.   We must look to the other concepts of value to weigh against the disadvantages incurred by paying a price in money, time, and manpower to produce the index.

Value-in-use can be illustrated by considering, say, a production line capable of producing N items per day at a unit cost of C dollars.   If a new machine tool can increase production to $2N$ units, then its value-in-use is NC dollars per day.   The purchase price, or cost, may be higher or lower.   Clearly, value-in-use varies with each user of the machine tool, although the purchase price does not.

Imputed value is a subjective judgment, rarely expressible in dollar terms.   The expression by library users of a preference between two choices, as a preference for key word indexing over hierarchical classification, is an imputation of value.   Imputed values will vary, not only among organizations that operate libraries, but among individual users of the same library.

Neither library science nor operations research has yet provided a truly useful measurement technique for evaluating the total performance, or value-in-use, of a library.   By total performance, we mean the net contribution made by the library to its users.   There are non-quantitative methods of great use in studying opinions about, or imputed values of, library service, these largely centered about interviews with users, catalogers, and administrators.   Bourne[3] gives a good resume of such methods.   There are highly useful methods of measuring the cost of specific tasks or subsystems (e.g., cataloging or searching files), but these usually are restricted to comparisons of how well the present procedure compares with a proposed new procedure for accomplishing the *same result*. We have no way of predicting how a *new* task procedure or subsystem, a change in the index language, for example, would affect the quality of the library's service or the contribution to its users.

In the author's opinion this is the reason why mechanization in documentation has not progressed as far as in some other fields—because we cannot predict performance and because tests involving the operation of full scale libraries, *and* the research organizations they support, are so expensive as to prohibit measurement of value.

4.5   USE OF THE RETRIEVED INFORMATION

So far we have implicitly assumed that a searcher wants to retrieve information from a natural language document, that he uses the information retrieval system as a means of acquisition, and that he would read the documents and extract the desired information without assistance from the system. While such a simplified view of the mechanism aids in the presentation of principles, there is no need to be so restrictive in practice.

In this section we shall consider the circumstances under which the retrieval system may be relied upon to extract information from a file and make some operational use of it, by which we mean to use the recovered information in some other process, possibly another information retrieval operation.

Certainly, to make operational use of information stored in a file, it is necessary that the retrieval programs be able to understand the information. Because computer interpretation of natural language is still a limited art, we shall emphasize more restrictive languages in the material to follow. In pursuing this point we shall first discuss the conditions under which information retrieval from files can be used operationally, then discuss cyclic retrieval or the use of such data to control successive retrieval operations.

4.5.1   Information and Credence

The physical removal or copying out of information from an index record is what we have chosen to call information selection. Recall that *index record* has a wide enough definition to include full documents, themselves, at times. To amplify the concept of information selection, we must first refine the concept, *information*.

Professional intelligence analysts (in the military or diplomatic sense) tend to draw an interesting distinction between information and intelligence; viz, intelligence is information whose credibility has been established. This is quite obviously a highly subjective, purely attitudinal relationship, but it has its place as an element of information retrieval. Let us briefly review a few notions about information in order to view them in perspective.

1. Information can be measured, but only in a limited sense—one useful to the communications engineer, but not the linguist or journalist. See Chapter 7 for a fuller treatment of this topic.

2. Information theory does not, at present, treat the semantic aspects of information; this remains the domain of the linguist or lexicographer. A person engaged in information retrieval is usually concerned much more with meaning than the communications engineering aspects of information.

3. To be credible, a message certainly must have meaning, but the converse is not always true.

To illustrate these points, consider Paul Revere's intelligence and communications operation. A code was established among Revere and his companions to warn of the approach of the British. "One if by land and two if by sea," referred to the number of lanterns in the belfry of the Old North Church, but might as well have referred to the transmission of the symbols 1 and 2 or, of course, no symbol, if no British came at all. The methods to be introduced in Chapter 7 to measure some of the physical requirements of this communication system would solve the engineering problem and confirm that at least two lanterns were needed to transmit the full range of possible messages (i.e., "no British," "by land," and "by sea"). The prearranged code tells the meaning. Now, assume Revere sees a signal, say a 1. The engineer would tell him he has received one and one-half bits of information. His code book tells him "By land." But, does he believe it? What if Tories have captured the lookout, and are sending the signal to prompt Revere into premature action and, perhaps, into the waiting arms of the British? As *technical information,* the message has been, "One lantern." As *semantic information,* the message has been, "A lantern signal has arrived and its coded meaning is 'The British are coming by land.'" As *intelligence,* the message means either "The British are coming," or "One of their agents is in the belfry of the Old North Church." Hence, in the effective sense, to put the information to immediate operational use, Revere must decide what degree of credence he will assign to the signal. Military messages in more sophisticated communication systems often have additional characters, beyond those needed to convey the actual message, which are devoted to authenticating the message—verifying that it was sent by the stated originator.

What has this to do with information retrieval? The more credence a user assigns to the index file, the more effective, or operationally useful, information he can get out of it. In one of our previous examples, we described the retrieval of an author's birth date as a way to retrieve *information* from an index. Some readers may protest that a scholar does not base his conclusions on a catalog card entry, and this will, in general, be true; but, if scholars saw to it that other scholars made up the index cards and that these scholarly indexers were of sufficient stature that their facts could be relied on, then even a scholar could and would retrieve information from an index.

We have taken this circuitous path to point out that credibility of the data, although not affecting the mechanics of retrieval, can affect the willingness of retrievers to make full use of retrieval mechanics. Let us now resume our discussion of retrieval mechanics in this light.

The librarian, indexer, or cataloger normally adds only one item of information to the document, as received, and that is the call number— the most often retrieved index term. The other terms are mostly transcriptions or encodings of contents of the document—author, author's affiliation, publisher, and subject (recalling that the latter is a re-encoding of the author's idea). Occasionally, the cataloger will seek out true names of authors who use pseudonyms, or their dates of birth or death. In a faceted key word or natural language system, we have a great deal of breadth in the index and, potentially, more intelligence than in a classification index. We may have names associated with places, organizations, or disciplines. We may have chemical compounds associated with diseases for which the substance is a treatment, or a number of home runs associated with a baseball player.

By "associated" we mean nothing necessarily more than co-occurrence. A library user, interested in the effect of a given drug in treating various diseases, might ask, simply, for "All documents pertaining to chemical compound, X, and **disease**." If the requestor had sufficient confidence in the index, he could ask for selection of the name of diseases for which X a possible cure; that is, he could *search* for co-occurrences of X, and **disease,** and **cure** or its synonyms, and he could select any word tagged as a disease. The question of what drug will cure a given disease can be answered, to some degree, from the index file, without recourse to the documents. Similarly, questions such as: "Other incidents involving the person associated with home runs on team T," "Name of product associated with a rise in the stock price of company C" could directly retrieve information on a player trade or a new product.

We see, then, that it is *information* in the index record which is the objective of the activity called information retrieval. We find that even the most pedestrian of information retrieval systems operate this way—by retrieval of information (a call number) from an index (card catalog), and then use of the retrieved information in an operational sense (location of the physical document). It is as easy to retrieve other items of information and as easy to use them directly, if only the retriever has faith in the credibility of the data. Note that we call the use of a retrieved call number to locate a book "operational" use of information that is, the information is used to control a physical process. Many simple examples of this phenomenon exist: the retrieval of the figure labeled "on hand" from an inventory file, and its direct use in a stock reordering program; or retrieval of the number of seats available for a given flight, given date, and between given cities, and its use either to reject an airline customer's order or to sell him the space.

4.5.2 Cyclic Retrieval

Once we have a system in which the users have reasonable faith in the quality of the indexing, and the indexing is done in reasonable depth and breadth, we can begin to exploit the true potential of information retrieval. *Reasonable faith* does not imply that the users must have any faith whatever in the indexers' ability to draw conclusions from the data—merely that the user must have faith in the indexers' ability to produce a faithful translation of the document into the prescribed index language. This rather innocuous sounding requirement by no means prevails in all library situations.

Cyclic retrieval is the use of the results of one retrieval operation to guide another. There is nothing new in the concept, for we all do this whenever the first reference book we find in the library refers us to another. The use of the cyclic concept in automatic systems, however, is not common. It implies programmed feedback—the ability to instruct a program to select some item of information, and then use this item as a query to retrieve some other item. This, surely, is effective communication in Weaver's sense.

To illustrate the mechanism, let us take the following example. Suppose a large company has received an inquiry about employment from Mr. Applicant, and that he cites as a professional reference Mr. Friend, to whom he refers as a former college classmate, and who is already employed by the company receiving the inquiry. Suppose, further, that Mr. Friend is on vacation, and the company is anxious to make a quick response to Mr. Applicant. The personnel manager could order a search of his files for all other company employees who attended the same university and graduated in the same year, with the intention of asking them if they know Mr. Applicant.   To do this, it is not necessary for the personnel officer to know the name of Applicant's school.   His query can be worded this way, "Find the name of the university attended by Mr. Friend and the year of his graduation.   Then, use these items as search terms to locate the names of any other Company employees who attended the same school and graduated in the same year."   Assuming the file of employee records to be ordered on **name,** a search can easily be made for the record of Mr. Friend, as shown in Figure 4.3. Once this is found, the items **university** and **date of graduation** must be retrieved.   Now it is necessary to start the search of the file all over again, looking at each record and matching the query terms against the corresponding index terms.   When a match is made, the item selected is **name,** it being of no consequence to the personnel clerk or machine performing the search where and when Friend attended school. The original query term was a single name; the final output could have been a set of names.   Two searches of the index file were required, one to find some attributes of the first name submitted (Friend) and one to find some other names possessing these attributes.

The process need not stop after two cycles, although the need for it may drop off rather quickly in normal business or research applications.   We might continue the preceding illustration by using the re-

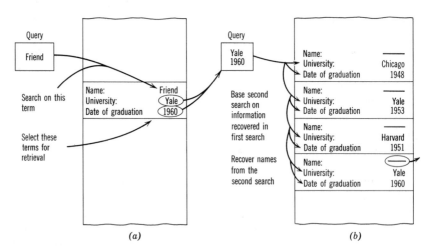

(a)   (b)

Figure 4.3   Cyclic retrieval.   (a) Part 1. Search the personnel file for information about a specific employee.   (b) Part 2. Use the recovered information to find the names of all other employees with the same attributes.

trieved names of classmates of Mr. Friend to retrieve their telephone numbers from a directory file.

The programming of cyclic retrieval requires no really new techniques or advanced programs. The only requirement is for a subroutine which will, upon retrieval of a prescribed set of index terms, enter them into a query format and return program control to the query routines. This is simply a generalization of the subroutine that selects the call number from the index record. Cyclic retrieval may be regarded as the specification of retrieval criteria by functional means rather than by specifying acceptable values of named data fields; that is, the value of terms used in retrieval operations after the first one is given by giving the functions that must be performed to find the values. Since little is required of programs to implement cyclic retrieval, the entire burden of making best use of the technique falls upon the retrievers. More positively, this capability can be provided at a relatively low cost, but cannot be used effectively until sophisticated users have developed a methodology.

REFERENCES

1. Becker, Joseph, and Robert M. Hayes, *Information Storage and Retrieval: Tools, Elements, Theories,* John Wiley & Sons, New York, 1963, p. 368.
2. Birkhoff, Garret, and Saunders Maclane, *A Survey of Modern Algebra,* The Macmillan Co., New York, 1949, p. 311.
3. Bourne, C. P., *A Review of the Methodology of Information System Design,* Stanford Research Institute, Menlo Park, California, September 1962.
4. Bourne, C. P., and Donald F. Ford, "Cost Analysis and Simulation Procedures for the Evaluation of Large Information Systems," *American Documentation,* **15,** 2 (1964), pp. 142–149.
5. Doyle, L. B., "Semantic Road Maps for Literature Searchers," *J. Assoc. Computing Machinery,* **8,** 4 (1961), pp. 553–578.
6. Hall, Arthur D., *A Methodology for Systems Engineering,* D. Van Nostrand Co., Princeton, 1962, pp. 253–55.
7. Hoel, Paul G., *Introduction to Mathematical Statistics,* John Wiley & Sons, New York, 1947, p. 202.
8. Kessler, M. W., *An Experimental Study of Bibliographic Coupling Between Technical Papers,* Massachusetts Institute of Technology, Cambridge, Massachusetts, Nov. 1961, Revised June 15, 1962.
9. Lipetz, Ben-Ami, "Compilation of an Experimental Citation Index From Scientific Literature," *American Documentation,* **13,** 3 (1962).
10. Luhn, H. P., "The Automatic Creation of Literature Abstracts," *IBM J. Res. Develop.,* **2,** 4 (1958), pp. 159–165.
11. Potter, Stephen, *Gamesmanship, The Art of Winning Games Without Actually Cheating,* Holt, Rinehart & Winston, New York, 1948.
12. Salton, Gerard, et al, "Progress in Automatic Information Retrieval," *IEEE Spectrum,* August 1965, pp. 90–103.
13. Stiles, H. E., "The Association Factor in Information Retrieval," *J. Assoc. Computing Machinery,* **8,** 2 (1961), pp. 271–279.

14. ———, *Word Analyzer Final Report,* International Business Machines Corp., Thomas J. Watson Research Center, Yorktown Heights, New York, 1962.

EXERCISES

1. Explain the difference, if any, between the queries in each of the following pairs:

   a. United States ∪ United Kingdom   United ####### (# is the universal match symbol)
   b. Iberia   Spain ∪ Portugal
   c. Airplane ∩ (jet ∪ (propeller))   airplane ∩ jet
   d. 3.8#   3.8 ∪ 3.81 ∪ 3.82 ∪ 3.83 ∪ 3.89 (see Figure 2·4)

2. Replace the following natural language statements of information require-ments with queries using key words of ACM subject headings (Figure 2.4), where appropriate, in Boolean expressions:
   a. Use of linear programming in the physical sciences.
   b. Design of special purpose computers for monitoring biomedical phe-nomena in manned space flight.
   c. European research on heuristic techniques in language translation.
   d. Names of people engaged in legal information retrieval projects in Great Britain.
   e. Publishers of programming text books published since 1963.

3. From the body of documents indexed for Exercise 3 of Chapter 3, write down 5–10 topics known to be covered, to some extent. Write a query using the index language previously used and *and* and *or* connectors. Search the index you previously compiled. Examine the records retrieved and comment on the appropriateness of your query. Include a recommenda-tion for enhancing the query, if necessary.

4. Translate the following expressions from key words into ACM codes, or *vice versa.* Use Boolean expressions if necessary (e.g., 5.5 = statistics ∪ probability). Comment on translations causing special difficulty.
   a. Data processing application to space science, technology, or operations
   b. Mathematical theories of information retrieval
   c. Computer translation of Russian language into English
   d. Copyrighting of computer programs
   e. Industrial training courses in analog computers
   f. 3.21 (Note codes 3.11 and 3.83)
   g. 6.35 (Note 4.41)
   h. Mathematically-oriented computer languages
   i. 4.19
   j. 4.3

5. Select a document at random from the set of those indexed for Exercise 3 of Chapter 3. Make up a query consisting of one or two index terms.

(Do not use title or other unique descriptor.)   Search the full index with this query.   If you retrieve more than the one original document, modify the query, as a result of analysis of the response, and try again.   Continue until unable to improve the query.   Repeat with a different initial document for a total of 10 times.

6. Make up a set of criteria for evaluating the performance of an information retrieval system such as that in use in your class or the library you regularly use.   Discuss and justify the measures used.

7. Make up a set of questions to use in polling library users to gain insight into their attitudes toward the library.   Discuss and justify the questions selected.

8. Discuss how the library or retrieval system you usually use (or are using in class) could eliminate one type of error (either type).   Discuss what would be the effect on the other type of errors.

9. In the retrieval system available to you, try several queries utilizing alternate strategies.
   a. Try for the best result in one "shot."
   b. Assume you will have four tries; plan and discuss a strategy to use in this case.
   c. Discuss the results of each query.

10. Discuss the role and extent of syntax deficiency, vocabulary deficiency and search logic as error-inducing factors in the information retrieval system you use.

II

The Organization
of Information

CHAPTER 5

The organization of records

5.1 INTRODUCTION

The discussion of information in Chapter 1 pointed out that we represent information, or ideas, by symbols. This representation is a form of *coding,* the use of one symbol to represent another, as is done in conventional communication. Even the simplest communication system consists of links involving several successive transformations of the input symbols. This was shown in our illustration of a radio transmission in Figure 1.2.

There are also many *levels* of coding in communication systems, successive combinations of basic symbols to produce higher symbolic concepts. For example, letters, words, and sentences are successive levels of coding in natural language. There is no obvious base level. We have no reason to say, for example, that the *word* is the most meaningful code level. Words are made up of letters. Letters, in communications, are made up of bits. Bits, in turn, are made up of rising and falling electrical voltages induced by magnetic fields. The point of view of the observer determines what level is important at the time. For example, the recording engineer is interested in the pattern or waveform of these voltages; the computer designer, in the bits they represent; the programmer, in characters; the accountant, using data prepared by the computer, in words or fields; and the company president wants a complete financial report, of many words. *Word* has two meanings in computer technology. There is a natural language word, a set of letters or phonemes with a defined meaning, and there is a computer word, usually a fixed number of characters. A *field* is any set of characters with a defined meaning. While often equivalent to a natural language word, it may also be a number or code. For example, a field designated *sex* may contain either **M** or **F**, standing for male and female.

This chapter is about records and fields. A *record* is a set of fields, all descriptive of some individual or class of individuals. A broader concept than a field, it is the use of a collection of fields to enlarge

151

upon, or further delineate, a subject which cannot be adequately described by any one of the individual fields. When we group records
together we produce a *file,* the concept of which is a higher level abstraction than that of a record. A file describes a class of things, of which
a record describes an individual or sub-class. For example, if a record
is about an individual person, each field of the record will describe
some facet of the person, such as his name or birthdate. A file made
up of such records may be descriptive of all people employed by a
given company. We can also have a record about a class. We might
have a file in which each record is a summary of the performance characteristics of all members of a particular class or type of aircraft operated
by a given airline company. A file of such records consists of records
covering all the aircraft operated by the airline. The data processing
world does not have a name commonly used for the next higher level
of abstraction in information assembly. This level is a *set of files.* A
set consisting of files covering aircraft, ground equipment, personnel,
sales, reservations data, and so on, would comprise a description of an
entire airline, which operates the aircraft described in one of the files
of the set. This is a higher level abstraction than description only of
the aircraft. Chapter 6 covers files, Chapter 8, sets of files.

In our coverage of records we first go into some general principles
of record organization related to computer processing. We then describe
a range of record organizations.

5.2   PRINCIPLES OF RECORD ORGANIZATION

Essential to the ideas to be presented here is the fact that symbols
can be combined to represent higher concepts. To make such combinations meaningful, they must follow some prescribed structural rules. The
set of symbols 0, 1, 2, 3, 4, 5, 6, 7, 8, and 9 can be used to represent
any positive integer if we follow the accepted rules for representation
of numbers in the decimal system, namely that the rightmost digit gives
the number of units, the next digit the number of tens, and so on. It
is logically possible to write numbers starting from the left, but the
results are meaningless unless all readers are familiar with the structure
used. Similar structural rules apply to the combination of numbers
or words into phrases, as a mailing address is generally understood to
be a street number, street name, city, and state. The rules for combining
fields to make phrases, which may or may not be complete records,
are collectively called *syntax.*

The principles on which the succeeding sections of this chapter are
based are the following:

1. A defined structure or syntax is required to be able to combine

symbols into new symbols, such as phrases or records, representing higher order concepts.

2. The complete definition of a symbol, as a part of an information structure, includes a requirement for the specification of the role it plays relative to other symbols within a higher level symbol (as a field within a record)—of its syntactic relationship to other symbols.

3. If information-bearing symbols are to be interpreted by a transducer, their structure must be comprehensible to that transducer.

4. The structure of a record can be changed by rearranging the symbols contained in it, but the extent to which this is possible without information loss depends upon the syntactic role of the symbol. A rearrangement which destroys original context can destroy meaning.

5.2.1   Record Structure

The letters that make up the English alphabet can also be used to make up words in French, Spanish, Portuguese, German, and other languages. The symbols *dot, dash,* and *space* are used in more than one telegraphic code. While all modern digital computers use a form of binary number representation, they combine the basic 0's and 1's differently to represent characters. The basic symbols in each case are not enough to make a language. There must be a morphology or a syntax—a set of basic structural rules—to guide the communicator in combining the basic symbols into more meaningful symbols.

We have shown that a record is merely a point along a chain of successive encodings of information. It consists of a set of fields, and it combines with other records to form a file. When we talk of the structure of a record, we mean both the specification of the positioning of fields within the record (that is, its format) and the relationships of each field to each other field.

A field of a record is definable several ways and may be said not to be completely defined unless all these facets are specified.

1. Its position in the record, for example, *characters 11–16 of a 100-character record*

2. Its function within the record, such as a special end-of-record symbol, or tag

3. Its name, which is actually the name of the class of referents of the field, such as a set of birthdates

4. Its value, or an individual referent or instance of the named referent set, as *July 4, 1965*

We may have a field whose name is *serial number,* whose position is in digits 11–16 of the record, whose function is to modify the *name* field, and whose value is 123456. By combining field name and position description, we produce a powerful manipulative capability. One of the simplest methods of organizing information is the use of a matrix, simply defined as a rectangular array of elements, which can be any agreed-upon, information-bearing symbols. Mathematical tables and airline timetables are examples of this form. One of the advantages of the matrix is that the elements can be referred to in the abstract by their positions, rather than their name or content. Mathematicians use the notation a_{ij} to refer to the contents of the cell of a matrix located in row i, column j. Similarly, the conventional method of referring to symbols in a computer program uses position (address) of the symbol as distinct from value (content of a memory location). In order to manipulate information, we must know its position within a structure of other information-bearing symbols. In order to convey semantic information, we specify a value. Any of these structural attributes can be defined directly (position is columns 11–16, or value of *date* field is 070465) or functionally (*serial number* occupies the next 6 characters after *name,* or *price* in an inventory record is copied from *price* in an invoice record).

In Chapter 1 we said that for a message to be successfully communicated between a transmitter and receiver, the coding of the message must be compatible with both transducers. There is a requirement analogous to this for processing data by a computer. A computer may be defined as a signal transducer in that the net result of its operation on a set of input symbols is to produce another set of symbols, with a defined logical relationship to the input. The computer must be able to understand the coding used in the input message, just as a radio receiver must be able to demodulate an incoming signal if the proper sound responses are to be generated as output. A radio receiving system must recognize more than one level of coding. It must first recognize electromagnetic waves, select only those within a given frequency, and then demodulate the signal which is conveyed as coded perturbations of the basic carrier signal. A computer may be required to recognize even more levels of coding. It must first recognize and read bits, then interpret these as characters, out of which the basic semantic elements, words or fields, are created. While bit and character interpretation are normally wired-in functions of a computer, interpretation of higher level codes is generally the province of a stored program. As an example, a magnetic tape of data prepared by a variable word length, or character, computer may not be readable by a fixed word length computer if the word length on tape exceeds the fixed word size. This situation can occur even when both computers use identical tapes, tape transports, and character encoding rules.   It is the procedures for creating and interpreting character strings that cause the incompatibility.   A program may be designed to prepare paychecks for employees based upon records of hours worked and permanent payroll records containing rates of pay and tax deduction data.   This program may not be able to perform at all if used with records having the same *information* about the employees, but which *organize* the fields differently.   On the other hand, computers have been successfully applied to certain tasks involving the interpretation of natural language where the organization of words is far more difficult to describe than is that of a payroll record.   The reason is that some model* of the organizational structure is required to be made known to the program, and, if this model is sufficiently accurate, the job can be done.   If it is inaccurate, the job cannot be done even though the organization may be simple.   Once again, we point out that this is but a corollary to the requirement that both parties to a communication use compatible languages or codes.

Knowledge of the organization of input data permits its reorganization without information loss.   For example, punched card payroll data can be read by a computer, fields rearranged, and all numeric fields converted from binary-coded-decimal to pure binary representation.   A natural language text may be read in and a concordance prepared by use of a program which is designed to take advantage of only two organizational concepts—that a space separates words and that a period ends a sentence.†   A concordance is a data organization completely different from text and used for a completely different purpose.   If complete, it and the textual organization are recoverable from one another by sorting, or resequencing, of the words.   There are limits, however, to the extent

---

* A model is a representation of one system by another, or "by means of a structure . . . aimed at answering certain questions about the problem. . . . However, a model may be present without one's knowing all its theoretical implications."² The model system normally represents only certain attributes of the original and ignores others.   A child's model airplane represents spatial attributes of the original.   A mathematical model of an airplane may represent its flight characteristics in the form of equations which, certainly, do not *look* like an airplane.

† That a word is whatever lies between two spaces, and a sentence whatever lies between two periods, is admittedly an inaccurate definition, or model, of a sentence so far as the grammarian is concerned.   However, the purpose of a concordance is location, and there is not so strong a need for grammatical accuracy as long as location is accurate.   For example, our definition would make two sentences out of, "Mr. Smith goes to town."   Yet all occurrences of *Mr.* and *Smith* could always be found.   This illustrates how a model, of even so complex a structure as natural language, need only be as accurate as its intended use demands.

of the modifications that can be made to a message without loss of meaning. If the characters of this book were sorted into a random order, no natural language communication would take place between author and reader, because the reader would have no means for reconstituting the original structure.

Another form of transformation takes place when we take in a string of numbers, perhaps temperature readings and times of the readings as taken by a weather observer, and fit a polynomial to this data. The result is a mathematical expression by which, given a time, temperature can be computed. Although there may actually be some loss of information in using this method, the memory space required for storing temperature data is quite drastically reduced. We cannot reorganize a Shakespearean sonnet without losing much of the author's message, although it is fully possible to restate the temperature table as poetry!

We can see, then, that the methods of organization that are possible for a given set of symbols are limited by the semantic and syntactic nature of the message. The meaning, or semantic content, of a message is often quite subjective, depending upon a complex interplay between the value of a field (particular word chosen) and the syntax of the record. This means that the possible organizations of a message are dependent upon its content as well as the receiver's knowledge of its structure. For a person who speaks only English and has no interest in linguistics, there would be no loss of meaning in sorting a Sanskrit text randomly, since it had no meaning to begin with. On the other hand, rearranging the sequence of an English language text will not destroy all meaning for an English-speaking person. In Figure 3.15 is the high-frequency portion of a list of frequency-ordered words from the newspaper article shown in Figure 3.16. The word list still conveys much of the sense of the article.

Before reviewing the various forms of record structure, we shall briefly introduce the factors that will later be used as a basis for analysis of the structures. A record structure and the set of values that its fields may take together constitute a language according to our definition in Chapter 2. The positioning of fields corresponds to format, functional relationships to syntax, and values to vocabulary. However, our presentation in Chapter 2 was oriented toward semantic content, essentially to the relationship between the index terms and that which they represented. Here we wish to stress structure, and as a result will modify our comparison factors somewhat.

The factors to be used for record structure comparison are expressiveness, positional ambiguity, semantic ambiguity, and compactness. We have omitted cost of term selection, used in Chapter 2, because it is far more a semantic than a structural problem. Also we have taken special note of the fact that some ambiguity can be caused by uncertainty of the position of information as well as by uncertainty of meaning.

5.2.2   Expressiveness

The expressiveness of a record structure refers to the ability of parties to a communication to convey ideas using the structure. Primitive structures limit communication. Complex ideas demand complex information structures. The potential expressiveness of a record structure is as important a factor in record design as it is in design or choice of an indexing language. By and large, the more rigidly structured a record (i.e., the more completely are the locations of its fields specified and known in advance), the less expressive it is capable of being. If the position of each field in a record is rigidly fixed, in order for a concept to be expressed, the need for expressing that concept must have been anticipated by the record designer and it must be expressible in terms of the facets he has selected for his record. In a natural language record, new concepts can easily be introduced. A new concept can be an entirely different facet, such as adding *height* and *weight* to *name, rank,* and *serial number* in a record, or merely a refinement of an existing field, as extending a numeric field to an additional decimal position of accuracy.

Expressiveness is not a directly measurable quality, but comparisons can frequently be made between record organizations on the basis of whether or not they can handle a given problem in expression.

5.2.3   Positional Ambiguity

When a record is being tested for the presence of a query term, the first action that must be taken, before a match can be attempted, is to locate the field that will be matched with the query term. Difficulty in doing so can cause two problems—it can slow the search and make the results ambiguous.

If the record structure is such that exact location of sought-for information cannot be found to any high degree of certainty, the match is ambiguous, for we may not be sure we have matched with the correct field. Such an occurrence is easily possible in searching natural language text. If we are searching a natural language text for the subject *iron* (a metal), and we do it by independently testing each word of a text to see if it matches the symbol, *iron,* we can easily err when we find *iron* in other contexts, especially when used as a verb meaning *to press.* If the searcher or search mechanism knows where in the record the type of information being sought is located, we say there is *prior knowledge of location.* The location of a term within a record structure is a function of the syntax of the record.   Prior knowledge can be provided by use of record structure, or format tables, or by explicit statement in the query.   It can also be provided by implicitly incorporating record structure information in the search program, about which more is said in Chapter 7.   In some records no prior knowledge is possible.   In general, then, we are concerned with whether prior knowledge of location of information is available, and the degree to which it is available.   The greater the amount of information available, the less positional ambiguity is present in the record structure.

If the field cannot be located immediately, the search will take extra time.   The extent to which prior knowledge of the location of information sought in a query is available to a searcher is a major determinant of search time.   When searching a file, we wish to know where the records are that might satisfy the query.   We shall cover this aspect of information location in Chapter 6.   When searching a record we want to know where the fields are that are to be matched with the query.   If, for example, a record consists of fields *name, rank,* and *serial number,* and if we are searching for all people named Smith, we must know where within the record the *name* field lies.   The alternatives are to search first for the name field, then compare it with the query term, or to treat all fields of the record as possible name fields and compare each with the query terms.   Clearly, either of these alternatives extends the time of a search, and the second alternative could induce errors.   We shall show in Chapter 7 that lack of information about record structure has some of the characteristics of noise in a communication system.

5.2.4   Semantic Ambiguity

The meaning of this factor has been amply defined in Chapter 2.   It refers to the possibility of plurality of meaning of any given field, or to the existence of more than one value with the same meaning.   There can also be semantic ambiguity about a field name, where, for example, it may not be possible to differentiate between the author of a collection of essays and the editor or anthologist if the field were defined simply as *author* and no field is provided for *editor.*

5.2.5   Record Compactness

Of concern, here, is how much memory or how many characters are required to store a given amount of information.   Each organization

Figure 5.1 Packing of fields into fixed-length words. (*a*) Three 4-character fields as closely packed as possible into 6-character words. (*b*) Three 4-character fields placed into 6-character words to minimize search time.

or language will express a given concept differently and each will use a different number of characters in doing so.

Although memory use is a direct economic problem, search time is also an economic problem and one that is partly dependent on memory use. A highly compact record, although using little memory, may require some unpacking before matching can be performed. For example, if a computer has a six-character word, and a record consists of three four-character fields, the most compact mode of storage is as shown on the left in Figure 5.1. To compare one of these fields with a search term requires unpacking of the record to bring the desired field into a position in the computer word comparable with the query term. Such unpacking can be so uneconomical as to preclude use of such a tight, memory-conservative structure. Placing one field in each machine word, although wasteful of two characters in every word, enables faster searching of this field.

5.3   THE PROGRESSION OF RECORD STRUCTURES

There are far too many ways of organizing information to be able to discuss each one individually. There is the tabular organization of digital data, previously described. There is pictorial representation. There is the use of highly symbolic mathematical formulas. There are analog recordings of information which may permit finer gradations of physical variables than can digital systems. Information can be represented and transmitted by gesture or facial expression. The discussion here is restricted to the communication forms most commonly used in libraries and data systems, the tabular arrangements of digital data. We consider that natural language is such a form. Although it lacks some of the characteristics of a matrix arrangement, we shall see that it nonetheless possesses other characteristics in common with tabular arrays.* In fact, we shall show that there is an almost continuous progression of methods from the most highly organized information to completely unorganized, and we shall describe representative points along this progression. An analysis of the differences among these methods follows. We are considering, here, language *structures,* not languages, in that we are omitting discussion of vocabulary. We shall cover a wider range than we did in Chapter 2, in which we talked about specific languages.

5.3.1   Invariant Structure

We can illustrate the most highly organized end of the spectrum with the following example. Consider a convoy of ships on the ocean, trying to maintain a prescribed formation. In such a formation, each ship will be assigned a position, in terms of distance and bearing, from a guide ship, normally the flagship. Each ship is concerned with two position records, one telling the location of the ship relative to the earth's surface (latitude and longitude), and one telling its location relative to the flagship. As the ships make headway, all following the same course at the same speed, their positions on the earth's surface will, of course, change. Minor navigational errors and differences in ships' handling characteristics will also induce small changes in relative position within the formation. However, aboard the flagship, by definition, only one of these positions can change. The flagship's position relative to itself is fixed—it is always known and it is always correct. The record containing the field called *position relative to flagship* is important for all other ships, and varies in value to some extent. To the flagship, it is invariant, and as a result, of no interest or significance whatever. This situation is illustrated in Figure 5.2.

The information on relative position of the flagship might as well be carved on stone, for it will never change as long as the same ship remains the flagship. The structure of this record never changes; neither does the value of the field within it. We call this *invariant record structure.*

5.3.2   Bit Coding

The first truly useful organizational technique in our continuum is one we shall call *bit coding.* For each possible value that an information field might take, a single bit is set aside in a matrix, and this bit is

---

* A natural language message (e.g., this sentence) is a linear array of symbols, a matrix of one row. The fact that more than one line of print may be necessary to convey it does not change the logical relationships among the symbols.

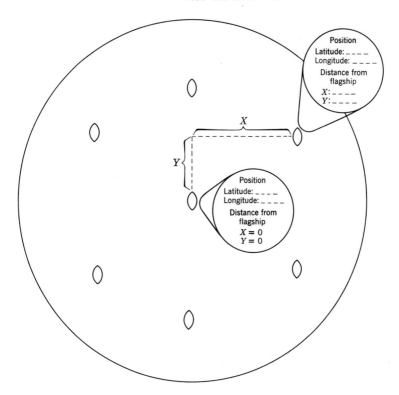

Figure 5.2 Invariant record structure. A fleet of ships in formation, each maintaining records of latitude and longitude and distance from the flagship. Latitude and longitude values are essentially the same for all ships in the formation and change uniformly for all ships. Distance from the flagship is different for each ship and is a function of minor variations in how each ship keeps its position. The distance from the flagship to itself, of course, is invariably zero.

set to *on* to indicate that that value has occurred, or to *off* to indicate the contrary. The method permits no variation in the topics covered or in the location of information; that is, a given bit always has the same *position* and *set of possible values*. The only variation is in the particular value, and, even here, we are restricted to a choice of one of two possible states. This is a technique in fairly common use, especially when the number of topics, or fields, and the number of possible values of the fields are both rather small. An example is the data coding scheme illustrated in Figure 5.3 A paper punch is often used with a format such as that shown to enter the date on such documents as

	Day		Month		Year 19__		Day		Month		Year 19__
Tens	Units	Tens	Units	Tens	Units	Tens	Units	Tens	Units	Tens	Units
0	0	0	0	0	0	●	0	●	0	0	0
1	1	1	1	1	1	1	1	1	1	1	1
2	2		2	2	2	2	2		2	2	2
3	3		3	3	3	3	3		3	3	3
			4	4	4		●		4	4	●
			5	5	5	5			5	5	5
			6	6	6	6			6	●	6
			7	7	7	7			●	7	7
			8	8	8	8			8	8	8
			9	9	9	9			9	9	9
(a)						(b)					

Figure 5.3　Bit coding: (a) general form; (b) "July 4, 1964."

railroad tickets or automobile inspection stickers by punching out the value of the bit being set *on*.　The right side illustrates how a particular date, July 4, 1964, would be entered.

5.3.3　Fixed Fields

Many very common data fields have enormous numbers of possible values, too many for efficient bit coding, but the users of the data wish to gain the advantages of a rigid structure.　In this case it is common to set aside a particular region of memory, of fixed size and location, for entry of the data.　On a paper form this might be an enclosed "box" for entry of a person's name, or it might be a group of contiguous columns on a punched card or character positions on a magnetic tape. Thus, the *positions* of the data fields are fixed, but there is no predetermination of the *values* that may be entered.　A record so organized, we call a *fixed field record*.

The difference between a bit-coded record and a fixed field record is entirely due to the range of values that may be entered at any given position in the record.　The practical significance of the difference would be apparent if we were searching, say, a personnel file of fixed field records for the names of people born in Chicago.　Although we might know exactly where, in each record, the birthplace field is placed, we would have no way of knowing whether the particular value, **Chicago,**

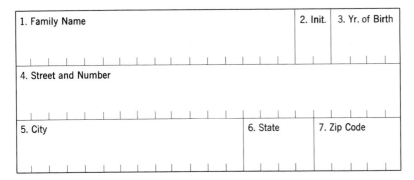

Figure 5.4 An example of a fixed field record. The trained reader of such records need not look at the numbers or instructions in fine print in each box; he interprets content on the basis of position.

would be found in the file at all; that is, whether there were any people represented in the file who were born in Chicago or even whether **Chicago** were a possible value of the *birthplace* field. A bit-coded organization would also leave the searcher in doubt that there were any people from Chicago represented in the file but would leave no doubt that it was a possible value, for **Chicago** would be either the name, or positional designator, of a bit or it could not be handled as a value of one of the bits within the set assigned to describe *birthplace*. A fixed field record is illustrated in Figure 5.4 Such a language structure could be used for index records that allow only one subject term. Then, *title, author, date, publisher, classification,* and so forth would each be represented by one field of the record.

5.3.4   Repeating Fields

Sometimes it is desirable to have more than one value of a field entered into a record. A job applicant, for example, may find that his application form contains the following legends, "Enter, in chronological order, all previous employers," or, "List all schools attended." In what exact position could we find the field value *x*, if it occurred? Recall that in a fixed field or bit-coded record, if the value *x* is to occur in a given field, it will occur in a precisely predictable location within the record. Now, if we wish to find whether a job applicant has ever worked for Widget Brothers, Inc., this value may be in any one, or a variable number, of lines devoted to former employers, but we cannot tell which one, if any. An additional complication has been introduced into our search procedure, and additional uncertainty as to what we may expect

Previous addresses (use additional sheet if necessary)

Street Address	City	State	ZIP	From		To	
				Mo.	Yr.	Mo.	Yr.
1.							
2.							
3.							
4.							
5.							
6.							

Figure 5.5   Repeating fields.

at any given location.   We give the name *repeating fields* to those fields, in an otherwise fixed field record, for which more than one value can be entered in one record.   Figure 5.5 shows an example of a set of repeating fields composed, in turn, of fixed fields.   In this illustration uncertainty arises because people do not choose their residences in any prescribed order, and, if Phoenix, Arizona, is to occur here, it cannot be predicted on which line it will fall.   Considerations of ordering among repeating values of a field are the same as for ordering among records of a file.   This topic is covered in Chapter 6.

The repeating field structure is well suited for recording index data involving subject heading or key word languages in which the subject terms are likely to have more than one value per index.

5.3.5   Tagged Fields

Because memory space is often at a premium, either on a paper form or in computer storage, problems arise with fixed field or repeating field record organizations over the amount of space to be set aside for a field or for the range of allowable field values.   A simple example is the number of digit positions to be set aside for a person's name or his city of residence.   To leave enough space for all possible family or place names would place an undue burden on the storage capacity of many record filing systems, since few such names are very long.   A calculated risk would be taken if a name field were restricted to twelve digits, and some special provision were then made for entry of longer names.   The problem is compounded when these fields of uncertain size are repeating.   In the case of either a variable length field or a variable number of repeating fields, if more space is allocated than can ever be used, there will be no loss of data but there will be very inefficient use of memory.   A common solution used with computer files is to precede the set of repeating field values with another field whose value is, "The number of field values to follow."   An alternative is to precede and follow the set of fields with a special character whose role is to define the boundaries of the set.   Either solution can also be used in the case of a single field value of variable length.   The method of special character boundaries may be used with variable-word-length computers to denote the beginning and end of fields.   We call these extra fields *tags* and note that, in the examples so far, they have been used to direct a processor in the physical interpretation of information—to find information, not to analyze its semantic content.   *Tagged field records,* then, are modifications of fixed field records by which new fields are introduced to denote the boundaries of a field or set of field values.

We can extend the use of tags by using them for explicit denotation of field names.   Let us assume we wish to design a record for a job applicant's name, residence, all previous cities of residence, all previous employers, and all schools attended.   Rather than creating a fixed field record with *previous residence, previous employers,* and *schools attended* as repeating field sets, with either a fixed number of entries or tags showing the number, a uniform format for all fields can be used.   This structure would consist of a tag denoting the field name for each occurrence of each field.   The tag *might* show structural information but would *have* to show content information.   At the very least, there would have to be a code to differentiate between cities, employers, and schools. This is illustrated in Figure 5.6.   This variation of a tagged field record

	Type of term	Number of characters	Start date	End date	Entry
1	Residence	7	1958	1962	Chicago
2	School	22	1954	1958	University of Illinois
3	School	19	1950	1954	Central High School
4	Employer	21	1958	1962	American Computer Co.
5	Residence	9	1945	1958	Milwaukee
6	Number of schools	1			2
7	Number of residences	1			3
8	Number of employers	1			1
9	Residence	8	1940	1945	St. Paul

Figure 5.6 Tagged field record. An example of a possible organization of residence, employer, and school data; format is uniform for all entries.

organization does not require that field values occur in any particular order. Entries numbered 6–8 provide structural information only, by stating the length of each field and the number of values of each field type, using the same language as is used for the values. With this type of organization, then, a search program has not even the benefit of knowing the region of a record in which the sought-for information will fall, and it may have to examine every tag-value combination in the record on any search. However, when the *number of repetitions* of any field can vary widely from record to record, this method of organization is very conservative of memory space. As pointed out in Chapter 2, such a record structure could be used with a key word system to denote the general class of the key word. This structure can also handle faceted terms.

5.3.6   Phrases

A language can be constructed which permits virtually the full vocabulary of natural language but makes use of a very limited number of grammatical forms.* A simple version would permit only statements of the general form *subject-predicate-object,* although the object position may also be used for an adjective. In effect, this is equivalent to *name-relationship-(name* or *attribute).* We can say, in this language, "Queen Elizabeth-is-(a) ship." or, "(The) ship-is-large." The structure can be expanded to permit multiple subjects, verbs, or objects. Such an expansion would allow "Queen Elizabeth"-is-(a) large ship." or "Queen Elizabeth-is (the) wife-(of) Prince Philip." It is not possible, however, to say, "If I were King, I'd build the greatest palace in the world." In a phrase each element of an expression contributes something to the meaning of the others. There is really no base word to which tags are appended, but a set of mutually dependent words, which, together, build up a concept. We call this a phrase, and note that it is but an expansion of the tagging concept. Even though we have used a three-facet structure as an illustration, each facet can be a single term or a set of terms, as, "(The) King and Queen arrived today."

5.3.7   Natural Language

We now come to *natural language,* the language of normal human communication. There is a structure to this form of communication, but the rules governing it tend to be vague and ambiguous, almost

---

* Such a language is in use at IBM's Thomas J. Watson Research Center for testing information retrieval concepts.[1]

impossible to list in full, yet able to be learned fairly well by small children everywhere. Some structural aspects of natural language were covered in Chapter 2. Just as is true for phrases, natural language has the attribute that the meaning of any term might be dependent upon the meaning of surrounding words. There is no single tag, nor even necessarily a single searching or reading procedure, that will always recover the meaning of any given word as the author intended it. This is as true for students struggling with the symbolism of *Moby Dick* as it is for a mechanical language translator.

5.3.8   Random Ordering

Natural language shows the least rigidity of structure of any organizational method in common use. To complete our description of the organizational continuum, let us consider the effects of loosening even this structure by randomizing the sequence of the words that may have appeared in a structured record. Although this procedure would destroy all order among words, it does not affect the order of characters within words; hence it destroys only one level of coding. Not all information is lost, for the vocabulary used in the original message is retained, as is implicit information on word frequencies. If, however, the element of reorganization were the character, and a natural language text were reorganized by randomizing the character sequence, we would lose any indication of character frequency. Although not very meaningful normally, character frequency is an important statistic in cryptanalysis, in which the input message is supposed to appear random to all but the code holders but in which cryptanalysts look for pattern or organization as an essential step in "breaking" the code. If we go one more step down the structural ladder, we come to the random rearrangement of a message by bit. The resulting message contains, at most, information that the sum of the bits is odd or even—a parity check. This information is devoid of semantic content.

5.3.9   Combinations

The final structural concept of interest is the use of a combination of the techniques described here. A combination does not necessarily fall on the continuum, but it is in common usage and is best understood when viewed as a combination of "pure" methods. A single example will suffice to explain combination records, and this is the baseball example shown in Figure 5.7. In the upper portion of the record we have a column of names of players, with each name tagged with the name

Washington

	AB	R	H	RBI
Doe, lf	2	0	0	0
ᵃ Jones, lf	2	1	1	0
Black, ss	3	1	1	0
Brown, 2b	4	0	2	2
White, rf	3	1	1	0
Silver, cf	2	1	1	1
Gold, 3b	3	0	1	1
Green, 1b	3	0	0	0
Gray, c	2	0	0	0
Blue, p	3	0	0	0
	27	4	7	4

Baltimore

Mason, 2b	3	0	0	0
Carpenter, 3b	4	0	1	0
Miller, lf	4	0	0	0
Cooper, cf	3	0	0	0
Sailor, 1b	2	0	0	0
Taylor, rf	3	0	0	0
Farmer, ss	2	0	0	0
Smith, c	3	0	0	0
Miner, p	3	0	0	0
	27	0	1	0

ᵃ Singled for Doe in 6th

Washington	0	0	0	0	0	4	0	0	0	−4	7	2
Baltimore	0	0	0	0	0	0	0	0	0	−0	1	1

PO-A Baltimore 27–6, Washington 27–8, DP-Brown and Green, LOB-Baltimore 1, Washington 2, U-Manny, Moe, Jack, T-2:35, A-24,567

Figure 5.7 A record organization using a combination of structures.

of the position he plays on the baseball team. This column, consisting of a set of repeating fields, is not titled. It is identified to the reader by its position within the record and by the fact that the field values, names, are so easy to recognize as such. To the right of this column are four columns of numbers, each headed by an identifying tag (**AB** = at bat, **R** = runs scored, etc.). These repeating sets, then, are tagged to enable the reader to select the desired field. Occasionally, a special tag (α) precedes a player's name. This refers to a footnote which is in natural language. The note gives such information as when a player entered the game and whom he replaced, information which could be entered in a fixed field for all players. This is not done because there are a relatively small number of such explanations that are needed in any case, but there are many possible notes to encode. Here, then, we find a natural language field replacing a fixed field or repeating set of fields and resulting in the saving of memory space. Individual tagged items are found in the lower portion of the record. Examples are **PO–A** for *put-outs and assists* and **DP** for *double plays*. Each of these tags is followed by a number or a full-text value of the field.

5.4   SUMMARY

We have introduced four attributes of record structure: expressiveness, positional ambiguity, semantic ambiguity and compactness, which correspond, roughly, to expressiveness, ambiguity, and compactness, used as attributes of index languages in Chapter 2. We are, once again, unable to provide numerical measures of the performance of any record structure against any one of these measures. Our approach remains to indicate by rough comparison which record structures have the capability to exceed others on each factor.

5.4.1   Expressiveness

We must rate an invariant structure as totally unexpressive. It can only convey information which is already known and requires no amplification or repetition. Similarly, a completely random arrangement of bits conveys almost no useful information, although randomizing by letter or word still permit some information to be expressed. Natural language is, by far, the most expressive of the structures we have considered. Indeed, within the realm of written communication, we may say that, *by definition,* natural language is the ultimate in expressiveness, for, while we can express the words of any other language in natural language, the converse is not necessarily true. Music, painting, and other nonverbal art forms permit expression that might be said to transcend that of verbal language; hence, natural language is not the ultimate mode of expression by man. Nonetheless, it is the mode of expression used to discourse about music, and the like, especially in libraries. A "curve" of expressiveness as a function of record organization is shown in Figure 5.8.

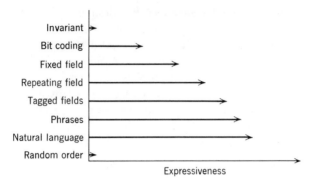

Figure 5.8   Relative expressiveness of record structures.

5.4.2   Positional Ambiguity

Invariant structure permits no doubt about location of information. A completely randomized message, on the other hand, leaves its interpreter with an irresolvable problem of finding where information is stored, for there are no guides. Bit coding and fixed field organizations provide no doubt, either, about the location of their constituent fields. Repeating field records leave doubt about the location of values within a set of repeating fields, and, if the repeating set is of variable length, may leave in doubt where the field following the repeating set begins. Tagged field or phrase record organizations do not necessarily impose any ordering restrictions among fields or phrases, relying on context

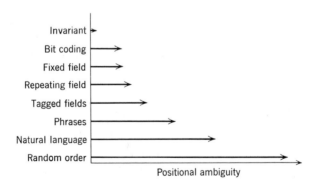

Figure 5.9   Relative degree of positional ambiguity of record structures.

to explain what information is being conveyed. Yet, since there is likely to be a restriction on what information is to be covered within a record, the possible interpretations of such fields or phrases is limited. Natural language imposes no restrictions except that of natural language syntax, which is extremely flexible and often ambiguous. Figure 5.9 shows these relationships graphically.

5.4.3 Semantic Ambiguity

Semantic ambiguity is nonexistent in invariant structures. In bit coding, although there should be no misunderstanding of the meaning of a bit, the searcher has no prior knowledge of the exact value of each bit. However, he does know the range of possible values, 0 and 1, and he may know the probabilities of occurrence of each. Fixed field, repeating field, and tagged field record structures may share with bit coding the attribute that all possible values of the fields have been specified and defined before use, but not necessarily so. For example, if we have a field called *marital status,* we may permit field values corresponding only to: single, married, divorced, separated, widowed. Thus all values that may occur are known in advance. If, in the same record, we have a field called *name,* we never know what name may be entered, and we must allow for an unlimited number of possibilities. Hence, although the functional meaning of any specified field within a record is well known, the values are far less predictable than the bits of a bit-coded record. As we move to phrase and full natural language, we are dealing with very large vocabularies, generally

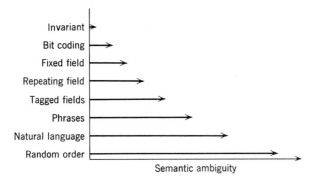

Figure 5.10 Relative degree of semantic ambiguity of record structures.

unrestricted, and with all the problems of semantic ambiguity discussed in Chapter 2.   These relative standings are illustrated in Figure 5.10.

5.4.4   Compactness

An invariant record has no information that we do not already know or that cannot change.   Hence any space devoted to storage of such a record is wasted.   Bit coding is quite wasteful of space if used as we have illustrated it in Figure 5.5.   Fourteen bits are set aside to express the day of the month, which requires only five bits if binary representation is used.   When the bits of a field are not mutually exclusive (in our date example, only one bit in each column can be used) but are used to indicate, say, a *go-no go* status of a set of independent variables, the method can be quite efficient.   In general, however, its value lies in ease of interpretation, not its compactness.

Fixed, repeating, and tagged fields and some phrase-structured records probably represent the greatest efficiency in information storage of all methods we have discussed, for they permit quite complex messages to be stated in relatively few characters, although they limit the nature of the message that can be transmitted using any given format.   Full natural language, because of the absence of a defined field structure, requires its users to define what information is being conveyed, as well as to give the specific facts of the message.   Records with defined structures convey this structural information implicitly.   Randomized records, because they completely fail to identify their structure, fail to transmit at least part of the information they could have transmitted before being randomized, hence are less efficient than their original, ordered versions. These relationships are illustrated in Figure 5.11.

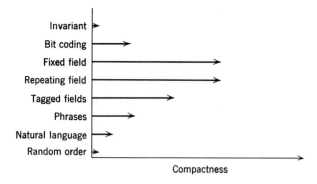

Figure 5.11   Relative compactness of record structures.

REFERENCES

1. Kochen, M., C. Abraham, and E. Wong. *Adaptive Man-Machine Concept-Processing*, International Business Machines Corp., Thomas J. Watson Research Center, Yorktown Heights, New York.
2. Saaty, Thomas L., *Mathematical Methods of Operations Research*, McGraw-Hill Book Co., New York, 1959, p. 32.

EXERCISES

1. Discuss the concept of an invariant, or unchanging, record structure in the context of the theory of word significance of Chapter 3.
2. Describe, in natural language, the record structure of the chapters of this book, of the index, of your automobile driver's permit.
3. Convert the baseball box score record illustrated in Figure 5.7 to a record structure using fixed and repeating fields only.
4. A college wishes to store the following information on each student: name, student number, high school attended, major subject, courses taken, date of completion of each, and grade received in each. Design a record for this information using a repeating field structure. Design another record using a combination of fixed and repeating fields and bit coding. Write a natural language example of such a record.
5. A postal address, in the United States, usually consists of: name, street number, street, city, state, and zip code. The syntax of this record is quite straightforward, but there are restrictions of the value of one field imposed by another. For example, if the zip code is 10016, the city must be New York. Describe other such relationships between other fields, in general terms, as: zip code determines city uniquely, city determines a set of zip codes.

CHAPTER 6

The organization of files

6.1 INTRODUCTION

A file is a set of records with some structural elements and some semantic attributes in common. Just as a character is built up from bits, a field from characters, and a record from fields, a file is created by grouping records according to some organizational rule. If we continue this logic, that of combining one level of information organization into a higher level, we would next arrive at a set of files. When we use a tape containing data to be operated on, we are using a set of files. More commonly there will be more than one data file in a system; for example, typical file sets are a master and a transaction file or a sales, a receipts, and an inventory file.

A file is said to be organized in that it consists of records which almost always are placed in sequence, according to some defined criterion, and that the records consist of fields organized to form the records. For any given system a file organization is completely specified if we know the following:

1. The data, or set of fields, present in the records of the file
2. The sequence of records within the file and the physical placement of records within the file
3. The characteristics of the storage media in which the file is stored

Before covering the details of file organization, we shall consider a basic approach to defining file processes and the elements of physical data storage. We shall then return to the problems and techniques of file organization.

6.2 FILE PROCESSING AND SEARCHING

A *file process* is a transformation of a file. When a transformation is defined, there must be specified not only what is to be done to the records of the file, but what subset of records of the file are to be trans-

174

formed. We define the *domain* of a process as that portion of a file, or subset of its records, which is to be processed. In many computer applications the domain is understood implicitly, and is usually the full file. In some the domain is explicitly defined by the input. This is the case when a sales transaction file is used to modify an inventory file. Each input record in the sales file contains a stock number which defines the records of the inventory file to be modified. The set of sales records defines the set of inventory records which constitute the domain for this process. In a file searching system the domain is defined normally by stating attributes of records rather than by explicitly naming them, whereas the transformation to be performed may be understood, namely, retrieve or reproduce all records in the domain.

File searching is the process of isolating a defined domain from the file. Isolation need consist of nothing more than flagging the search program whenever a member of the domain is found. Anything done to the isolated records, such as reproducing them, deleting them, or modifying them is then being performed on all members of the domain of the next process. Thus we say that a file process is not selective. It performs its function on *all members of its domain.* If the domain is not equivalent to the full file, a search must be carried out to segregate the sets. We use the term *file operations* to refer either to searching or processing.

A second useful distinction among processes is whether or not the records of the domain are altered. In the example just given the inventory records in the domain of the sales-posting process will be changed to reflect decreases in stock levels. An important class of processes, however, alters only the relative position among records. These are sorting and merging functions.

One purpose that is served by introducing the concept of a domain and differentiating between a *search,* to isolate a domain, and a *process,* to transform it, is to emphasize that naming a domain is not equivalent to processing it. Because one or the other of these items often is not stated explicitly anywhere in a program, it is easy to forget the difference.

6.3   THE ROLE OF STORAGE MEDIA
IN FILE ORGANIZATION

Although this book is not concerned with specific computer "hardware," it is necessary to introduce some of the basic concepts of physical storage, or memory, because of the large effect that memory configuration has on the carrying out of information retrieval functions. Memory design affects the cost and speed of file operations, and these are among the most important measures of performance of any data processing system. If a file is seldom used, has modest requirements placed upon it for search completion time, and if, when it is used, it is always searched on the same field, it can safely be placed on a slow, inexpensive memory. A file that is frequently searched, requires quick responses, or is of such a nature that the fields used as search parameters are unpredictable, calls for faster memory. Economic factors often change the relative merits of the various memory media. For example, it may be cheaper to maintain multiple copies of files on less expensive, sequential-search media and to search in parallel, than it is to obtain a single, high access speed, very expensive memory unit.

We consider two main aspects of physical storage. The first is the balance between reading and writing capability and the second, the accessibility of information in storage.

6.3.1   Read-Write Balance

The computers produced during the 1950's, the first decade of the electronic computer as a commercial product, were generally character-ized by the use of memory devices which were equally easy to read data from or write new data on. Magnetic tape, magnetic drums, mag-netic core, and cathode ray tube memories all have this characteristic. Paper tape and punched cards, which cannot be erased and rewritten as can magnetic media, can be punched anew somewhat less quickly than they can be read. Thus we have an approximate balance between reading speed and writing speed in these media, even though it is some-times necessary to do the writing on a "clean" memory element. The industry is now developing memories for which reading and writing times are not balanced. These are especially interesting in information retrieval because of their special challenge to file organization. An ex-ample of an unbalanced memory is a photographic film used for record-ing, on which bits are fixed permanently in memory by a photographic emulsion, and, like a hole in a punched card, cannot be changed. The photographic memory, formed into a disk, can be read as fast as magnetic memories, but writing or preparing a complete new disk can take several hours. The benefit of such memories is the high recording density and low cost of the raw material. As a memory with opposite characteristics, we must stretch a point and consider the printed page as a form of computer memory in which characters are imprinted on paper forms at speeds on the order of 1100 130-character lines per second, to be later read by a character reading machine at a much slower rate. The printing can go at a much higher rate than does the reading, and we have a memory which is heavily write-biased. There is no reason, then, to assume that memories must always have the same speed characteristics for reading as for writing. The memory can be slightly unbalanced in one direction or the other. Some of the immediate gains of using an unbalanced memory may be partly offset by other factors. For example, a photographic memory which is inexpensive and can be read quickly but which takes a relatively long time for writing, places a great burden on file maintenance activities. In some systems (see Chapter 10), file change operations are greater consumers of time than are search functions. If the posting of changes to a file becomes too expensive a process, the low cost of the memory is overshadowed. Such memories, then, must be carefully selected, and ordinarily would be used only in a situation in which changes are infrequent.

6.3.2 Accessibility

So far, in our discussions of both record searching and file searching, we have been very concerned with knowing where information is. Now let us consider the problem of actually getting at it. Data can be considered as placed at a certain distance away from the search mechanism, in the sense that a certain amount of time is required for the reading mechanism to go from the starting position of a storage device to the location of the information in question. For example, if we have information on a magnetic tape, which must be searched sequentially, the information can be as long as five minutes away, at an average tape speed. On the other hand, information of known location in a magnetic disk memory is usually available in a few milliseconds; however, if it is in a magnetic core memory, it may be only microseconds away. Our distance measure is certainly not the normal linear distance measure. We do not care how long a tape is; we only care how long it takes to search it and how expensive the search will be. We want, then, a relative measure that will permit comparisons of different ways of using computer equipment with fixed characteristics.

As an example of such a measure, we shall adopt an *accessibility measure, a,* which is

$$a = 1 - \frac{R}{A + R} = \frac{A}{A + R} \tag{6.1}$$

or the ratio of record access time (A) to record read time (R), plus access time. *Read time* we define as the time required to read a record into the memory of a processor exclusive of search and start-stop time. *Record access time* is the time required to move either the memory or the read mechanism to the position required for reading the desired record. This measure is a dimensionless quality which we shall henceforth call the *access coefficient*. Its value ranges from zero (when the access time is zero and there is no delay in reading information) to near one (when the access time is so high that read time is insignificant by comparison). We stress again that this measure is merely an example of a measure, not a universally suitable one.

The coefficient can be applied in three ways: to measure the characteristics of a memory or configuration, to measure the combined characteristics of a file stored in a memory, and to measure the accessibility of a given point in a memory to a read mechanism.

When applied to a memory, the measure would have to be based upon an average value of access time. The coefficient would be

$$a = 1 - \frac{R}{\bar{A} + R} = \frac{\bar{A}}{\bar{A} + R} \qquad (6.2)$$

where R is, again, record read time, and $\bar{A}$ is the average access time of all records in the file. The accuracy of this measure could be improved if we included components of access time, such as the time for an access mechanism to move between tracks of a disk, and the different probabilities associated with reading data, traversing tracks, moving between disks, and so on.

When we wish to consider a specific file stored in a specific memory, we must recognize that all records are not equally likely to be searched for. We may not know the distribution of search probabilities and may be forced by this lack of knowledge to use unweighted averages, but it should be recognized that unweighted averages are only an approximation. The term $\bar{A}$, rather than an unweighted mean, for the case of unequal search probabilities, will be an *expected* value of record access time which reflects the unequal access probabilities. An expected value[4] is an average value of a function, over all the values it may take on, weighted to reflect different probabilities of occurrence for different values. If record i has access time A_i and is searched for with probability p_i, the expected access time is

$$E = \sum_{i=1}^{n} p_i A_j \qquad (6.3)$$

If all the probabilities are equal, then $E = \bar{A}$. The access coefficient of a file for which the distribution of search probabilities is known is:

$$a = 1 - \frac{R}{E + R} = \frac{E}{E + R} \qquad (6.4)$$

Finally, the access coefficient for a particular record, i, when the read mechanism is in a particular position, j, and where A_{ij} is the access time from position j to i, is

$$A_{ij} = 1 - \frac{R_i}{A_{ij} + R_i} = \frac{R_{ij}}{A_{ij} + R_j} \qquad (6.5)$$

A sufficiently large sample of a_{ij} can give us an approximation to a, the coefficient for the entire file.

6.3.3   Levels of Accessibility

We define memories in terms of four levels of accessibility of information stored in them:

1. Parallel Access.   Often, somewhat misleadingly, called an "associative memory," this type of memory permits many records to be matched simultaneously.   We may load in it, say, one hundred personnel records and match all of them simultaneously against the query term, **John Jones,** in the same number of computer cycles normally required to test one memory word for the value **John Jones.**   The access coefficient is $a \approx 0$ for each record in the memory, since there is no access delay beyond the read time for a record.   (Since parallel memories to date are small, there will be an access delay in getting the information to fill the memory, but that is charged to the search of the main memory.)   The cumulative access, for the entire set of records in the memory that is being matched at one time, is also 0, for all records are searched in the same cycle.

2. Content Addressable Memory.   Such a memory is one which resembles a parallel search memory in that it is not necessary to give separate search commands for each record that is matched with a query, but the matching is done sequentially, not in parallel.   This has been called an *intrinsically addressed memory* by J. E. Griffith[3] who outlined the logic of a processor based entirely upon this concept.   Access times for records after the first are far less than would be the case if each increment of search required the control section of a computer to return to the search program for new instructions, as is commonly done.   A computer using a content addressable memory is faster than a computer of the same construction would be if it did not have this feature.   But, as a class, content addressable memories are not inherently faster than other forms of memory, regardless of logic used.   If the access coefficient for the first record searched is a, the access coefficient of each of the next records searched is a', where a' is less than a, and is probably very nearly a constant.   The access time to the next sequential record is usually a constant for a given memory, but may vary when the next record is on a different track, disk, or tape.

3. Equal Access.   In this form of memory, any given location is as readily accessible as any other, but we can gain access to only one at a time and, if content addressable logic is not used, each access requires the same number of computer time cycles.   The term *random access* is sometimes used to mean that any point in memory chosen at random can be gotten to as quickly as any other point.   The term, however, is usually used to apply to a *direct access* memory, which we shall describe next.   The magnetic core memory of most modern computers is the best common example of a truly random access device.   A magnetic disk memory, regardless of common usage, does not meet this definition. The access coefficient for an equal access memory is $a \approx 0$, for the access delay is negligible; but, if n records are to be searched, the total search time is n times search time for one record.

4. Direct Access.   In this category falls what is most often, but mis-leadingly, called random access.   It is best illustrated by magnetic disks. The characteristic of disks, of importance here, is that access to any given disk can be gained by moving the read mechanism directly to the desired track, at high speed, without reading all intervening data. This is fast compared to magnetic tape access time, even when data read rates are comparable.   Reading from a disk is sequential within a track, usually a fixed-length, annular region within a disk.   Access time to a point on a disk includes a starting time for the read mechanism to overcome inertia, stopping time, and the time required to move at a constant speed across the face of the disk.   In a system with multiple disks it is necessary to include a separate calculation for moving from one disk to another.   Magnetic drums are also a form of direct access memory.   Reading speeds here may also be quite fast, but there is an access delay until the proper point on the drum surface comes under a read head.   Direct access, then, applies to memories that do not have equal access characteristics, but which do allow an access device to move directly to the desired information without reading all intervening information.

The numerical value of a depends upon individual memory design. However, as a broad generality, we can assume that access time is the same order of magnitude as read time, so that a will be somewhere in the range between about $\frac{1}{2}$ and, say, $\frac{9}{10}$.   Drums may have a slightly lower coefficient than disks (lower = faster access) because they are kept constantly in motion and there is no inertial time required.   Clearly, actual coefficient values depend on the specific memory used, and the record sizes stored thereon.

5. *Sequential Access.* Magnetic tape, paper tape, and a deck of punched cards stacked in a card reader are illustrations of a sequential access memory. For these media it is necessary to start at one end of a file and work sequentially down toward the other end to do a search. It is not normally possible to skip or bypass any portion of the memory, but prepositioning of the read mechanism or file, to save time, is possible. It is also possible, with various machine and program designs, to avoid excessive, time-consuming stops in a sequential search. But there must be a certain minimum amount of time spent traversing from one end to the other, and this, on the average, is much longer than the time required to move over the same number of records, directly to the desired track on a direct access memory.

The access coefficient will be quite large for these memories. For a typical magnetic tape, record read time may be several tens of milliseconds, but average access time may be several minutes. The coefficient, then, would be on the order of 0.999, again, actually depending on specific machine design and record size.

For some combinations of file organization and search methods, the record access coefficient of direct and sequential access memories can be nearly equal. Tape and disk data read times are close to equal so that file organization and record search probabilities become very important to the accessibility calculation. A file organization that cannot use the direct access capability will gain nothing from having it available. Put the other way around, file organization can overcome some disadvantages of memory design.

A factor to be considered in evaluating memories is the capability to overlap search time with other functions. If this can be done, even though the same amount of time may be required to reach a given location, search cost goes down because the time is being put to good use. Overlapping is done in many ways. One is to command a disk memory to position its read head at a given location, then some other function can be performed which does not require the information stored there, nor use of the disk arm. Later the computer returns to the first task, with the arm now positioned for minimum delay. Even core memory access times can be overlapped with computation or instruction interpretation time.

6.4 PRINCIPLES OF FILE ORGANIZATION

We have identified three components of the specifications of a file's organization: the data contained within the file, the position of records within it, and the storage media in which it is stored.

We discussed record content in Chapter 5 and have no need to repeat that discussion here. There is, however, a special aspect of record content that is highly important to file organization. To discuss it, we must presuppose that we are ultimately concerned with file sets. The special problem is, given the complete set of fields that are to be grouped into records and files, how shall fields be divided among the files? In which file shall key words go? In which synonyms? In which access numbers? We call this *data assignment*.

Next, we are concerned with the sequence of records, the order in which they are stored or will be encountered, and with their actual placement with respect to each other, for sequentially entered records need not be placed contiguous to each other.

Finally, file organization is affected by two external factors, the storage media, which we have already discussed, and search logic, which we shall define as the interface between the files and the searcher or system user. Since we have already reviewed the effect of storage media, we shall confine our attention in this section to the effect of search logic on file organization.

6.4.1   Data Assignment

Why do we speak of dividing fields of information among more than one file? Why not put all information we have pertaining to a given subject into one file? The answers to these questions are best given by example. We might choose to separate data records and files from records which contain largely structural information about the data. The content of the latter is not meaningful outside the system, and we do not wish to have to repeat it with every data record. We might, on the other hand, wish to organize our files with high redundancy in order to plan for any possible system component failures. Finally, we might wish to organize our files by splitting information among several files in order to make higher searching speeds possible.

As a simple example of information assignment, let us consider the problem of synonyms in an information retrieval system. Any given key word may have several synonyms. It would be quite wasteful of memory space, and ultimately of search time, to include in each record the complete list of all synonyms for all words therein. The conventional approach is to create a separate dictionary file and let this file show, once and only once, all semantic relationship between words. In the actual data records, then, words need be entered only once and in only one form. Another example of why information might be divided between files concerns reliability of equipment. Consider a magnetic drum unit. In addition to access speed, drums differ from magnetic tape in that, if any portion of a drum unit fails to work, the entire unit, with its recorded data, is out of action.   Unlike a malfunctioning tape drive, we cannot simply dismount the magnetic material and remount it on another drive.   If a drum unit is out, it is totally out.   Now suppose that we have an information retrieval system which must operate continuously and with high reliability so that we must guard as much as possible against the consequences of any component failure.   Any tape, disk, drum, or other machine has a certain probability of failure, and we must consider this in designing the system.   Because we assume that we cannot interchange drums in event of failure, it will be necessary either to maintain complete spare units with duplicate files, or to use redundancy in file construction.   An example is given below of a complete file system in which each file is increased in size slightly, creating sufficient redundancy in the total system to guard against the failure of the components holding any file.   The system can be so designed that it can operate with any one drum unit out of operation.   Such a situation might be as follows.   Assume a computer has attached to it three drums, each with a capacity of 1,800,000 characters.   For the purpose of this example we assume no spare units to be available.   The principal file to be stored is an index file with these characteristics:

5 subject descriptors, of 18 characters each, per record
1 document number term, of 6 characters, per record
30,000 documents (hence index records) in the library
5000 subject descriptors in the vocabulary, evenly distributed

The index file has $((5 \times 18) + 6)\ 30{,}000 = 2{,}880{,}000$ characters in it. The file will be evenly spaced across the three drums, 960,000 characters stored on each drum.

A second file to be maintained is an inversion of the first and consists of a record for each descriptor in the language, the record containing the accession or document number of every index record in which the descriptor appears.   There is an average of:

$$\frac{30{,}000 \text{ documents} \times 5 \text{ descriptors each}}{5000 \text{ descriptors in the vocabulary}}$$

$$= 30 \text{ references for each descriptor record}$$

Each record has 30×6 characters per document number $+\ 18$ characters per descriptor $= 198$ characters, and there are $198 \times 5000 = 990{,}000$ characters in the complete file.   The reduction in size of the inverted file from the index file is gained by not having to repeat the 18-character descriptor so often. The placement of this file in memory is described below.

In normal operation, a search would be conducted by using both files, the inverted file being used to locate quickly those document numbers which correspond to records in the larger index file. An explanation of this mode of searching is given in Chapter 4. Although this method requires the use of half again as much memory as the index file alone uses, searching is very quick because the alphabetic ordering of the inverted file quickly locates the index records that must be examined, greatly reducing the number of records in the larger file that must be read and matched.

We shall assume the inverted file also to be split over the three drums in such a manner that two thirds of the file are on each drum, each one having a different combination of thirds of the file. This results, of course, in duplication of the file. The configuration is shown in Figure 6.1 where I_1, I_2, and I_3 represents the thirds of the index file and V_1, V_2, and V_3 represent the thirds of the inverted file.

With this organization, we can easily carry on conventional searches, paying no attention to the second copy of the inverted file. If any drum unit becomes inactive, we lose the ability to retrieve one third of our index file records. However, by determining which unit failed and modifying our search addresses, we retain the capability of (a) locating any query term in the inverted index file and retrieving

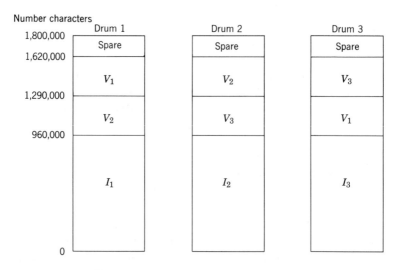

Figure 6.1   Data division for reliability.

corresponding accession numbers which can be used for direct document retrieval and (b) continuing to retrieve index records two thirds of the time.

Thus, by judiciously assigning and replicating data, we have guaranteed continuous operation in the event of a partial memory failure, even though we cannot provide all normal services. This recovery capability is accomplished entirely by changing addresses and search sequence, including barring searches directed to one third of the index file. Note, by the way, that the memory does not quite allow for the approach of assuring reliability by replicating the index file and not having an inverted file.

In addition to dividing to save memory space and to guard against system failure, we may divide information simply to speed searching. The use of a dictionary to save space in a system may also lead to time savings. For if we are searching for a given key word we may find it much more quickly in the shorter dictionary file than if we have to search each record of the full index file, although this does, of course, depend upon the number of index terms in use, the number per index record, and the number of index records. More important than finding it quickly, is finding out quickly that the word will not be found at all in the index file. The dictionary will tell, after a short search, that this term is not in the file and, therefore, that the full file need not be searched. The time that can be saved in such a situation can be very significant.

In summary, we find that, given a large set of information, the manner by which fields are selected and formed into records, and records formed into files can lead to memory space or search time savings. It is quite apparent that the access coefficient of records and files can be changed quite considerably by different assignment schemes.

6.4.2 Record Sequencing

File sequence is the relative position of records with respect to each other. File sequence information is analogous to knowledge of record structure. There are, however, some slight differences. First, it is possible to search and interpret a file without knowledge of its sequence, whereas to search a record without knowledge of field positioning almost denies any possibility of sensibly searching the record, for each field means something different and, if it cannot be distinguished from any other, matching is meaningless. Second, even when full knowledge of file sequence gives the exact location of desired information, some machine designs require a pause after each record read, and it may be necessary to test to see if we have gotten to the record we knew we wanted. For example, on some magnetic tape systems, if we know we want the sixteenth record on a tape file it is necessary to read each of the first 15 and to count them or check record numbers to tell when we have arrived at the sixteenth record—records cannot be accessed by number. Therefore, it may not have been necessary to have such complete information as to know that we wanted record 16. It may have been sufficient to know that we wanted the record with Mr. Jones's name in it, for to search each record for Jones may take no more time than to search for, or count to, 16.

It is interesting to ask the question, "Does knowledge of file sequence always give us exact knowledge of the record we want?" The answer, unfortunately, is "No." Knowledge that the white pages of the telephone directory are organized alphabetically by name of subscriber does not provide us with a means for searching by street number or by type of business. If we know only that the subscriber whom we wish is a motion picture theater located on a given street, and we do not have a yellow page directory sequenced by type of business, the phone book might just as well be in random order so far as we are concerned. A file is usually sequenced on its most often used or its most important field, called the *sort key*. A telephone book is most often searched by the family or business name of the subscriber. When we wish to search such a file on a field other than that which determines the sequence, we are not really lacking information about the structure of the file, but we are unable to find beforehand where the record we wish is located. This is a condition we call *relative random order*. The file is in sequence on one field, but there is no correlation between this sequence and the resultant sequence of values of our search field. A file that is sequenced, for example, on employee's names, will be in random sequence relative to date of birth. There are gradations between a file in sequence on a field and in random order relative to that field. These result from minor sort keys and correlation between field values.

A *minor*, or *subordinate*, *sort key*, is a field used to determine relative position among a set of records when the primary key, or sequencing field, has the same value in each record of the set. A book publisher's catalog may be in sequence by subject, and all books on the same subject then sequenced by title. An automobile manufacturer might keep a cumulative sales file sequenced on *make* (e.g., **Chevrolet, Buick, Pontiac**, etc.), *body style* (e.g., **sedan, convertible**), *color*, and *region* of the country where sold. (See Figure 6.2.) This file has four sort keys and two other fields (*sales registered* and *orders received*) relative to

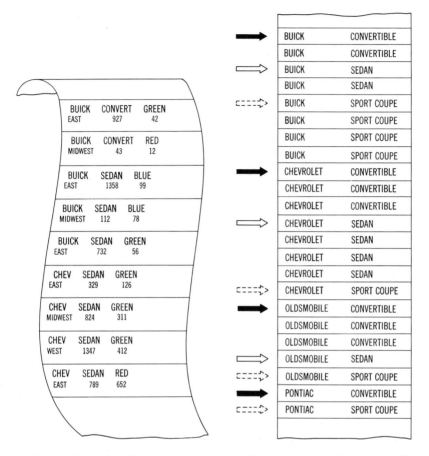

Figure 6.2 A file sequenced on four sort keys. The data fields are *make, body type, color, region of country, sales, orders;* the first four are sort keys.

Figure 6.3 Searching a partially ordered file.

which the file is in random order. If a search is to be conducted on *make,* it could quickly find exactly the right location for the desired make because this is the primary sort key. For a search on *body style,* once the beginning of a set of records having the desired body style is found, the first record with an unwanted style signifies the end of the set for that make, and no more records need be tested under that make. Figure 6.3 illustrates a search for all *sedans* in a file in sequence by *make* and *model.* Other information in the record is not shown in this illustration. The solid arrows show the point where each group of records with a new value of *make* starts. The hollow arrows show the beginning of the *sedan* group of records under each make. The dotted arrows show the record which can be used to decide that the last sedan record has been seen within a *make* group. Thus we see that some location information is available and that the location search by *body style* is not random but will take longer than a search for all members of a particular make.

Correlation among fields is illustrated by an index file sequenced on document accession number. If access numbers are assigned sequentially as new documents arrive, then a file in this sequence is *approximately* in sequence by date of publication of the documents being indexed. Over time, a pattern will probably develop for lag between publication and receipt date. The probability that the index record of a document of a given publication date will fall in a defined region behind the first record with a given receipt date, can be well established and can be used to speed file search.

An interesting aspect of file sequence is that the precise location of information it affords is not always necessary or useful. Consider a disk unit, which has up to three access arms, individually controllable. If a search of this disk is to be performed, one that calls for very rapid retrieval of a large number of scattered records, it may be possible to develop a mathematical expression that will enable the program to compute the optimum path of the disk arms through the file. It is also easily possible, however, that the calculation will use more computer time than can be gained by using the "best" path over a merely "good" one, with only approximate positioning, but with locations quickly computable. We have already given another example, that of a magnetic tape search, where, because records must be examined as they are read, it may not pay to compute which record is wanted or to find out from an inverted file. It may be faster and cheaper to search all records using the actual search criteria. More information on the value of location knowledge is given in Chapters 7 and 8.

6.4.3   Record Positioning

Memory or search program design may indicate a mode of file storage wherein the next record to be searched is not necessarily contiguous to the last one. For an example of a condition where this mode is desirable, suppose we are using an inverted index file and we wish to put a new index record into the file. If the word **cat** is an index term, and if the **cat** record is stored on a particular disk track which has no space left, it would be necessary to start using the next track for new document numbers referring to **cat**.   But, if this track is occupied (perhaps with the **catalog** record), we would have to recopy the entire file below **cat**, moving almost the entire file to open new space for **cat**, while keeping the file in sequence.   An alternative is to take the **cat** record out of its physical position in sequence, place it wherever two adjacent tracks are available, and replace it in its original position with a note referring the search program to the new location.   This is illustrated in Figure 6.4.

By breaking away from the traditional idea that a fixed amount of

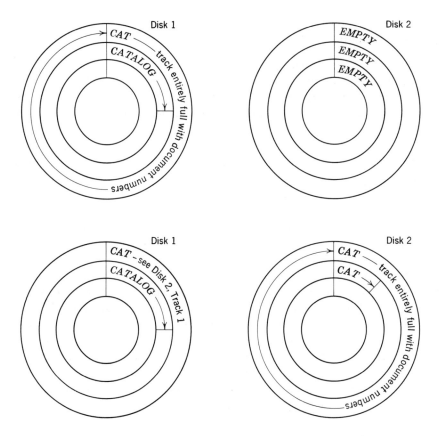

Figure 6.4 Noncontiguous record storage. Track 1 of Disk 1 is completely full when new information, to be filed under *CAT* arrives. In order to place this information in the next track, the data already there would have to be moved. To avoid this change, two contiguous empty tracks are sought and the overflowing record is moved over; a reference to the new location is left in the old location.

memory, at a fixed location, must be allocated for each file, it is possible to make far more efficient use of memory or of the computer time required for a search. It is also possible to so reduce the bookkeeping burden on the programmer, who must keep track of these fixed locations. that he is enabled to concentrate his full attention on the processing of the data, instead of the storage of it, thereby being more efficient in the use of the programmer, as well. We leave until Section 6.5 illustration of some of the methods of positioning records, but they are principally characterized by use of more sophisticated techniques for allocation of storage space to files and for representing information about record location.

6.4.4   The Effect of Use Patterns on File Organization

The logic permitted in a query affects file organization (and vice versa) in that the file system and search program must be able to carry out searches as directed by the query, and this dictates that the files and programs must be responsive to the functions, sequences, and priorities stated in queries.

A query will specify on what terms to search and what fields of the matching records are to be retrieved. There may be many ways of meeting the formal requirements of the language, but these can be narrowed down considerably by taking into account user search patterns. If, for example, a sufficiently large majority of queries include a document access number, there may be no need to maintain an inverted index file, for a search of the complete file in the small number of cases of unknown document numbers may be the most economical way to operate the system.

If many system users show, or are expected to show, a need for a synonym dictionary for browsing, it is probably best to make this file separate from others, even though other information could be combined with it, to enable the dictionary search to proceed quickly and smoothly. Similarly, if users frequently want to look at full index records, even though some economy may be achieved by dividing the record in storage, or using highly compact codes, the requirement to display them in readable form, and often, may negate such economies.

Perhaps the greatest single effect of the query, or of query patterns, on file organization is in response time specification. Response time is the elapsed time required to perform a search and present the searcher with the information requested. In designing a system, specifying its response time characteristics is not a simple matter. Within any user group, while there are often a number of users who insist on very rapid responses (perhaps within 2–15 minutes) there will be many for whom tomorrow is good enough. The designer must decide whether he will provide the high-speed service to all users, to provide the service that the majority request, and leave the minority to fend for themselves, or to provide the degree of speed needed in each case, but no more. Ideally, he should know the entire distribution of response time requirements. It is even desirable to know how the arrival of these queries will be distributed in time throughout the day. In attempting to meet requirements, he must consider what is actually being retrieved in any stated response interval. Does the user want hard copy or will he be satisfied with citations or index records? The engineering problems associated with high-speed retrieval of hard copy from files can be formidable. If a conversational, or browsing, mode of search is used in which the searcher uses a succession of queries, do we aim to minimize his total search time, or only to give him immediate response to each single query?

Unfortunately, the user patterns of a mechanized information retrieval system are different from the patterns of the same users before the library was mechanized. Hence a system designer does not normally find a well-established historical record of system use as a basis for his design. Equally unfortunately, users are hard put to tell a designer what they really need or what value they assign to various service speeds, because they do not know themselves.

6.4.5 Summary

The organization of a file implies the specification of its information content, the sequence of its records, and the physical positioning of its records relative to each other and to the memory. In making a design choice in each of these areas, we are influenced by two external considerations—that is, external to the files. These are the physical characteristics of the memory on which the file is stored and the pattern of use of the files. The latter, in turn, covers such factors as desired system reliability, response time, or frequency of search of various files. In the design phase of a new system the user patterns are rarely available in the sense of being well-defined, statistically valid figures.

6.5 METHODS OF FILE ORGANIZATION

Below is a brief survey of four principal methods of organizing files. The major differences among them will be seen to be the manner of positioning records and the manner of representing information about how records are positioned. Representation of such information is the topic of the next chapter, but it can be seen here that, if we can always assume record $n + 1$ immediately follows n in physical position, then there is no need to state this fact explicitly in the file. If on the other hand, physical position is entirely divorced from logical sequence, as we shall find in list structures, then at record n we must tell the searcher where he will find record $n + 1$. There are costs and values associated with either approach.

6.5.1   Contiguous Sequential Placement of Records

Overwhelmingly, the most common method of placing records within a file is to situate them so that the $(n + 1)$st record is adjacent to the nth record, both physically and in logical sequence. All users of the file would be aware of this arrangement and all programs used with the file would be designed with this placement in mind. The method is conservative of memory because no information fields need be devoted to telling where the next record is, the records are stored in a compact form, with no blank spaces separating them. On the other hand, a change in the file structure can be difficult to handle. So simple a change as the insertion of a new record between existing ones requires moving all the records beyond the new entry position. In the case of tapes, drums, or disks this means recopying all or most of a file in order to make a single change. A change in record structure, since it applies to each record of a file, would require moving or recopying the entire file.

6.5.2   Chaining

Chaining is a file organization which uses information embedded in a data record to locate the next record, which need not be contiguously stored. In non-computer files, chaining is often accomplished by the use of the notation "See _____" or "See also _____" that might appear on a library catalog card or a telephone directory. It tells the searcher that there is more information of potential value, and tells where he must go to find it. When the referenced item is found, it, too, may contain a "See also _____" reference, and so on, until a chain of references has been established among a set of related, but not contiguous, records.

In computer systems chaining is used when there is some reason for not placing the referenced record contiguous to the referring record. One reason for avoiding contiguous placement is that rigid allocation of memory space to files can be wasteful when one storage area is ready to overflow, but another has empty space. Another is that it can be too costly to interleave new records in their proper sequence immediately on their arrival in the file. An example of a chained file organization is one composed of records ordered on, say, names, which are assigned to disk tracks such that each different initial letter is assigned to a single, separate track to simplify initial access to the file, A's in track 1, B's in track 2, and so forth. As new name records are added, or more information is added to existing records, the tracks fill up at a variable rate. When the first one is about to spill over, instead of completely rearranging the file, the next record can be inserted in the next available track in a disk reserved for spill-over, and a reference address inserted in a reserved area at the end of the first track. When the first spill-over track is filled, another is "opened." Gradually, most of the first 26 tracks will spill over, so that only the initial disk of data for each letter group is fully in sequence. Therefore, while data within a track are in alphabetical sequence, the tracks are not in sequence. This technique is illustrated in Figure 6.5. Here, using a file of name records, we see that, initially, one track of disk 1 was allocated to each

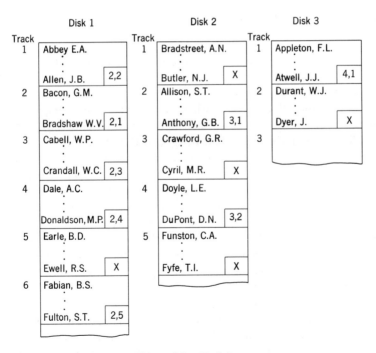

Figure 6.5   Chaining.

letter of the alphabet. As the tracks fill, a spill-over area on disk 2 is used, tracks there being assigned as needed. On disk 2 the initial words of each track are not in alphabetical order, but, within any track on disk 2, order is maintained among records. At the end of each track is a field which either specifies that there is no spill-over (**X**) or gives the address of the next block of data on disk 3. The process may be repeated as often as necessary.

Use of such a file organization requires a full, sequential search of each letter group for each query. It may be possible to make the reference address the first word on a track so that, as soon as a read is initiated, the next arm movement command can be set up and accomplished while the remaining data are being read into core memory. By this means it is possible to avoid undue delay in searching the file. Perhaps the file could be sorted, periodically, into a sequence to decrease search time. The key point is that this can be done when convenient. It is not necessary each time a new record is added or a track filled.

This method can be used to great advantage when the number of file changes far exceeds the number of file searches as is, in fact, often the case.

6.5.3   Branching File Structures

An extension of the chaining concept provides us with a positioning mode which has the advantages of using fixed-field records and contiguous placement of records, but which can handle repeating fields, can save space when the value of a field or group of fields can recur often throughout the file, and when record structure changes are frequent. A structure such as we shall outline was described by Bachman and Williams[1] in the context of an Integrated Data Store.

To illustrate a branching structure, let us assume we have a file of fixed-field records, but with one repeating field set. One group of the fixed fields is such that the same set of values recurs often, as would happen if, in a file of stock items, we wished to store the manufacturer's name and address. Then a large number of records would have these field values in common, at a considerable waste of storage space.

We could organize such a file by removing the set of repeating fields from all records and placing them in a separate file, ordering the values alphabetically, and omitting repetitions or duplicates. We replace the set in the original record with a single address referring to a record in a file of addresses. Each record in the address file will contain the record numbers of repeating field values that pertain to the specific record in the main file. This is illustrated in Figure 6.6. Here, we first show a sample record with one repeating set and the remainder

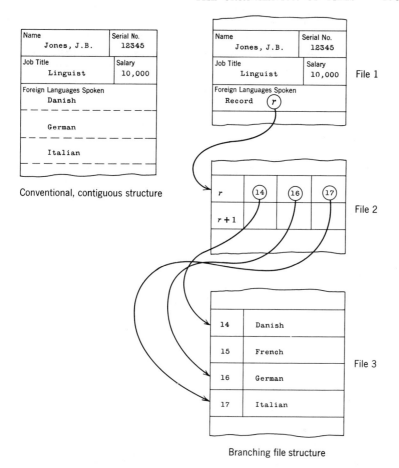

Conventional, contiguous structure

Branching file structure

Figure 6.6 A branching file structure compared with a contiguous structure.

all fixed fields. On the right is another file set organization which handles the same material. File 1 consists now only of fixed fields, the list of languages being replaced by a reference to a record in File 2. File 3 consists of all the values, of *foreign languages spoken,* less duplicates, taken from the repeating sets of all records in File 1. In place of these values in File 1 we store an address in File 2. At that address in File 2 are to be found the list of records in File 3 that would have been stored in the base record of File 1 under a conventional organization. In so reorganizing our data we have created three files, two of them (1 and 3 in the figure) being of fixed length records and one, the address file, having variable-length records. What we have done, then, is to change the file in which the variable-length records occur, we have not eliminated the variation. However, the main file is now of fixed length records, and it is easy and economical to search. The only time variable-length records will be encountered is when the particular field which repeats is one of the fields being searched upon, in which case the variable-length record search is unavoidable. When such a search is avoidable, it is bypassed, at a saving in search time and search program complexity.

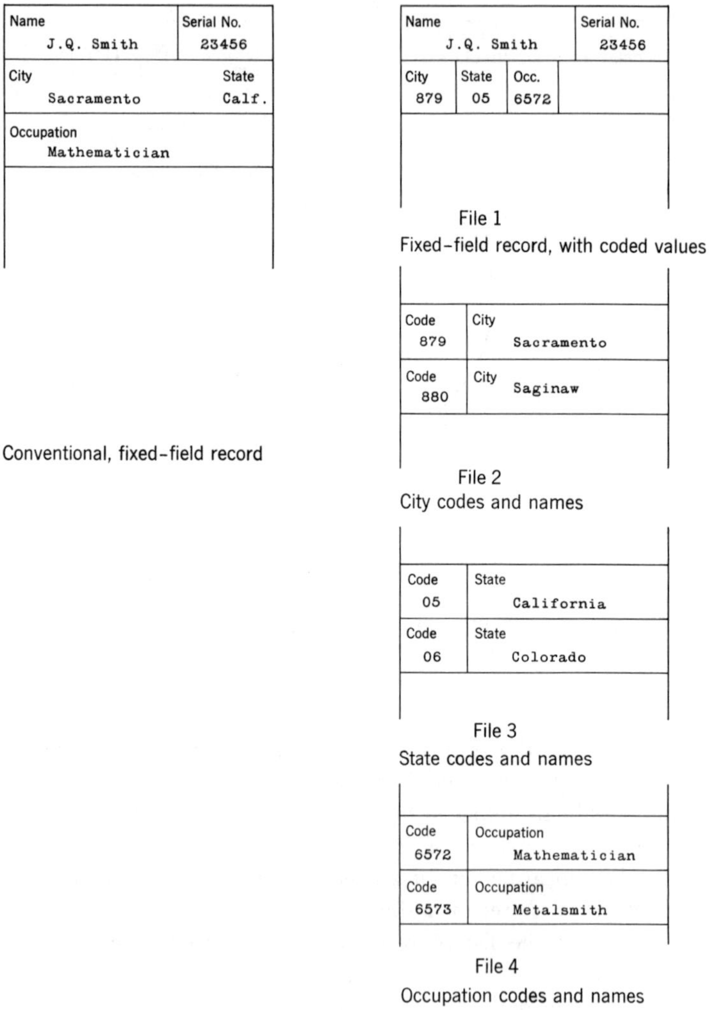

Name J.Q. Smith	Serial No. 23456
City Sacramento	State Calf.
Occupation Mathematician	

Conventional, fixed-field record

Name J.Q. Smith			Serial No. 23456
City 879	State 05	Occ. 6572	

File 1

Fixed-field record, with coded values

Code 879	City Sacramento
Code 880	City Saginaw

File 2

City codes and names

Code 05	State California
Code 06	State Colorado

File 3

State codes and names

Code 6572	Occupation Mathematician
Code 6573	Occupation Metalsmith

File 4

Occupation codes and names

Figure 6.7   Removal of often-repeated data from a file.

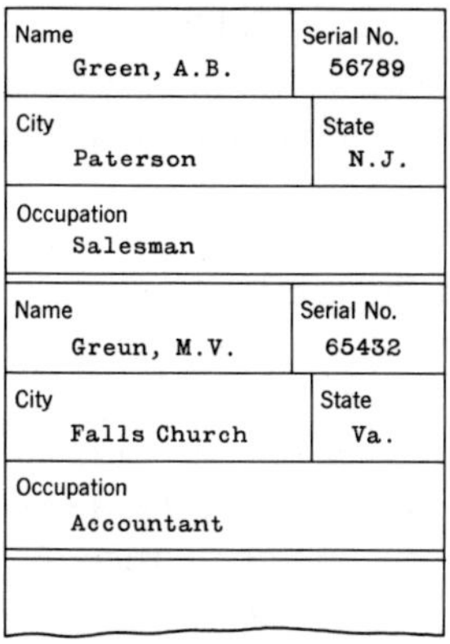

Name	Serial No.
Green, A.B.	56789

City	State
Paterson	N.J.

Occupation	
Salesman	

Name	Serial No.
Greun, M.V.	65432

City	State
Falls Church	Va.

Occupation	
Accountant	

Fixed–field record to which it is
desired to add a new field:
county

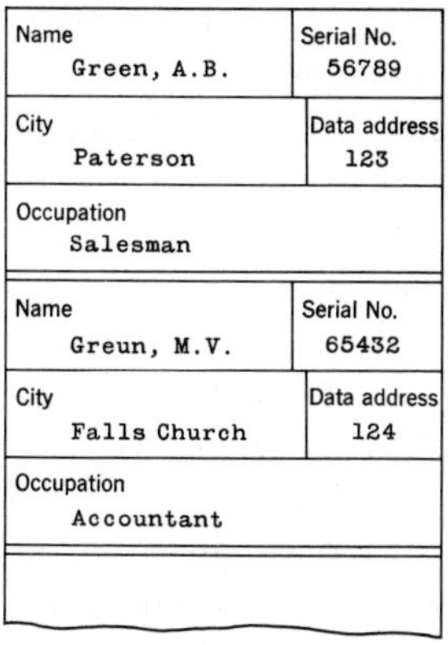

Name	Serial No.
Green, A.B.	56789

City	Data address
Paterson	123

Occupation	
Salesman	

Name	Serial No.
Greun, M.V.	65432

City	Data address
Falls Church	124

Occupation	
Accountant	

Original record in which a data
address has replaced the *state* field.

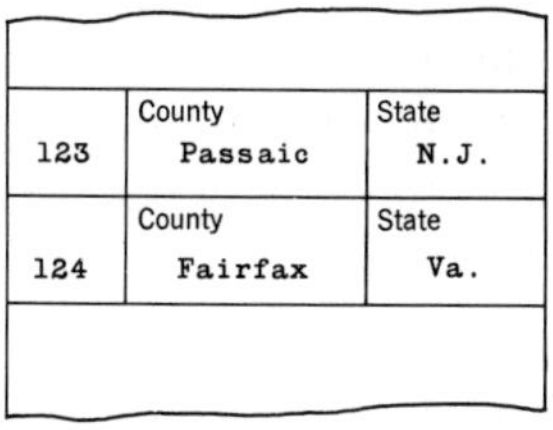

	County	State
123	Passaic	N.J.
	County	State
124	Fairfax	Va.

New file that contains the new
county field and the old *state* field,
linked to the original file by the
date address.

Figure 6.8   Branching structures as an aid to record modification.

We return now to the group of fixed fields with often-recurring values. If we remove them from the main file, we will reduce the number of times the same information must be repeated. This step should be taken, obviously, only when such a saving will actually result, as witnessed by actual data distributions. We place in the main file, instead, a reference to the record of the new file containing the transferred information. This is illustrated in Figure 6.7.

If we wish to change the structure of records in the main file of a branch structure, we need not recopy the entire file. Suppose we wish to add one new field to each existing record, thereby expanding the size of the file, and, in a normal organization, requiring rewriting of the file. We might, instead, replace one of the existing fields with an address in a new file at which the replaced and the newly inserted fields will be found. This is illustrated in Figure 6.8, where we wish to change the structure of the original record by adding a new field, *county of residence*. This is done by creating a new file and changing the meaning of one field in the original but does not require modification of the first file's structure.

Any of the branch files created by removing data from the main, or trunk, file can, in turn, be subjected to the same procedure, creating a tree-like structure. Usually, we call a data structure a tree if the branches do not intersect, or cross-refer, except at a single point. The organizational technique we have described here permits more than one record to refer to a common point in another file. Thus there can be more than one path from any given point in the structure to any other point, a phenomenon which cannot occur in a true tree structure, by definition. The structure that is created is quite versatile in its adaptability to change, and provides for simplicity in the physical composition of its files that enables most searches to be carried out expeditiously. This is done at the cost of some memory wastage due to the number of references between files that must be accommodated.

6.5.4   List Structures

A list structure is an organization of data that removes completely any requirement that records be placed in any particular way connected with their membership in a file. The structure can also be used to connect physically displaced fields into logical records. These structures are highly adaptable to change in record structure or content. The logic of searching a list structure is quite simple, but the physical dispersion of the data can make such searches slow and expensive. The languages of list processing offer concise symbologies for record and file structures. We have not adopted any of these because they are not yet in common use. The notation we use is derived from Newell.[5] There is a variety of others, tending to differ on minor points only. A review of the principal languages has been compiled by Bobrow and Raphael.[2]

The basic element of a list is a symbol stored in a cell, an accessible area of memory. Cells can consist of a bit, character, fixed length word, or variable number of words. The symbol stored therein can be a bit, character, word, or field, of fixed or variable length. A *list* is an ordered set of such elements. By *ordered* we mean that position is important, that *a c b* is a different list than *a b c*. If a list contains only basic symbols in its membership, it is called a *string*. If at least one element of the list is itself a list, then the containing list is called a *list structure*.

A list consists of a *name* which is, or represents, the location in memory

| Memory | Contents | |
location	Data	Address
14	*cat*	18
18	*dog*	11
11	*mouse*	143
143	*pigeon*	56
56	END	

Figure 6.9   A simple list.

of the first item on the list, *data elements,* and the *locations* of the
data elements, or *pointers.*   A list, then, is a chain, according to our
definition.   A simple list is shown in Figure 6.9.   This represents the
set: *cat, dog, mouse, pigeon,* ordered alphabetically.   The list starts
at memory location 14, and **14,** or a synonym for 14, such as **animals**
is its name.   The last entry in the list is at location 143, but it is necessary
to go to location 56 to discover this, for at this address is a special
symbol terminating the list.*   The list elements are not stored in contiguous memory locations, nor is the sequence of storage addresses in
numerical order.

Any element of this list can be a list, itself.   We might have a structure
such as *cat, (dogs), mouse, pigeon,* as shown in Figure 6.10, where we

* Either the data element or the pointer can be used to flag the end of a list.
Our illustrations use the data element for this purpose.

| Memory | Contents | |
location	Data	Address
14	*cat*	18
18	*78*	11
11	*mouse*	143
143	*pigeon*	56
56	END	
78	*collie*	79
79	*retriever*	2
2	*setter*	194
194	*terrier*	22
22	END	⑱

Figure 6.10   A list structure.

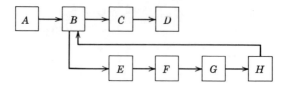

Figure 6.11   Diagrammatic representation of a list structure.

have replaced the word *dog* with a list of types of dogs.   We can easily convert our list structure terminology to show this by replacing the word *dog* with the address of the list of dog breeds.   This is shown in Figure 6.11.   This structure can be represented symbolically as: *A, (E, F, G, H), C, D.*   An optional field, in the address portion of the last element of the subordinate list, gives the location of the next element in the parent list, enabling a search program to resume its search.

The beauty of this, both as terminology and as a way of actually storing information, is that the programmer is freed from having to make up storage allocation tables and constantly moving data around in memory, into and out of working or buffer areas.   An item can be added anywhere in the list structure, with equal facility.   Any item of a list can, equally easily, be expanded into a list, itself, as we showed above.   There is the further advantage that, if there is an abundance of one kind of data in memory at any given time, any available space in memory can be used for it; there are no reserved memory blocks. Unused space is kept track of by another list, the elements being addresses of available cells.   "Bookkeeping" this list is quite easy to program.   As a new item comes into memory, a look in the *available* list gives the address of the next vacant cell.   That cell's location is deleted from the available list, the new data stored in whatever relative position is desired, in the containing list, the address of the next data item on the list or the termination symbol is added to the new item, and the pointer of the element preceding the new one is adjusted.   These mechanics are easy to perform in list processing languages, although tedious in normal programming languages.   The process is illustrated in Figure 6.12.

The reason list processing has yet to acquire universal popularity in non-numeric data processing is that, while these mechanics are easy in the list processing language, they can be very time-consuming when performed by a computer, so much so that the economics of use of present-day list processing languages in most information retrieval

Data list				Space available list	
Location	Cell content	Pointer		Location	Pointer
14	C_1	18		100	15
18	C_2	3		15	16
3	C_3	104		16	17
104	C_4	76		19	20
76	END			20	etc.

(a) The data list consists of a set of data items and pointers to the next cell.   The space available list can consist simply of a set of pointers, each location pointed to being available.

14	C_1	18		100	16
18	C_2	3		16	17
3	C_3	104		17	19
104	C_4	76		19	20
76	C_5	15		20	etc.
15	END				

(b) When a new item is added to the data list, the next available location is found in the space available list, that list modified, and the new item added to the data list.

Figure 6.12   Modifying a list structure.

applications is questionable.*   Because of the saving in programming time that is possible, however, we may anticipate future hardware and software developments that will enable these methods to be made practical.

We emphasize, in conclusion, that the major difference between list structures and conventional file organizations is that all location information is explicitly stated in a list structure, there being no assumption at all about relative placement of fields of a record.   This allows great freedom to change record content or structure, but searches may require jumping around the memory, at a sizable increase in search time.   Furthermore, because each field must have an associated address for the next field, the memory required to store a file can be as much as double that required for the same data under a contiguous placement.   It is even possible to use more than twice the minimum amount of memory because there can be more than one pointer with each field.   There may be one to the next field and one to another value of the same

---

* As this book is being written, the author notes an increase in the use of list processing techniques on research projects.   Perhaps this indicates that their use in operational projects is not far behind.

field, and possibly, one to the next record, or to the previous field, as needed in any particular case.

REFERENCES

1. Bachman, C. W., and S. B. Williams, "A General Purpose Programming System for Random Access Memories," *AFIPS Conference Proceedings, 1964 Fall Joint Computer Conference,* Spartan Books, Baltimore, 1964.
2. Bobrow, Daniel G., and Bertram Raphael, "A Comparison of List-Processing Languages," *Communications of the Association for Computing Machinery,* **7,** 4 (1964), pp. 231–240.
3. Griffith, J. E., "An Intrinsically Addressed Processing System," *IBM Syst. J.,* II, September–December, 1963, pp. 182–199.
4. Hoel, Paul G., *Introduction to Mathematical Statistics,* John Wiley and Sons, New York, 1947, p. 128.
5. Newell, Allen, Ed., *Information Processing Language-V Manual,* Prentice-Hall, Englewood Cliffs, New Jersey, 1961.

EXERCISES

1. For the file illustrated in Figure 6.2 compute the access coefficient a for all records if searched on *make, body style,* and *color.* Repeat for the file illustrated in Figure 6.1.
2. A university maintains the following files: *Student File,* containing: *name, student number, high school attended, major field, course taken, date completed, grade* (the latter three fields constituting a repeating, faceted term).
Facilities File, containing: *building number, room number, room capacity, classes scheduled* (the latter being a set of repeating fields, one for each class period).
Schedule File, containing: *department name, course offered, instructor, building, room, hour* (the latter five being a repeating, faceted term).
Faculty File, containing: *department name, instructor name, course taught* (the latter being a set of repeating descriptors).
a. Design record structures for each file.
b. Design file organizations for a tape-only memory, a high-speed disk memory, a mixed tape-disk memory where there is enough disk capacity for about one fourth the total file. Compute a for each file. Find the organization of the mixed memory that minimizes the sum of a's for all fields.
3. Design a file organization for the information described above that uses the least amount of memory, yet permits searching on all fields defined. In other words eliminate as much redundant information as possible.
4. For a file using contiguous sequential placement, compute or derive an expression for the additional amount of storage required to convert to chaining or list structure organizations. Clearly, this is a function of file size, memory configuration, and so forth. Use as many such factors as possible, defining each, in deriving your expression.

CHAPTER 7

The storage and measurement of structural information

7.1 INTRODUCTION

In several of the examples of the last two chapters we showed how knowledge about the location of information within a file could be used to reduce search time and how this information is sometimes stated explicitly and sometimes implied by the nature of the file. For this information about file structure there are problems of storage, retrieval, and use of data that are independent of the information stored in the files whose structure we must describe.

The essential items of information about file structure are a description of record structure and a means of finding the new field or record from any given point in a memory. Such information is often provided implicitly. Optional information may tell about record sequence and the distribution of data within a file (such as where the M-records start in an alphabetically ordered file). If a large body of structural information is built up within a system, all the problems of searching the main files are also present in searching files of structural data, and there may have to be files of structural data about the structural data files.

It is not always clear when information serves a purely structure-defining purpose and when it does not, nor is it necessary to be able to distinguish. For example, an inverted index file, as defined in Section 4.2.4, serves very much the same function as the list of pointers described in Section 6.5.4 as a constituent of a branch structure. The sole difference is that the inverted index file does not necessarily have actual addresses in it, although it may have them. It usually has document numbers which are the primary sort key of another file, and are not the same as record numbers, even though highly correlated.

Our concern in this chapter is primarily with the methods used to represent structural information. We shall also consider some problems of measuring this information, and some of the effects of doing without it, or having ambiguous information present. We start with a brief introduction to information theory and then proceed to representation and measurement of structural information.

7.2   CONCEPTS OF INFORMATION THEORY

Communication may be defined as the successful transfer of a symbol from one point, or transducer, to another. Receipt of an erroneous symbol, or misinterpretation of a received symbol, is unsuccessful symbol transference. The symbol transmitted may represent a physical object (the tree outside my window), a class of objects (oak trees), or an abstract concept (nature). The symbol may also stand for another symbol, and there is no requirement, in any of these cases, that the transmitted symbol look or sound like what it represents. The Morse Code symbol · — certainly bears no physical resemblance to A, nor does the symbol A to the variety of sounds which, in turn, are represented by A. If there can be no variation in the symbols transmitted by a transducer, there can be no semantically meaningful communication; no information transfer. If there is variation, or choice, by the source as to what symbols will be sent, there must be uncertainty at the destination, in advance of the transmission, as to what will be received. Information theorists measure the amount of information transmitted by measuring the degree of uncertainty that is dispelled between transmitter and receiver.

Information retrieval has not been a classical area of application of information theory, and the results of our effort are more intended to show the possibilities than to present conclusive findings. For readers desiring a more comprehensive treatment, we recommend Shannon and Weaver,[4] Cherry,[1] or Pierce.[6]

7.2.1   What Is Information?

We cannot, unfortunately, take back our statement in Chapter 1 that we have no real definition for information. We have alluded to some equivalence between degree of choice of symbols and information. If there exists a large degree of *choice* by a transmitter in the selection of the symbols to be transmitted, then there must exist a great deal of *uncertainty* as to what symbol will be selected. It is important to realize that the sense in which we use the term *uncertainty* is that of having a number of choices, the selection not being predetermined. Uncertainty does not imply indecisiveness, or the inability to choose; it

refs to the range, or number of decision alternatives.   When a deci-
sion-maker, even with a large number of alternatives, almost always
chooses the same one, there is not much uncertainty.   For example,
although a larger number of political parties is active in New York
than in most American cities, over the last few decades voters have
shown a decided tendency to select a Democratic mayor.   In spite of
the number of choices here, the uncertainty of choice is low.   We may
say, then, that not much information is conveyed when we hear that
a Democrat has won the mayoralty of New York.*   The governorship
of New York State has shown a much greater tendency to shift back
and forth between the major parties.   Because there is more real
choice—greater uncertainty—in this "system" we can say that an announcement of the victor in a gubernatorial election provides us with
more information.

7.2.2   The Measurement of Information.

The basis of information measurement is the probability of selection
of each of the decision alternatives facing an information source.   As we
pointed out in the election illustrations above, it is not just the *number*
of choices, but their *probabilities of being chosen,* as well, that contribute to a measurement of information content.

Information theorists have chosen the logarithm of the probability
of occurrence of a symbol as the means for measuring information transmitted.   The actual measure is found by multiplying the probability
of occurrence of each symbol by the logarithm of the probability, and
summing over all symbols transmitted.   Mathematically, this is expressed
as

$$H = - \sum_{i=1}^{n} p_i \log p_i \qquad (7.1)$$

where H is the average information content of n symbols whose probabilities of occurrence are $p_1, p_2, \ldots, p_n$.   We use the minus sign to achieve
a positive value of H, since probabilities range from 0 to 1 and the
logarithm of a number in that range is negative.

If a probability is zero, then $p_i \log p_i = 0$ and no information results.
If a probability is 1, $p_i \log p_i = 0$ and, again, no information results.
Since both 0 and 1 probabilities represent certainty—an event either

* This statement remains true as a generality over the last several decades,
in spite of the Democrats' defeat at the hands of Mr. Lindsay in 1965.

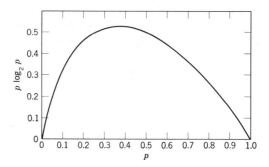

Figure 7.1   Plot of $p \log_2 p$.

cannot happen or always happens—we find a mathematical representation of our intuitive idea that information is the dispelling of uncertainty, and, if there is no uncertainty, there can be no information. In Figure 7.1 we show a plot of $p \log_2 p$.

If we use logarithms to the base two, the units of H are called *bits* or binary digits. For example, if there are 32 (2^5) letters in an alphabet, each equally likely to occur, the formula says that five bits of information are represented. A bit as a unit of measure should not be confused with what we might call a *physical bit*, a magnetized area on magnetic tape or a single magnetic core in a computer memory, which can have value zero or one. Each *physical bit* does not necessarily convey a *bit of information*. When we use a six physical bit computer code (capable of representing $2^6 = 64$ symbols) only for the ten decimal numeric symbols, there is obvious redundancy in our coding. Even the use of only four bits still represents every decimal digit ($2^4 - 16$) and still has some redundancy. Figure 7.2 shows how an alphabet of 32 symbols is coded using five bits.

Let us consider this from another point of view.* Suppose the alphabet to be used in communicating between two points consists of three symbols: *a, b,* and *c.* We do not wish to have to transmit the full Morse or Hollerith letter representations, as this would be a waste of communications facilities. Instead, we shall store a table of symbols in both transmitter and receiver, and transmit, not the symbols themselves, but instructions on how to retrieve the symbols from the table. Assume, further, that there are unequal occurrence probabilities for the latter, say: $P(a) = \frac{1}{2}$, $P(b) = \frac{1}{4}$, $P(c) = \frac{1}{4}$. The table used to

* See Cherry[2] for a fuller treatment of this approach.

locate letters would reflect the unequal probabilities, and might be as shown in Figure 7.3a. The transmitter will send, in this scheme, not the actual symbols a, b, c, but the instructions on where in the table the receiver can find the symbols that the transmitter means to send. The transmitter assumes the receiver will start its table search in the center of the table (start position), and will move up or down on receipt of a single bit command, whose values are 0, for up; or 1, for down. If the signal is 0, the receiver moves to the upper half of the table which is composed entirely of a's. There can be no doubt which symbol was intended, since all a's are the same. If the initial signal received was 1, the receiver moves down to the bottom half of the table, finds that the symbols here are different, and that another selection bit is needed. The receiver now awaits the second signal. A 0 selects the b and a 1 selects the c. Figure 7.3b shows all the possibilities. Here, we see the messages that must be sent to select a symbol from the table. A single bit can select an a, but two bits are needed for b or c. In effect, we are simply replacing the symbols 0, 10, and 11 with a, b, and c, respectively. In this scheme, the minimum number of bits required to specify a symbol is used in the transmitted signal, and the number of bits required to choose a symbol is variable. If fixed-length, binary codes for a, b, and c were to be transmitted, it would require at least

1. 00000	17. 10000
2. 00001	18. 10001
3. 00010	19. 10010
4. 00011	20. 10011
5. 00100	21. 10100
6. 00101	22. 10101
7. 00110	23. 10110
8. 00111	24. 10111
9. 01000	25. 11000
10. 01001	26. 11001
11. 01010	27. 11010
12. 01011	28. 11011
13. 01100	29. 11100
14. 01101	30. 11101
15. 01110	31. 11110
16. 01111	32. 11111

Figure 7.2   The coding of 32 different symbols using five bits.

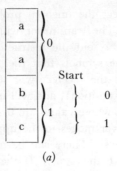

(a)

Intended symbol	Transmitted symbol	
a	0	
a	0	
b	1	0
c	1	1

(b)

Figure 7.3 Use of positional commands to transmit information: (a) symbol table and search positions: (b) summary of transmitted symbols.

two (physical) bits each time. The *average number* of bits required to specify an element of the table under the variable scheme is

$$H = -p(a) \log_2 p(a) - p(b) \log_2 p(b) - p(c) \log_2 p(c)$$
$$= \tfrac{1}{2} \log_2 \tfrac{1}{2} + \tfrac{1}{4} \log_2 \tfrac{1}{4} + \tfrac{1}{4} \log_2 \tfrac{1}{4}$$
$$= 1\tfrac{1}{2}$$

It is interesting to note that the expression for H has its greatest value when all the probabilities, p_i, are equal[5]; when all transmitted symbols are equally likely to occur, or there is complete freedom of choice. When all symbols are not equally likely, some constraint is imposed upon free choice, and the amount or rate of information should decrease. Using example rather than proof, in an alphabet of two symbols, we would have if the probabilities were $\tfrac{3}{4}$ and $\tfrac{1}{2}$

$$H = -(\tfrac{3}{4} \log \tfrac{3}{4} + \tfrac{1}{4} \log \tfrac{1}{4})$$
$$\approx 0.8$$

but, if the probabilities were equal, both $\tfrac{1}{2}$, we would have

$$H = -(\tfrac{1}{2} \log \tfrac{1}{2} + \tfrac{1}{2} \log \tfrac{1}{2})$$
$$= 1.0$$

7.2.3   Noise

A final concept which we shall touch on only briefly is that of *equivocation,* or the effect of *noise*.   In traditional communications usage, noise is a spurious signal, an unintentional but positive transmission that may cause the receiver to interpret a symbol as one different from the one intentionally sent.   The reader is undoubtedly familiar with noise on a radio receiver that might have been transmitted by a home vacuum cleaner.   To overcome this, communicators introduce redundancy, so that, when the receiver is unsure of the meaning of a symbol, it can make use of redundant, or extra, signals to resolve the doubt.   A computer's parity bit is an example of this, although a single bit can only serve to detect errors, and cannot correct them.   An elaboration of the same concept uses additional bits to provide the information needed to correct an error.   The phonetic alphabet used in military radio communication (A = alpha, B = bravo, etc.) uses a full word of several letters to help the receiver discriminate between similar-sounding letters such as E and T (echo and tango).

The equivocation caused by noise is measurable.   This can be seen in the fact that the probabilities of occurrence of field values may be different for the transmitter and receiver in the presence of noise, and the difference leads to a measure of the equivocation.   For example, the spoken letters E and Z have different probabilities of occurrence in English, but on a noisy voice radio they may be undistinguishable by the receiver.   Hence the receiver rates the occurrence probabilities as different from the transmitter's values.

Redundancy is often intentionally introduced into an alphabet or language to help overcome equivocation or ambiguity.   This is usually caused by noise—unwanted but positively transmitted signals—but can also be caused by untransmitted information, as, for example, an internal failure in a computer causing a timing pulse to fail to "fire" may cause misinterpretation of information being read from magnetic tape at the time.   Similarly, failure to provide information about the structure of a record, even though the record may be faultlessly transmitted to a computer, can result in its being erroneously decoded.   The lack of full information on the location of field values that is characteristic of repeating or tagged fields or of natural language is an example of noise.   In the case of searching a record, the probability of finding a field value at some particular position may be less than the probability of its occurrence in the record, because there may be more than one possible position for it.   For example, if there are ten repetitions of the field *previous address,* even if a given value is known to be in the set (the probability of being in the record is 1), its probability of being in any given repetition of the field is only 0.1.

7.3 REPRESENTATION OF FILE STRUCTURE INFORMATION

We must bear in mind that structural information is only of value if the processor can take advantage of it. For example, if data are stored on a magnetic tape, and, if the reading and searching of this tape cannot be overlapped with any other computer operation, there is little use for a table of record locations, for each record will have to be examined anyway. On the other hand, if the same file were stored on a disk, and if the disk read head could be positioned while the computer is performing some internal calculations, the availability of an index to record locations can reduce effective record access time to almost nothing, in the sense that the central processor will hardly ever have to wait for data as it often must in a tape system. A system designer, in considering the ways of representing information within his system, must also consider whether he wants this information in his system. We review in this section the three most common ways of representing information about file structure: tabular, formula, and implicit.

7.3.1 Tabular Representation

Use of a table is probably the most common way to represent location information, and is becoming common as a method of representing record structure information. The table of contents and index of this book are examples of such tables. The index is a detailed table showing the actual page number where a word (the argument) appears. The table of contents is far broader if considered as a subject indexing file, in that chapter titles are not always very descriptive of subject content and there is no cross-indexing. A "thumb-indexed" dictionary also provides a relatively general location table. The beginning of the section for each letter in the alphabet is marked so the searcher knows a particular word falls between two markers, and his search time is thus reduced, even if the exact location is not given. This is a good example of a case where perfect location information would save very little time, if any, for inclusion of an index in a dictionary would nearly double its size and probably also the price. The arguments of the index would be the same as the arguments of the main table, and the net gain to the user would be nil.

The tabs of a thumb index essentially point to bench marks in the file, places where the initial letter of the record being defined changes. Of about equal value and cost would be an approach whereby the dictionary is divided into 26 sections of equal length, with the index tabs showing the first three letters of the first word in each section. This is a common form of index in multi-volume encyclopedias, which are books of about equal size, varying in number of entries beginning with any given letter.   Either technique depends for its effectiveness on the implicit assumption that the records of the file are in alphabetical order. If we wish to make a table of the locations where values of a field occur, and if this field is not the primary sort key, our table will have to be quite long.   This is so with a book index.   The book's text is not ordered alphabetically.   Its index is not only longer than an index to an ordered file, the user cannot interpolate in it.   Hence every word that may be searched on in an index must be explicitly mentioned. Knowing where *cat* and *catapult* are mentioned in the text does not help to find where *catalog* is mentioned.

In recent years tabular representations have been used to describe record formats to a search program.   Doing so enables search and match programs to be written in a general way, which can accommodate themselves to any record structure submitted, as long as the structure-defining table is also submitted. The data description features of COBOL[7] provide for such tables, which can then be interpreted by the COBOL compiler. If a programmer writes a statement such as ADD A TO B, the compiler, by examining the data description tables, can decide exactly what machine-language instructions are necessary to extract variables A and B from their files, and add them together.   An example of a COBOL data description is reproduced in Figure 7.4. This shows a portion of a personnel file being described.   The *name* field is defined as consisting of 15 characters.   The arrangement of the numbers in columns 8–11 show that the *name* field is subordinate to (has a higher valued tag than) the personnel record, as are the *sex, age, height, weight,* and *eye color* fields.   The code 88 in columns 12, 13 denotes a definition of a particular value of the field defined above the number, as, on line 080, **88 MALE VALUE 'M'** means that M is a code for *male,* and is one of two permissible values of the *sex* field.   If a field were to have subordinate fields, as *name* might have *family name* and *initials* as components, this would be shown as follows:

```
02    NAME
  03    FAMILY NAME
  03    INITIALS
```

where the indentation and the use of a number, 03, greater than 02 designate that the latter two fields are subordinate components of the field, *name.*

IBM

COBOL PROGRAM SHEET

PAGE 3	PROGRAM	FILE SEARCH		SYSTEM		SHEET 2 OF 4
020	PROGRAMMER			DATE		IDENT 73SEARCH 80

SERIAL / A / B

010	FD	PERSONNEL-FILE
020		LABEL RECORDS ARE OMITTED
030		DATA RECORD IS PERSONNEL-RECORD.
040		
050	01	PERSONNEL-RECORD.
060	02	NAME PICTURE X(15).
070	02	SEX PICTURE X.
080		88 MALE VALUE 'M'.
090		88 FEMALE VALUE 'F'.
100	02	AGE PICTURE X.
110		88 UNDER-20 VALUE 'Y'.
120		88 20-TO-50 VALUE 'M'.
130		88 OVER-50 VALUE 'E'.
140	02	HEIGHT PICTURE X.
150		88 OVER-6 VALUE 'T'.
160		88 5-AND-A-HALF-TO-6 VALUE 'M'.
170		88 UNDER-5-AND-A-HALF VALUE 'S'.
180	02	WEIGHT PICTURE X.
190		88 OVER-185 VALUE 'H'.
200		88 185-TO-120 VALUE 'M'.
210		88 UNDER-120 VALUE 'L'.
220	02	EYES PICTURE X.
230		88 BLACK VALUE 'L'.
240		88 BROWN VALUE 'R'.
250		88 HAZEL VALUE 'A'.

Figure 7.4 Excerpt from a *COBOL* data description. Reprinted by permission from *General Information Manual, COBOL* © 1961 by International Business Machines Corp.

The set of pointers of a list structure also constitute a tabular representation of location data, although they, of course, are not contiguously stored. These give only the minimum information, the location of the next element in the list, and tell nothing about the distribution of element values, while even the thumb index, by spacing between tabs, gives a visual description of the distribution of words by initial letter. Again, the reason why an index can provide information on the distribution of field values in the file is the assumption that the file is ordered on the same field that is the argument of the index.

7.3.2 Formula Representation

A second approach to the storage of location information is to store only a formula which would provide the location of the record. The independent variables of the formula would be attributes of the record. As a trivial example, in our discussion of chaining in Section 6.5.2, we assumed a file to be so organized that, at the beginning, each succeeding track of a disk contains records starting with a different initial letter of the alphabet. Overflow from these tracks is placed elsewhere. Let us now assume such an arrangement based on a numeric field, with the first digit used as an index term; that is, all records whose sort key starts with 0 are found on track 1, those starting with 1 on track 2, and so forth. The formula, where D is the first digit of the sort field, and T the track number, is

$$T = D + 1 \qquad (7.2)$$

To store this information as a table would require ten entries, with the computer instructions for table look-up equally time- and space-consuming as the formula evaluation instructions. A more realistic and useful example would involve taking advantage of the correlation between a sequentially assigned document accession number, date of document publication and receipt, and location of the corresponding index record. In a large library that does not often purge its files or holdings, the size of the collection, as a function of time, probably follows an exponential growth curve. Certainly, each succeeding year results in the storage of more documents than were stored during the previous year, and all are cumulated indefinitely. If we note the access number assigned to the first document received in each new year, and plot this against time, we will probably find a reasonably smooth curve, such as is shown in Figure 7.5. We can then derive a mathematical expression to fit this curve, such that, given a document access number, we can compute its probable date of receipt, or given a date, we can compute limits on its probable access number. Of course, a tolerance limit must be put on the latter computation, so that a block of numbers is retrieved for any date search, with the probability high, but less than one, that all documents received or published on that date lie between stated document number limits. By changing the scale of the function, we can compute the approximate storage location of a document number, by date or by access number. For example, the points plotted in Figure 7.5 are well fitted to the mathematical expression

$$A = (D - 1949)\ 12{,}000 \qquad (7.3)$$

where A is the access number, D the date of the index record, and 12000 represents the rate, in records per year, at which new records are assumed added. The constant 1949 represents the year 1949, a date on which it is assumed the library was founded, but had no documents. To compute the access number of a document received in July, 1960, we set $D = 1960.6$ and compute $A = 139{,}200$. Experience may

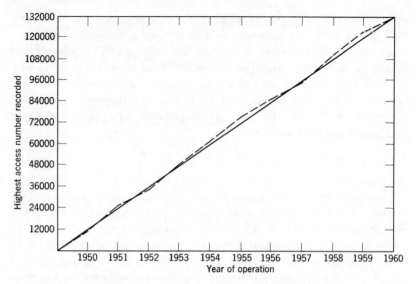

Figure 7.5 A plot of the highest access number recorded in each year of operation of a library.

show that 90% of documents are received within a year of publication. Another calculation for $D = 1961.5$ gives an upper bound on the document number within a 90% confidence limit. Memory location assuming fixed-length index records will be a function of A, such as

$$T = \frac{A + k}{c} \qquad (7.4)$$

where k is a constant depending upon how the access numbers are assigned, and c is track capacity. k is selected so that the first record is found on track 1.

Where this method can be used at all, it can achieve great savings in memory space, but in many cases it is unable to provide the accuracy needed for a complete location, and its use may have to be followed by a table search which might then have been used for the whole job. Unfortunately, few information fields have such a distribution of values that use of formulas alone can accomplish an accurate location.

7.3.3   Implicit Storage of Information

Information is represented by symbols. The symbols that represent information descriptive of, say, a fixed field record are often stored as a part of the logic of a program, although they may also be separately

stored as a table.   If stored within the program, the structural information is represented by a sequence of memory-to-register transfer instructions together with appropriate shifting and masking operations.   The
structure is defined, then, by a series of computer operation codes whose
execution accomplishes decoding, rather than by an explicit description
of the structure from which decoding instructions can be compiled.   The
cost of the memory used, and the organizational methods of storing
structural information in a program are very difficult to include in an
analysis of the total cost of using one method of file organization over
another.   The reasons are found in the many complexities of programming and computer design.   Machine instruction repertoire and programming language variations can alter relative costs, so can programmer
efficiency, memory space-running time trade-offs, and the frequent need
to conform to a standard system of programming or file organization,
within a computing center.   These latter variables are all independent
of the processor.   Thus, if structural information is present in a data
record as a tag, we tend to charge it to the data record for cost-analytic
purposes, but if the same information is stored in a program or on
a program tape, even though it may consume the same total amount
of space, we have a tendency to ignore it when analyzing space utilization.   This practice is not without justification because, often, there
is no need for great precision.

Similarly, knowledge of value, content, or field value distribution may
be stored in a program.   The simplest example is found in any program
switch or variable transfer command which is operated by successively
testing an input value for a set of expected values of a data field.   It
is not logically necessary to test for all n possible values of the field.   It
is sufficient to test for $n - 1$ values and, failing these, assume the input
value must be the nth possible one, without ever recording the nth
value in the program.   In testing a single bit, for example, it is only
necessary to test it for the value 0; if it is not zero, the assumption
can be safely made that is one, but the value 1 need never appear
in the program.   If the switch depends upon sequential testing of a
number of values (is it 1?, is it 2?, etc.) then the values tested can
be arranged in decreasing order of probability of occurrence of the value.
Such an arrangement implicitly stores information about record content
in a program, but the storage requires no more space than if random
or alphabetical sequencing were used.   In other words, the additional
information on frequency of occurrence is stored free of cost, as far
as memory is concerned.   What cost there is is borne by the programmer
who takes the time to order the list of values.   This is an example
of the use of physical data organization to store information.   Often

the contents of a data field are placed directly into an index register to serve as an address increment in locating other data or transferring to an appropriate subroutine. This is another example of how knowledge of content can be used to direct a program, although there is no explicit storage of the information used (the information used is an address) in the program.

7.4   MEASUREMENT OF FILE STRUCTURE INFORMATION

Our approach to the content of record or file structure information will be to indicate, by example, the differences in search time or computer memory required, with and without structural information.

7.4.1   Measuring Value Information

First, consider the illustration in Section 7.2.2 of transmitting the *position* of a character in a table, rather than a conventional symbol for the character, itself.* In the transmission demonstrated an average of 1.5 bits of information were conveyed, per message, regardless of which symbology was used. If the positional notation was used, an average of 1.5 physical bits were needed to carry this information while if a conventional, fixed character size notation was used, at least two physical bits were required. We could look at this situation as one in which the receiving computer serves as an index, telling where the desired information is located. The transmitter, then, supplies file structure information. The facts that the file to be searched by the retrieving computer is ordered, this order is known, and it is taken advantage of, enable the saving of an average of one-half bit out of every two that might otherwise have to be transmitted.

The general problem of not having the information required to interpret a mesage is essentially the same as that dealt with earlier in Section 4.5.1 under the title "Information and Credence." We are dealing, not with the physical problems of how to transmit a character, but with problems of interpreting messages that we assume to have been transmitted correctly. We can always make some interpretation of a signal, but we cannot always be sure that we are interpreting it as the transmitting agency intended. Our next example illustrates the problems of interpretation without a key.

Suppose a set of bit-coded records are to be read into a computer,

---

* The positional notation is also a symbol for the character, as well as a descriptor of the character's location. We draw the distinction simply because a location descriptor is not the conventional way to transmit characters.

and the information contained in them posted to an existing file. The computer, however, is not given the organization, and, having no other way to decode the message in a record, is reduced to making a random selection of a value for posting. With such a method of "interpreting" input messages, we will be right half the time, for a bit-coded field has values 0 or 1, and, if these are equally likely to occur, we can achieve the results stated.

If, under the same circumstances, we have some information about the distribution of 0's and 1's, even without knowing the record organization, we can improve our accuracy. Assume that $P(0) = 0.9$ and $P(1) = 0.1$. Still following our previous procedure, we shall randomly assign values to the bit positions we wish to modify, without regard to the value transmitted, but with the same probabilities as used by the transmitter. The table in Figure 7.6 shows the result. It shows the probability of transmitting each input value, the value that will be assigned to the bit position by a random assignment process, the probability of making that assignment, and the probability that the given output value will have been assigned to the given input signal. The only cases in which incoming signals were correctly interpreted are the first and last, where a 0 input led to an 0 result, and a 1 led to a 1. The total probability of these events, of a correct assignment, is .82, and the probability of an error is 0.18. The apparent increase in accuracy, over the example in the preceding paragraph, is certainly not due to a change in the method of assigning values, for we have continued to use a random selection process. Therefore, the increase must be due to the only factor that changed, prior knowledge and use of the probability of occurrence of each symbol. Even if the probabilities at the transmitter were 0.9 and 0.1, as assumed, but this were not known

Bit value	Probability of transmitting value	Bit value randomly assigned	Probability of assigning value	Probability of assigning stated value to transmitted value
0	.9	0	.9	.81
0	.9	1	.1	.09
1	.1	0	.9	.09
1	.1	1	.1	.01

Figure 7.6   Results of random assignment of bit values.

at the receiver, then $P(0) = P(1) = 0.5$, and the probability of correct assignment reverts to 0.5. Thus, it is the knowledge about the data organization held at the receiver, not the organization itself, that governs.

7.4.2   Measuring Sequence Information

In the bracketing search procedure described in Section 4.3, we assumed that the program would always look first at the middle of the table, test the value of the appropriate field of the record found there, and either move up or down according as the stored value was greater or less than the search value. When the processor made its second move in another part of the file, it moved, not half the "length" of the file, but one-fourth, repeated the comparison, and moved up or down one-eighth the file length, then repeated this procedure until the correct record was found or only so small a segment was left that it could have been economically searched sequentially. So long as the file is ordered on the search term, this method will require $\log_2 n$ comparisons to find the desired record, where n is the number of records in the file.* Incidentally, because a binary, or two-valued, choice is made at each decision point in this procedure, the search method is usually known as a *binary search*.

If this same file were stored in random order, or, equivalently, if we had no information about its sequence, it would have to be searched by examining every record to see if it matched the query term. For an average search in which it was known that only one record in the file would satisfy the query, there would be $n/2$ records examined. At the other extreme, if an index file gave us exact knowledge of the location of records in this file, we would only have to examine one record.

The number of bits of information needed to describe the location of every record in a file is $\log_2 n$, where n is the number of records. (See Section 7.2.2.) We can see that this is the same as the number of required comparisons in a binary search if we know the file is in sequence but do not know the distribution of sort key values. If we have no information at all, the number of comparisons required is n. If we know that there is only one record containing a given field value—that values are unique—there will be $n/2$ comparisons, on the average. This is summarized in Table 7.1 which shows the number of records that must be accessed and examined when a file is searched for a single record matching the query term and we are given the type and amount of information stated.

---

* After b brackets, when there is only one record left to examine, the file has been cut in half b times. Then, $(n/2)^b = 1$ or $b = \log_2 n$.

Table 7.1   Number of file comparisons as a function of amount and type information.

Information known	Amount of information	Number of comparisons
None	0	n
Unique field values	–	$\dfrac{n}{2}$
File is in sequence	–	$\log_2 n$
Exact location of each record	$\log_2 n$	1

This would seem to fit a relationship such as*

$$c = n^{(\log_2 n - a)/\log_2 n} \qquad (7.5)$$

where c is the number of comparisons required in the search of a file of n records if a bits of information are known about the file's positioning of records. Solving the equation for a gives us a means of estimating the amount of information in a system in which we know, by other means, the probable number of comparisons.

$$a = \log_2 n - \log_2 c \qquad (7.6)$$

This amount of information is stored implicitly in the computer program that might, for example, use a binary search technique and presume the file to be in order. For a file of 1024 records which is known to have unique field values of a search field, but not known to be in order, there are

$$a = \log_2 1024 - \log_2 \frac{1024}{2} = 10 - 9 = 1$$

bit of information. If we have a file of 2^{20} records, in sequence and with unique sort keys, we have:

$$a = \log_2 2^{20} - \log_2 \log_2 2^{20} = 20 - 4.32 = 15.68 \text{ bits}$$

7.4.3   Comparison of Methods of Information Representation

We shall now carry the last example a little further and show, in more detail, what information is made available by an index to a file,

* We have fit a curve to only two points, and must recognize that the relationship is only approximate.

what the cost of storing that information is, and what it can save when searching a file.

Assume a file of n records, where n is a large number, say in the hundreds of thousands. Also assume the records are of considerable length, say over 500 characters. These numbers serve only to put the problem within realistic bounds, and do not affect the logic of what follows. The file is to be stored on magnetic disks which have a capacity of 100 records per track and 100 tracks per disk. We need, then at least $n/10,000$ or 10 to 100 disks. Further assume that the file is in sort on an alphabetic field which is ten characters in length, and in which each letter is equally likely to occur, and that field values are unique (i.e., no two records have the same value of the sort field).

Let us consider six ways of indexing this file—describing it to the computer.

Method 1 provides no information at all—not even that sort keys are unique—and forces the search program to assume the file to be in random order. Hence, all n records will have to be searched every time there is a query.

Method 2 provides only the information that the values of the field on which the file is searched are unique. Having no information about order, it is still necessary to test each record, but the search can end as soon as the desired record is found. On the average, $n/2$ records are searched.

Method 3 provides two facts: that values of the sort key are unique and that the file is in order. This information is provided in *Methods 4, 5,* and *6,* as well.

Method 4 also tells the value of the sort key in the first record of each disk (i.e., the first record of the first track of each disk).

Method 5 gives the value of the sort key in the first record of each track.

Method 6 provides an index to the exact location of the record bearing a given value in its sort key, and provides this for all values present in the file. The index file, which we shall call I_1, has n records, one for each record of the main file. Each record in I_1 represents a six-digit address field* of a record in the main file, F, but the address will not be stored explicitly. Instead, when we have found the record in I_1 that we want, we will use its position or sequence number within the file to find the address we want in the main file, thereby saving the memory required to store addresses of records in F. To search I_1, another index, I_2, is created which gives the exact address of the first

---

* Two for disk number, two for track number, and two for record within track.

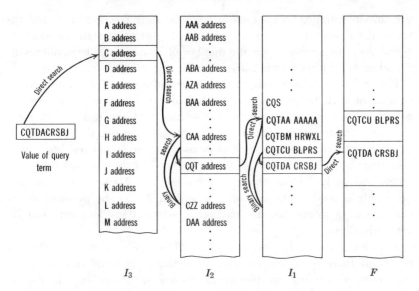

Figure 7.7 Nested indexes to a file providing exact location.

record in I_1 to begin with a given trigram, for each trigram present in the file. I_2 contains as many as 26^3 records, of three characters, plus a four- or six-character address.* A third index, I_3, gives the address in I_2 of the first record to begin with a new initial letter. It consists of only 26 four- or six-character addresses and will be searched by inserting the initial letter of a query term into a computer index, or address modification, register, and directly retrieving the corresponding address in I_2. The operation of this nested set of indexes is illustrated in Figure 7.7.

Here we see a query, consisting of a field value, **CQTDACRSBJ.** In step 1, the initial letter is used to operate a program switch which locates the third record in I_3. This record contains the address of the first entry in I_2 beginning with **C.** We go to this address in I_2 and perform a binary search within the C-area, finally locating a record which contains the first three letters of our query value, **CQT,** and an address in I_1 of the beginning of all **CQT** records. We use this address to locate the first entry in I_1 beginning with **CQT,** again use a binary search to find the full requested value, **CQTDACRSBJ.** We need not explicitly retrieve an address from this record in I_1, for, if we know where in I_1 we are, we can

* Address length, in this case, is a function of how storage space is assigned and whether, for example, a new trigram always starts in a new track.

use this information to compute a corresponding position in F, and retrieve the desired data record. The exact number of searches required is unknown, depending upon the number of records in I_2 beginning with C and in I_1 beginning with CQT.

Figure 7.8 contains a comparison of the index length, the information content of each index, and the number of searches required to retrieve a record from a file, F, which is the object of the search. In each case, the length of the file, F, is n records. We use the notation I_1 to represent any index to F that is used. The I_1 file for Method 6 was described above. For Methods 4 and 5, I_1 is the index of first records in each disk or track, respectively. In Methods 1, 2, and 3 no I_1 file is used. The size of a record in I_1 can be as small as 10 characters, as is the case in Method 5, where track location must be explicitly stored.

I_2 is an index of I_1, and I_3 of I_2. These are used only in Method 6. I_2 contains up to 26^3 ($= 17,576$) records. It could have less, but not more, depending on the actual values appearing in records. A record consists of three characters, plus an address, as shown in Figure 7.7. I_3 consists simply of a list of 26 addresses, of four to six digits each.

As to information content, the nonexistent indexes of Methods 1, 2, and 3 provide none; but, because we have some information about the structure of F in Methods 2 and 3, namely the uniqueness of field values (2 and 3) and ordering of records (3), we attribute this information to the nonexistent I_1, for it is the function of that index to describe F. Here F is described implicitly but the I_1 function is still present. The expressions are derived from Eq. 7.6. The figures shown for Methods 4, 5, and 6 are the $\log_2$ of the index length, in records. In Method 6 the information content of I_2 and I_3 cannot be considered additive to that of I_1.

The number of searches is calculated both for the main file F and for the index files. In Method 1 we must look at every record in F, not stopping when we find a match because there might be another match. In Method 2 we start the same way, but, on finding a match, we can quit. We shall do so after an average of $n/2$ records. In Method 3, and in all other searches of F or an index, unless otherwise stated, we shall be using binary searching. In Method 3, then, we must search $\log_2 n$ records in F. In Method 4, we search $\log_2 (n/10,000)$ records in I_1, and then $\log_2 10,000$ records of F in the disk referred to in I_1. In Method 5 we search more index records, $\log_2 (n/100)$, but fewer main file records, $\log_2 100$. In Method 6 there is one search of I_3, up to $\log_2 26^2$ searches of I_2 (we know the location of the initial letter and

Method of describing file structure

		1	2	3	4	5	6
File length	F	n	n	n	n	n	n
	I_1	not used	not used[1]	not used[1]	$\dfrac{n}{10,000}$	$\dfrac{n}{100}$	n
	I_2	not used	not used	not used	not used[2]	not used[2]	$26^3 = 17,576$
	I_3	not used	not used	not used	not used	not used	26
Information content of file:	I_1	0	$\log_2 n - \log_2 \dfrac{n^{(3)}}{2}$	$\log_2 n - \log_2 \log_2 n^{(3)}$	$\log_2 \dfrac{n}{10,000}$	$\log_2 \dfrac{n}{100}$	$\log_2 n$
	I_2	0	0	0	$\log_2 \dfrac{n}{10,000} - \log_2 \log_2 \dfrac{n^{(3)}}{10,000}$	$\log_2 \dfrac{n}{100} - \log_2 \log_2 \dfrac{n^{(3)}}{100}$	$\log_2 26^3 = 14.1$
	I_3	0	0	0	0	0	$\log_2 26 = 4.7$
Number of comparisons required in file search:	F	n	$\dfrac{n}{2}$	$\log_2 n$	$\log_2 10,000$	$\log_2 100$	1
	I_1	0	0	0	$\log_2 \dfrac{n}{10,000}$	$\log_2 \dfrac{n}{100}$	$\log_2 \dfrac{n}{26^3}$
	I_2	0	0	0	0	0	$\log_2 26^2 = 9.4$
	I_3	0	0	0	0	0	1
Total number of comparisons		n	$\dfrac{n}{2}$	$\log_2 n$	$\log_2 n$	$\log_2 n$	$\log_2 n - 2.7$

Figure 7.8 Comparison of file description methods. (1) These files are not actually present as such, but information is available on the structure of F, the storage of which is the function of file I_1. (2) Here we have the same situation described in Note 1. Information on the structure of I_1 is available, but not in I_2. (3) These measurements are for the explicitly stored information referred to in Notes 1 and 2.

223

are searching through a maximum of 26×26 second and third letters by the binary method), and $\log_2 (n/26^3)$ searches of I_1, the n records of I_1 being divided by I_2 into 26^3 subgroups, of known location. There is only one search of F required in Method 6.

If we now total the number of searches required by each method the results may appear rather anti-climactical, for we arrive at nearly the same result for all methods that use an index and bracket searching. This should not be surprising. An index does not make decisions; it permits them to be made at lower cost or in less time. Hence the indexes of Methods 4, 5, and 6 provide faster search capability than can be achieved through Methods 1, 2, or 3. The speed is achieved at the cost of storage space for the indexes.

We can see that providing even so little information as that sort key values are unique can reduce the expected number of searches from n to $n/2$ records. Further information that the file is in sequence reduces the number of searches by $n/2 - \log_2 n$ records. Further reductions are difficult to accomplish. Method 6 can provide some reduction, but the amount depends upon the distribution of sort key values and is limited to a small amount.

In conclusion, we have shown that the information available about a file's structure is not always measurable, nor is it always explicitly stated. The value of the information is in the reduction in cost or time of file searching, and where these factors are not pressing, it does not follow that all possible structural information should be made available. We have also shown that, regardless of the organization of a file or the distribution of its sort key values, a search program cannot take advantage of the structure unless it is informed about the structural feature. Structural information, then, must be postively conveyed to the search program.

REFERENCES

1. Cherry, Colin, *On Human Communication,* MIT Press, Cambridge, Massachusetts, 1957.
2. *Ibid.,* p. 177.
3. Gaines, Helen Fouche, *Cryptanalysis,* Dover Publications, New York, 1956, p. 219.
4. Shannon, Claude E., and Warren Weaver, *The Mathematical Theory of Communication,* University of Illinois Press, Urbana, Illinois, 1959.
5. Ibid., p. 21.
6. Pierce, J. R., *Symbols, Signals and Noise: The Nature and Process of Communications,* Harper & Bros., New York, 1961.
7. ———, *General Information Manual, COBOL,* International Business Machines Corp., White Plains, New York, 1961.

EXERCISES

1. Take a text of 100–200 words. Delete every fourth word and recopy the text so that a reader cannot tell the length of the deleted words. Have someone try to reconstitute the original from the reduced text and the knowledge that every fourth word was deleted. It might help to put a special symbol in place of the deleted word. Repeat, with a different person, deleting every third, then every second word. Repeat the entire process deleting every nth letter, instead of word. Compile scores showing the ability of your test subjects to reconstitute text as a function of the amount of information deleted. What does this tell about redundancy in the English language?

2. H. F. Gaines[3] lists the following table of frequencies of occurrence of letters in English (in occurrences per hundred letters):

A 7.81	I 6.77	Q 0.14	Y 1.51
B 1.28	J 0.23	R 6.64	Z 0.09
C 2.93	K 0.42	S 6.46	
D 4.11	L 3.60	T 9.02	
E 13.05	M 2.62	U 2.77	
F 2.88	N 7.28	V 1.00	
G 1.39	O 8.21	W 1.49	
H 5.85	P 2.15	X 1.51	

From this information compute the average information content of a letter in English text. What is the maximum information, per symbol, that can be conveyed by a set of 26 symbols? What does this indicate about the redundancy of English?

3. For a dictionary or telephone book:

    a. Devise a tabular file of location information, showing on what page each new initial letter starts.

    b. Work out the best formula representation you can of this information.

    c. Flow chart a search program in which this location information is stored implicitly.

4. For a telephone directory, use the methods of this chapter to compile an estimate of how much information is represented in knowing the sequence and structure of the alphabetic listing. Do the same for the business listing—the yellow pages. To do so you will have to estimate the file size and the number of business types used as headings. If there is an index to the yellow pages, how much information does it represent?

CHAPTER 8

The organization of file sets

8.1 INTRODUCTION

We have already seen some examples of the use of a set of files to accomplish an information retrieval objective. A file together with an index to itself is such a set. In this chapter we shall follow the basic plan used in Chapters 5 and 6 by first developing a set of file set organizational principles, then giving some examples of their application.

A *file set* is any collection of files. We often find that an information retrieval system, mechanized or not, handles files which have no connection among themselves, in the sense of cross referencing. A computer center may handle both a company's personnel records and its library index records. Although these constitute a file set, their only common attribute may be that they physically coexist within the same computer center. To distinguish between such a file set and one whose members do cross-reference each other, we define a *file system* to be a set of files each of whose member files either contains a direct reference to an address in another file of the set, or uses data fields which are used in another file. An example of the former type of reference is an index to a file, which gives an address in another file at which stated information will be found. An example of a common reference is found in a dictionary file which gives information about index terms which have also appeared in a file of index records. This is done through common use of the index term fields, not by direct addressing between files.

8.2 PRINCIPLES OF FILE SET ORGANIZATION

The higher in a hierarchy an assemblage of information-bearing symbols lies, the harder it becomes to define it rigorously and to cover all the principles of its organization. The system designer has almost boundless options in organizing his file sets and, although his organizational decisions in this realm may dominate all other performance charac-

226

teristics, he will probably find less experience and fewer facts about user requirements and probable system performance available to guide him than he does in making some more detailed decisions.

Our review of file set organization principles will cover three topics. First, we consider types of files and analyze the various roles played in file systems by individual files. Second, we consider the sequence of searching files, noting here that a file system is not always searched by following the same progression through the individual files. If the sequence can vary, then it must be specified in each case, and we find ourselves confronted with a formidable decision-making problem. Third, we consider cost as the basis for comparison among file set organizations.

8.2.1   Types of Files

First, we distinguish between files whose records refer to entities external to the file system, and those whose referents are internal to the system. *Every meaningful record must contain information about something external to the record.* A record descriptive only of itself is of no value. Similarly, a file must refer to something external to itself, although some of the records of the file may contain only location or other structural information about that file, which is true of pointers in a list structure. The referent of some files may be internal to the file set, however. This is true of an index file. Other files, such as document files, may contain only references to entities outside the file set. Thus, relative to any file set, we may have *internal referent* files and *external referent* files. Both roles can be played by one file. A dictionary gives information on connections or relationships among fields within another file of the set (internal referent), and also gives definitions useful outside the context of the file set (external referent).

We can further subdivide these categories and recognize two sub-classes of each. Internal referent files may contain direct addresses linking the file to another file, or they may be linked by common field usage. External referent files may contain documents written in unrestricted languages whether in computer-readable form, microfilm form, or in original hard copy form, or they may contain information statements, in a language interpretable by a computer, such as, **Part number 1234. On hand: 12,000. On order: 3,000. Sales last month: 75.** Such records meet the formal definition of a document, but tend to be written in highly restrictive languages, and differ from index records only in terms of the referents, not content or structure. Such records are often created from information contained in the documents that are stored in the system.

We have, then, identified the following types of files:

1. Document Files. These comprise the documents, themselves, occasionally in machine-readable form. They may also be books on a shelf or microfilm files. The objective of the most common type of information retrieval system is to locate specific documents in this file and withdraw them, so that the actual information sought can be found.

2. Data Files. These contain information records which are not necessarily descriptive of documents. Within the context of this chapter, they are generally descriptive of utterances, messages, or facts which are possibly found within documents and abstracted therefrom. They were not necessarily found in any single document. Any single such item may be the result of careful analysis of many documents. The estimate of a hostile country's military strength, which might be written in terms of numbers of divisions, missiles, and the like, is the result of a long process of reading, interpreting, evaluating, and abstracting a large number of individual documents. Records in data files will usually be structured much as index records are, the structure being comprehensible to the retrieval system, but they need have no referent within the file system. Where such files are present, their search may be the prime purpose of the information retrieval system.

3. Index Record Files. These are sets of index records, each record being the index of a single document. They may have external referents, but an index record, by definition, always has at least one internal referent—a document.

4. Structure Files. These serve to speed the search of other files by providing information on the location or structure of data therein. There can be a structure file for a structure file, as shown in Method 6 of our example in Section 7.4.3. Structure files differ from index record files only in regard to their referents.

The examples that we use in this chapter are based on contiguously placed file structures and fixed- or repeating-field records. However, the principles apply to any file organization.

8.2.2   Search Sequence Considerations

In most of our examples so far, we have assumed that a file set is searched by proceeding in exactly the same sequence through the member files of the set—a sequence such as: dictionary, inverted index file, index record file, and document file. In making the assumption that searches are carried out this way, we have also assumed that we always start with the same information—a set of query terms—and seek the same information—a document. But these are not always the conditions under which a search is carried out. A simple example is a search in which document number is the only query term. There is no need for a dictionary or inverted file search here. The query term can be directly applied to a search of the index record file.

Similarly, the information sought can vary. We may wish only some information from the dictionary, or only an index record. If we combine variations in the information sought with variations in the information available at the start of a search, we can see that permitting such variation imposes an additional burden on the search program. Not only must the file be searched, but the search program must deduce which files are to be searched and what is to be retrieved from each of them. In an elaborate file system, this may be a problem of major proportions.

One solution to this problem is to have the searcher specify what files are to be searched, in what sequence, and what is to be retrieved from each. This can be a burden, for it demands from him thorough familiarity with the file system, an unrealistic requirement for a large group of users of a central library facility. Another approach is to have the search program determine, from the information presented in the query, just what has to be done. This is fine from the user's point of view. He simply states what he wants and what he knows, and awaits results. The logic requirements imposed on the search program by this approach are of considerable complexity, as we shall demonstrate in Section 8.5.

However the information is conveyed to the search program, allowing a variation in the sequence of searching the files of a set imposes two requirements. The first is that the sequence to be used for each query be communicated somehow, either as part of the query or as an output of a special program that would determine sequence. The second imposed requirement is that the search logic be describable independently for the search of each file rather than just once for the total query. As to the first requirement, we can simply postulate that the requestor will provide the search sequence as part of his question. The requirement that each file search be conducted independently adds very little burden to computer program design. It simply means that, for a search of any file, the search criteria be given, the fields to be retrieved be explicitly named, and, upon retrieval, that these fields can be directed to be placed in a query format, as search criteria, for the search of the next file. Something like this is done in any search operation involving two or more files. The search of an inverted file results in retrieval of record-number fields. These are used as request terms in searching the full index file. We are only requiring that this procedure be generalized so that the output of any file search can become part of the input to the search of any other file.

8.2.3 Comparison Factors

As we stated in Section 8.2, comparing file set organizations, either on cost or performance, is a difficult task. User patterns are needed for both, for the cost of using a given system may as well be a function of frequency or volume of use, or distribution of query types, as it is of record access time. Clearly, what performance the users need is a vital factor in weighing the value received for a given cost. Because of the constant dependence of value on user needs, there is no standard formula for evaluating file set organizations. We can, however, list some factors that will be important in any comparison.

The *absolute cost of a total system*—processor, memory, and files—is important because, however efficient the system is, it may have to conform to cost restrictions. A budget ceiling often means that we are not free to achieve greater efficiency if absolute cost must increase in the process.

The *absolute time required to perform a search* is the total elapsed time from submission of a query to receipt of the results. The time should be given in the form of a probability distribution, depending, for any given processor and file set organization, on query content and arrival rate. Batch processing and multiprogramming are both methods by which the resources of a computer can be more efficiently applied to processing data by overlapping or combining functions. If one or both methods are used, we become concerned with relative time required to perform a search; that is, with the portion of the total elapsed time that was used by a single search, or its prorated share of the total time. For users this becomes a cost consideration, for they are concerned with elapsed time, or service time, and with the cost of that service.

We are, then, interested in a *relative cost* measure, which can be used to compare one file set organization's use of resources with another's. Included in this measure might be a marginal measure that gives the additional cost of additional searches after a fixed minimum of queries have been handled. Usually, we will find an information retrieval system being justified by one set of requirements, but also find that there is another set, not important enough to justify the investment in themselves, which will result in increased use of the system once it is installed.

We may begin a comparison of organizational methods by answering the following questions:

1. What is the toal cost?   Regardless of value, can our budget afford it?

2. What is the relative cost of a search?   In other words, how much of a system's cost might we consider ought to be borne by the searcher?   (The question of whether this cost is balanced by the value of the retrieval output is one that ought to be considered, but is not specific to file set organization.)

3. How long will it take to accomplish a search?   This must be interpreted in light of a variety of system load factors and user needs.

4. Within the limitations of the total information available in a file set, what search capability is available to the searcher?   Can he, for example, use variable sequence searching?

The answers to all these questions must also be weighed against user needs, and the difficulty of quantifying them returns us to the conclusion of Chapter 4 that no general theory exists for evaluation of information retrieval systems.

8.3   FIXED SEQUENCE FILE SEARCHING

Below are described several methods of file set organization, all having the characteristic that every search of the file set involves searching the same files in the same sequence.

8.3.1   The One-File Set

The simplest file set organization, for information retrieval, consists of a single file containing all the index records of the library, ordered by accession number, or, perhaps, not ordered at all.   No attempt is made to sequence by a potentially more useful field, such as *subject, author's name,* or *publisher.*   Since *subject* or *author* may require multiple descriptors, they may be not representable by a single value of a single field.   Hence, a problem is created on how to sequence these index records, for there may not be any obviously most important subject or senior author.   Any arrangement of records other than by access number would require sorting all new input and merging it with old data, instead of merely tacking it onto the end of the file.   To perform a search, every record must be examined for every query, there being no prior information about where to find the desired data.   The file is in random sequence relative to any field descriptive of document content.   When records are found which satisfy the query, they are copied onto an output tape or printer.   This is the method we have described previously, in Section 4.2.4, and which is illustrated in Figure 8.1.

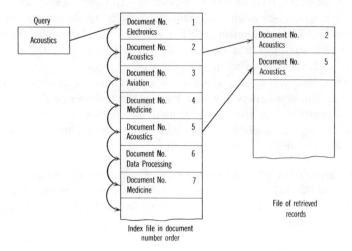

Figure 8.1   Search of a single file in relative random order.

Even this simple organization can be made more efficient for searching, by creating special code fields in each record which will tell quickly whether or not certain classes of information are present. A one-digit abbreviation of a subject classification code might be used, or the author's last initial, or the units digit of the year of publication, whichever field is likely to be often searched on. These techniques are valid only if the searching computer is able to, or needs to, capitalize on them. In a computer such as the IBM 7090 a small amount of time is available, after a record read operation has been initiated and before the tape stops, during which limited searching can be carried out and a decision made as to whether the tape needs to be stopped for more detailed searching. If the tape is stopped for each record, the cumulative restart time can become a serious time burden. Hence, the availability of what amounts to an abstract of the index record, contained within the record, could be very valuable. If, on the other hand, search logic is kept very simple there may be no need for the abstract, since it may be possible to carry out the entire search without stopping the tape.

Another organizational method is to sort the terms within each index record alphabetically, when they are first entered into the computer, so that a quick determination can be made whether any given query term is present in the index or not. This is generally applicable only to record structures where sequence of index terms is not important.

What benefit in search speed is derivable from this method is bought at the cost of sorting each input record.

8.3.2   Use of a Dictionary

In the file system described above synonyms must be handled by either so restricting vocabulary that there can be no synonyms, or by including in the query the union of all possible synonyms for desired terms. Another approach to the problem is to introduce another file, a dictionary, which will serve the purpose of resolving synonym problems before the index file is searched, and which avoids both restricting the language and making queries excessively long.* Since a basic function of a dictionary is to associate words together that have a defined relationship to each other, there are several possible ways to organize it:

1. The dictionary is a table converting an input word, in natural language, to a numeric value or other code. Words which are synonyms are given the same code. This means that if natural language output is desired in an intermediate output, the numeric values must be converted back to natural form, or both natural and coded versions stored in the index record. Use of such a shortened code, which must then be used in searching system files other than the dictionary, provides storage economy for other files. Such a dictionary is illustrated in Figure 8.2. Words are assigned numeric values when first entered into this file. A synonym for a word already in the file is given the same number as that word. Equating *airplane* and *plane* shows that the file can be used to serve very special subject areas, since these terms are not synonymous in all their possible meanings, but may be declared so in

* A query with a large number of terms, even if they are only a chain of disjoined synonyms, can severely restrict the operating efficiency of a program, for example, by causing an excessive number of tape stops.

Word	Code
AIRCRAFT	01
AIRPLANE	01
CALCULATOR	02
CANINE	03
COMPUTER	02
DOG	03
PLANE	01

Figure 8.2 A word-to-code dictionary.

Entry Word	Approved Equivalent
AIRCRAFT	AIRPLANE
AIRPLANE	AIRPLANE
CALCULATOR	COMPUTER
CANINE	CANINE
COMPUTER	COMPUTER
DOG	CANINE
PLANE	AIRPLANE

Figure 8.3   Word-to-word dictionary.

any given context where one meaning is overwhelmingly more probable than others.

2. To avoid the use of codes which can prove something of a burden in keeping files up-to-date the same dictionary concept can use a reference from a synonym to an approved spelling or form of a term in lieu of a common code for all synonyms.   Which, of several alternatives, is the approved form can be quite arbitrary so far as the program is concerned, since this term is really only serving as a code, but one which enables semantic communication with a human reader.   See the example in Figure 8.3.   This dictionary uses the same equivalences as that in Figure 8.2, but, instead of a code value, one of the terms out of a group of synonymous terms is selected as the approved version.   Although it serves the same role as the codes of Figure 8.2, the approved version is semantically meaningful to the human reader.   This organization reduces conversion time but, of course, requires a larger file than does the use of codes.

3. Although not a common requirement, there are systems in which it is important to retain the index term as it originally appeared, yet where a synonym dictionary continues to be needed.   In the first two illustrations the form of the index term being added to a file is changed by the dictionary before it is stored, so that, on retrieval, it cannot be determined which synonym was used originally.   In an intelligence library it is often important to know what terms were used by authors in the past to describe an object or concept, even though access to the term in the files may be through a synonym.   For instance, to retrieve information on the activities of a person who has used an alias, it is sufficient to convert all aliases to the "true" name by use of a synonym dictionary, but the intelligence analyst may be interested in what name was in use at that time, and perhaps by what name the person was known in his association with different groups.   Automatic conversion

of all input terms to a fixed standard destroys this kind of information. The requirement can be met by use of both the original terms and of a code designating the synonym group, or by a return to the method of changing a query term to the union of that term and all its synonyms. In Figure 8.4a, we show the original versions of index terms stored in the index record. The number designating a group of synonyms is gotten from the dictionary in Figure 8.2. The document illustrated could be retrieved on a search for **calculator** or **plane,** synonyms for the index terms used, by use of the codes representing each of these terms. Figure 8.4b shows an alternative method in which the document

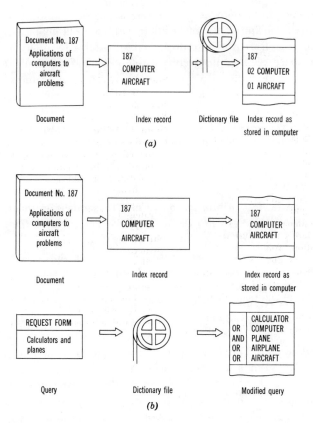

Figure 8.4   Retention of original terms.   (a) original index term stored in index record with synonym group number; (b) original term only stored in index record.

index uses only the original versions of index terms. Query terms are converted to the union of all synonyms for the stated word, using the dictionary of Figure 8.3 to compile the list of synonyms.

In all these forms a dictionary fits the definition of a data file in that it gives information that is independent of document content.

8.3.3   Use of a Structural File

With each of the dictionary techniques described above, we have assumed that searching of the file is serial, just as we have previously assumed with regard to the index file; that is, we have assumed no knowledge of the location of a word in the dictionary file. This assumption has much less validity for a dictionary file, however, than it had for the index file, for the entry to a dictionary is always by natural language term, and, if it is used as the sort key, good knowledge of location is readily obtainable. This is, however, an example of a situation in which perfect knowledge of location, although obtainable, is probably not worth the effort, for a complete table of term locations might take as much space as the dictionary it refers to and the time to search this table would easily offset the time advantage subsequently gained in the search of the dictionary. Partial location knowledge, which might be gained by any of the methods described in Chapter 7, would be valuable when applied to dictionary searching. Similarly, location files are useful in searching the index or any other file.

8.4   THE INVERTED INDEX FILE

A common device in information retrieval systems is an inverted index file, used to speed access into the index file. The inverted file is created by affixing the record access number to each descriptor of each index record, and then sorting the entire file by descriptor. The resultant file contains a series of records which contain a term and the location of the records from which the term was extracted. In the strict sense, then, an inverted index file is a structural file. However, because it can also serve the purposes of an index record file, as we shall demonstrate below, the inverted index falls in both categories and deserves special attention. The formation of an inverted index file is shown in Figure 8.5. When a search is to be made for all index records containing a given descriptor, the inverted file is searched first and the precise location of all records that satisfy the request can be retrieved. Any of the methods of storing location information described previously can also be profitably applied to this location file. When equal, or

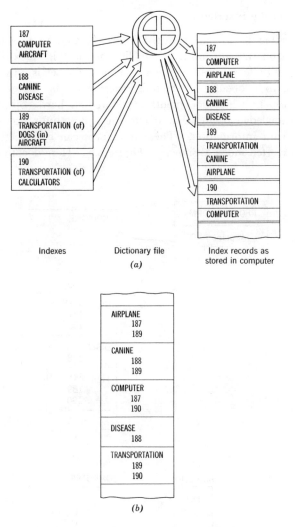

Figure 8.5 Inverted index file. (*a*) preparation of the index file; (*b*) resulting inverted index file.

direct access records are available, investment of a little extra memory for these index tables can result in much quicker pinpointing of the single record ultimately desired.

8.4.1   Use of the Inverted File

It is possible to use an inverted index, created to provide location information on the full index file, in lieu of the full index file. Sometimes the ultimate purpose of the search of a file set is only to retrieve a reference to a document which is external to the file system. This is what happens when documents are stored in hard copy form only, and the knowledge of in what document a descriptor occurred is the only significant information. These references can be directly retrieved from the inverted index as shown in Figure 8.6. Here document number

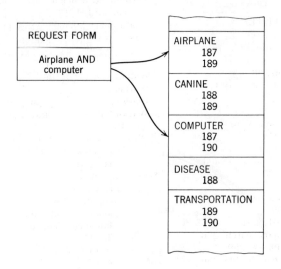

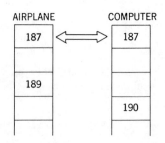

Figure 8.6   Use of an inverted index file.

187 satisfies the query illustrated.   This fact can now be used to retrieve an index record, or it can be used as a call number in a direct retrieval of a document from the document file.   Note that a regular index record shows, not only what documents contain a given term, but what other terms are contained as well, information not easily obtained from an inverted file.

Variations in search logic can improve the efficiency of a file set with an inverted index.   In the most common mode of usage, when the search specifies a Boolean combination of terms, the union and intersection operations can be carried out on the list of record locations retrieved from an inverted index.   Another method that has been proposed by I. A. Warheit[1] is to locate only one term of a request set in the inverted file, then search out the index records listed there.   The full logic is applied only to the index records retrieved by this term.   This method offers an advantage when the expected number of index records to be detail-searched is low, the number of comparisons to be made during the record search is also low, and the query terms are all intersected. The method works best if the least probable term can be selected from the request set and used as the one entry to the inverted file.   This technique is called *direct access searching* and is illustrated in Figure 8.7.   Only one of the two query terms is looked up in the inverted index file.   All index records containing that term are examined for presence of the other query term.   This method reduces searches in the inverted file and eliminates cumbersome logical operations on the lists of document numbers retrieved from the inverted file.   If a third table, an index of the inverted file, is used, it would be possible to include not only location of term records, but the number of index record references in each, and this could be used to select the single entry for the inverted file.   On the other hand, maintaining and retrieving relative frequency of use data may use up all the gains otherwise provided.

8.4.2   Benefits and Problems

In our discussion so far of inverted files, we have implicitly assumed that the index record is a uniformly structured, repeating field record. This need not always be true.   The index record can take any of the forms, including combinations, described in Chapter 5.   It is not always necessary or economical to provide location data on every field type in the basic record through an inverted file.   We might choose only subject descriptors, but not date or author, for example.   In such a case, a search for all documents by a given author would require a

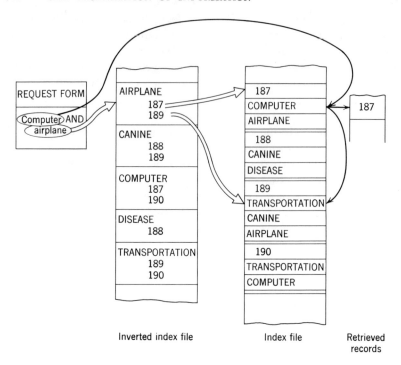

Figure 8.7   Direct access searching.

full file search.   It is even less desirable to invert a complete file in non-document-oriented files.   The low search probability of most of the many fields in typical data records makes allocation of extra memory to speed the occasional search uneconomical.   Consider what happens when the index file is sequenced on some more meaningful basis than accession number.   We must certainly bear in mind that one result is a requirement to sort all incoming index records.   Any sequence other than accession number must be sufficiently more efficient than access number order to overcome the penalty of sort time.   Sorting on subject would often be desirable, but many indexing systems permit and encourage several subject terms per index.   Sorting of index records by subject would then require each record to be replicated as many times as there are subject terms in the record.   The inverted file concept avoids this potentially excessive use of memory by simply providing a cross-reference capability without replicating the full index record.   We shall next consider, then, what advantage there could be to resequencing the index records if an inverted index is available.   We shall also examine the circumstances where the cost of maintaining an inverted file is too high, and see what the weaknesses of the inverted file method are.

Let us take the last question first. An inverted index requires that terms be extracted from all incoming index records, sorted, and merged into the existing inverted file. Given the record design, the sort technique to be used, and the computer characteristics, this time can be accurately predicted, and goes on the debit side of the ledger. In use, we enter an inverted index with search terms as arguments and retrieve record numbers for use in the index record file. The retrieved record numbers must then be sorted. The distribution of these record numbers will not, in general, form any pattern; hence, there is no reason to assume the records represented will be clustered in the index file. The record number may be looked up in a table of record locations, or the index file can be searched sequentially until all records in the domain have been found. The problem of locating records whose access numbers are known can be alleviated by using an access number that is coded to indicate location, perhaps a code with disk unit, disk track, and record number as fields. The weaknesses of an inverted file system, then, are: the processing cost to prepare the inverted file; the lack of correlation between position of a term in the inverted file and the positions of index records which contain that term, meaning that even after recovery of the record numbers we are still faced with a long search; and the necessity to sort the records retrieved from the inverted file in order to use them efficiently as the basis for index file search. For most systems, these are rather minor weaknesses, but they can be important where great speed or great efficiency of use of computer equipment is required.

8.4.3   An Illustrative System

Let us now address the questions of the advantage of another sequence for the index record file and the cost of maintaining the inverted file. For a resequencing of the index record file to be more economical than use of an inverted file, some of the following conditions would have to be met:

1. A low ratio of number of descriptors in use to number of index terms (high repetition rate of terms). Free key word systems would tend toward a high ratio (terms are constantly being added), while a hierarchical language will stay relatively stable for the same document input rate (high repetition rate).

2. Memory space relatively freely available, but processor time tight or relatively expensive. The large, relatively inexpensive memories of

magnetic tape strips or cards make storage cost, per character, very low. With such devices, optimization of processor utilization becomes more important than memory utilization.

3. A small number of terms typically used in queries. This probably indicates a subject heading or hierarchical index system.

Assume all three conditions hold, and let us consider how a system could be designed under these constraints. The following are plausible system parameters:

Total number of descriptors possible	5000
Average number of descriptors applied to document	5
Document input rate	10,000 per year
Average number of descriptors per query	3
Assumed size of library (hence, index record file)	50,000 records
Number of years of cumulated data	5

All descriptors have equal likelihood of appearing in any index.

Our file organization consists of sequencing index records by descriptor and replicating the record for each descriptor therein. Thus the file will consist of $5 \times 50,000 = 250,000$ records organized into about 5000 groups of about 50 records each, each group containing numbers of all the index records in which a given descriptor occurred. Within a descriptor group, records are sequenced on accession number. Some form of chaining will be used so that the complete index file does not need to be sorted or reorganized each time a new record is added. For a search, a variant of Warheit's method would be to locate the chain (descriptor group) for any one query term, then search for the presence of the other search terms in each of the (average of) 50 records in that chain. The 50 records contain an average total of 250 descriptors, and we must test each set of five for the presence of two values (the two search terms other than the one used to locate a chain). At most, 500 comparisons will be made. A table is required to give the starting point of the chain for each possible descriptor and the next available location for storing new inputs. This table can be quite concise, requiring only two numbers to be stored for each argument.

An example of such a file structure is shown in Figure 8.8. In the Index Record File (IF) are shown three records, of five descriptors each. The Replicated Index File (RIF) consists of one *record* for each *term* of the Index File. Each record of the RIF consists of the original IF record with a different term rotated to the top position, as in Records 2 and 3, or 4, 6, and 56 of the RIF. Record 5 of the RIF shows the use of chaining. A search on **computer** will recover Records 3 and 4, and then a jump must be made to Record 57 to continue the

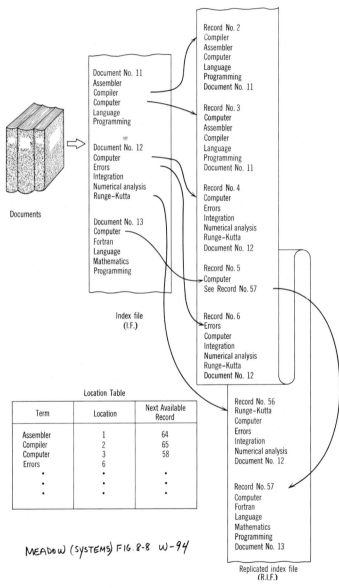

Documents

Document No. 11
Assembler
Compiler
Computer
Language
Programming

Document No. 12
Computer
Errors
Integration
Numerical analysis
Runge–Kutta

Document No. 13
Computer
Fortran
Language
Mathematics
Programming

Index file
(I.F.)

Record No. 2
Compiler
Assembler
Computer
Language
Programming
Document No. 11

Record No. 3
Computer
Assembler
Compiler
Language
Programming
Document No. 11

Record No. 4
Computer
Errors
Integration
Numerical analysis
Runge–Kutta
Document No. 12

Record No. 5
Computer
See Record No. 57

Record No. 6
Errors
Computer
Integration
Numerical analysis
Runge–Kutta
Document No. 12

Record No. 56
Runge–Kutta
Computer
Errors
Integration
Numerical analysis
Document No. 12

Record No. 57
Computer
Fortran
Language
Mathematics
Programming
Document No. 13

Replicated index file
(R.I.F.)

Location Table

Term	Location	Next Available Record
Assembler	1	64
Compiler	2	65
Computer	3	58
Errors	6	
.	.	.
.	.	.
.	.	.

MEADOW (SYSTEMS) FIG. 8-8 W-94

Figure 8.8 Use of a replicated index file.

search on that descriptor. A location table is illustrated, showing, for each descriptor, the location of its first occurrence in memory and the place where new records may be introduced to the file. This is similar to the space available list of a list structure, and eliminates the need to trace through an entire chain to find the spot to add a new record.

To use an inverted index file instead of a replicated index file, in the problem just described, means that the inverted file must have an average of 50 entries for each descriptor, making it larger by a factor of 25 than the location table. The incoming index records must be sorted, and the individual record number posted to the inverted file. Here, we can make a saving by the use of chaining, obviating the need for sorting or reorganizing often. Then we must use individual processor characteristics to compute and compare the distance and cost coefficients for the retrieval of this set of records by the inverted file method with the method discussed above, which omits an inverted file. In an all-magnetic-tape storage system, the replicated index method could easily be more economical, provided file sizes do not grow to such proportions that tape memory becomes too cumbersome a storage medium.

8.5   VARIABLE SEQUENCE SEARCHING

We use variable sequence searching whenever the searcher is free to specify what kind of output he would like retrieved from an information retrieval system, or to vary the nature of the query terms. In fixed sequence searching, we always start with the same kinds of terms and always retrieve the same kind of data. A simple example of variable sequence searching is given by a system which permits either subject matter or document number searches. If the index record file is the only file of a set, the variations in input do not affect the sequence of file search. A more complex and interesting example is given by the *multifile search problem*. Here, the searcher does not know the values of the search parameters he needs to recover the desired information. What he provides as an input is a query to one file which will retrieve the data that will then be used in another query of another file, from which the desired data are retrieved. Any number of file searches can be chained together in this manner. Although these searches can all be made to the same file, there is usually more than one involved, hence the name *multifile search*. If we consult a telephone directory for the telephone numbers of all airlines operating locally, then call them and ask for flight departure information on flights to Chicago, we are performing a multifile search, starting with airline names, ending with departure times, and using telephone numbers as

a link.   This problem is likely to occur operationally only with very
large file systems.   Even though it may occur with smaller ones, special
purpose solutions may be possible that cannot be used efficiently in a
larger system.

As an illustrative example of the use of variable sequence searching,
assume a file set consists of an index file, an inverted file, and one
or more data files.   The index system is presumed to dictate use of
a fixed key word descriptor list, plus indexing of all proper names occurring in the document.   Such a system would be useful in many technical fields where, in addition to searching for accomplishment in a
field, or background information, or the state of technology, it is important to be able to retrieve on product names, work done by particular
individuals, or at particular laboratories or factories.   Assume that one
of the files covers product data.   Figure 8.9 shows a schematic of this
file set.   We have, here, a product file, which is a data file containing
four fields of information: *product name,* and, for each product, its
manufacturer, location of manufacturer, and *unit price.*   There is also

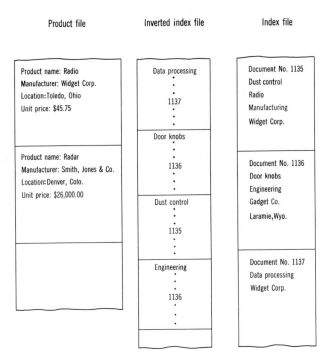

Figure 8.9 File set organized for variable-sequence
searching.

an inverted index file and an index record file.   An example of a query that might be posed to this file is, "Find all documents on dust control in the manufacture of radios by the Widget Corp., in Toledo."   **Dust control** is assumed to be in the fixed descriptor list.   Although **radio, Widget Corp.,** and **Toledo** are all terms found in the product file as values for *product name, manufacturer,* and *location,* respectively, there is no need to use the data file in this search, for all necessary field values are known and can be used directly in the index files.

For an example of the use of a data file, consider a question such as, "In what cities are transistor radios manufactured?"   Again, using Figure 8.9, it can be seen that the question can be *answered* solely by reference to the product file, by direct reference to **transistor radios.** The computer output need not be a list of references, or even a list of product records.   It can be the list of cities where transistor radios are manufactured, for selection of the *location* field as sole output of a search of the product file is possible in a variable sequence search. Thus, so long as data files are present in the system, there is no reason why they cannot be searched directly for the answer to a question that would otherwise lead to the retrieval of a set of documents in which the answer would be found after much reading.

In these examples, the sequence varies only to the extent that the starting position is either the product file or the inverted file.   The next example shows more variability.   Assume a file set consisting of an index and inverted file, a dictionary, and data files for people, products, and organizations.   The basic coverage of the whole system is scientific and technical information.   We can assume the index record consists of key words tagged to show their role—person's name, product, organization, manufacturing process, and so on—and that they are linked to each other, so that the product of a company (organization) is linked to the company name, but it cannot be inferred whether the product was bought, sold, or advertised by that company—only that the names are linked.   The dictionary shows synonyms, including class and class membership for each word.   A schematic diagram of this file set is illustrated in Figure 8.10.   The file set is assumed stored on a direct access memory.

In addition to routine queries directed through the dictionary to the inverted index to the index file, this file set can handle many other kinds of questions.   A few are illustrated:

1. We wish to find a list of all Harvard men in the electronics industry. We will use the same files as shown in Figure 8.10; thus we have no file sequenced on either *university attended* or *industry type.*   However,

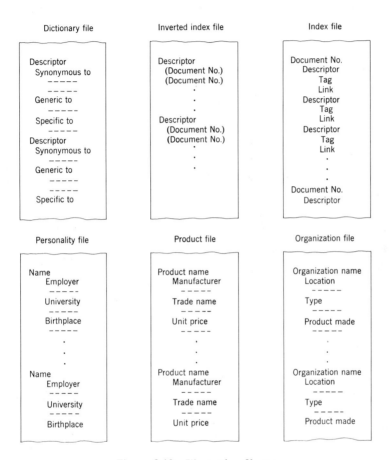

Figure 8.10   Illustrative file set.

these fields do occur in the personality and organizational records, respectively. Furthermore, these records were made up only from information that occurred in the documents whose indexes constitute the index file of this set. One approach is to do a full sequential search of the personality file for the names and affiliations of all Harvard men (step 1, Figure 8.11), and then, by a search of the organization file (step 2), delete all those names retrieved in step 1 whose organizations are not in the electronics industry. This would be a very long process, although not as long as if we entered the organization file first, looking for names

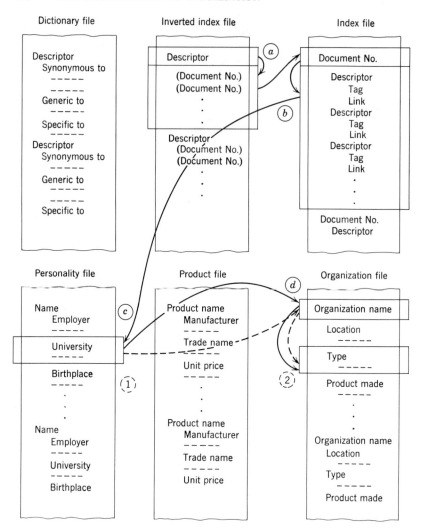

Figure 8.11   File search techniques (I).

of electronics companies.   In the method illustrated, the second search, that of the organization file, is done using the sort key as a search term.   If we had to search the personality file on *organization affiliation*, we would be faced with a full-file search, following a full-file search. Another approach it also shown in Figure 8.11 with the steps shown by solid lines.   We enter the inverted file on **Harvard** (step a), retrieve index record numbers, find all index records containing this term (step b), retrieve all personal names found in these index records, search the name file for these names (step c), delete those who are not Harvard graduates (the list of names will include many who were merely linked with Harvard, such as faculty members, visitors, and donors of gifts), and finally, back to the organization file for verification of type or organization (step d). The advantage of this method over the first two is that all files searched are sequenced on the search parameter, so that in spite of the number of files searched, the total operation can go quickly. Also, of course, the question has been answered directly, without the necessity of reading source documents, although the document indexes have been used. If documents have been correctly indexed, there is no possibility of this procedure leading to an error.

2. We have a tip that the stock of the ABC Company is a good buy. We have never heard of this company, and would like to know who else is in the same field and what information we have on the competition. A search technique is shown in Figure 8.12. We would enter the organization file first, on **ABC CO.**, and retrieve the names of all products manufactured (step 1). This list must be used to enter the dictionary (step 2) to find all synonyms, especially important where trademark names, rather than generic descriptors, are used to identify products. We then enter the product file (step 3) to retrieve the names of all producers of each product. This answers the first part of the question, "Who are the competitors?" Now, we could return (step 4) to the organizational file for a summary of information on the competitors, or go to the index file via the inverted file to retrieve documents about them (steps 5 and 6). Once again, every file entered was searched on a field on which the file was sorted.

3. Our company plans to erect a new manufacturing plant. The list of possible locations has been narrowed to five cities. The plant will need to be supplied with ten different raw materials, and we would like to assure a nearby supply to hold down delivery costs. We would like to know what materials are available near each city, and would like whatever information we have on the suppliers. For simplicity, we define "nearness" as "in the same state." To satisfy this request, we could enter the dictionary (step 1 of Figure 8.13) for synonyms for the names of the needed products, then the product file (step 2) to retrieve the names of all producers of them. The list of suppliers is then used, in step 3, to enter the organization file, where manufacturing locations are retrieved and compared with our list of prospective plant sites. Those supplier records not containing one of the prospective states would be deleted. The remaining records are sorted by state, and the resulting set of records satisfies the first part of the query. The second

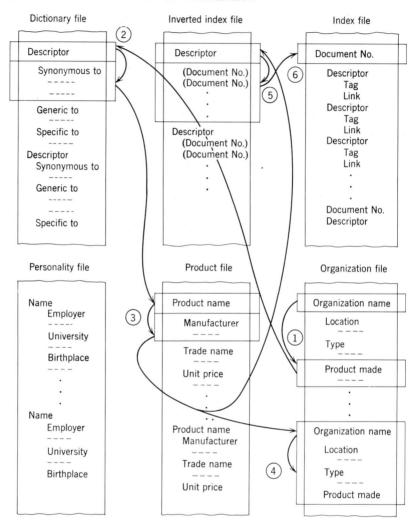

Figure 8.12 File search techniques (II).

part, just as in the previous example, is satisfied by a conventional index search on company names, steps 4 and 5.

In each of these examples the information could have been retrieved, eventually, by starting with a document request, and culling the required data out of the text, making additional queries along the way, if necessary. The procedure would be very time-consuming and tedious. It is in this sense that we made the statement that the variable sequence file organization can lead to improved quality of output compared with the fixed sequence methods.

A careful examination of the four examples of file-set searching given so far in this section will reveal that, not only can the sequence of file searches vary, but the purpose of searching any file can vary. Some file searches are performed only to retrieve information that will speed the next search by providing location data. This is not new; it is the purpose of an inverted index file. What is new is that the role of

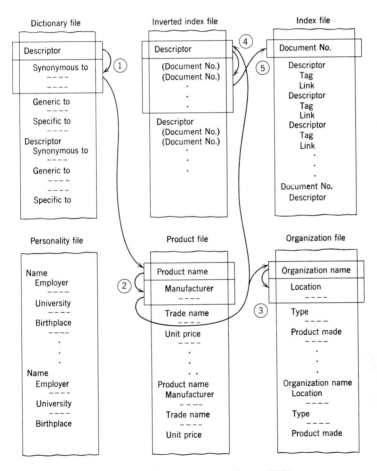

Figure 8.13 File search techniques (III).

the files can be made to vary between data retrieval and location retrieval. In the example of the Harvard men, we could have made a direct attack on the name file. The only purpose for searching the inverted index and index files was to locate the records in the name file that we wanted to examine. Thus, the index file served as a location device for another file. This returns us to one of the key points made at the beginning of this section, that each search of a file can be treated as an independent search, with its own search criteria and output requirements. In a system permitting variable sequence searching, it is part of the skill of the users of the system to plan a sequence which will answer the question and do so efficiently.

REFERENCES

1. Warheit, I. A., *The Direct Access Search System,* International Business Machines Corp., Advanced Systems Development Division, San Jose, California, Technical Report 16.01.011.081, June 4, 1963.

EXERCISES

1. Find an organization for the file system illustrated in Figure 8.10 that will be able to answer the queries illustrated in Section 8.5 without the use of variable sequence searching.
2. We are told by a friend that a Mr. X has written a technical paper that might interest us. No other information is given. Using the file system shown in Figure 8.10, devise a search plan that will recover the following:

   a. All papers by Mr. X.
   b. The name of the subjects Mr. X writes about.
   c. Other papers by colleagues (same profession, same employer) of Mr. X.
   d. Names of universities where similar work is done. (A university will be found in the organization file, tagged as a university but without any product.)

3. The value of variable sequence searching, we hope, has been made clear. Its costs would be reflected in higher programming costs and possibly higher operating costs. A problem remains of how to convey to the search program the sequence with which files are to be searched and what is to be retrieved from each file. How would you do it? Possibilities to consider range from a fully automatic method that, given the query terms and the desired information, computes the best sequence for searching the files, to a conversational query mode in which system users, not too familiar with the details of file design, step through a series of searches, one at a time. Intermediate outputs could be provided at each state. Work the problem of Exercise 2 into the discussion of your solution.

III

Processing of Files and File Sets

CHAPTER 9

Basic file processes

9.1 INTRODUCTION

In Chapter 6 we defined a file process as that which, in some way, transforms a file. Since we often prefer to be selective, the concept of a process *domain* was introduced and defined as that portion or subset of a file that is to be transformed. In other words, if we wish to operate on only a portion of a file, we must first isolate that portion, the domain of the process, consider it as a file in itself, and then process the sub-file so isolated. The act of isolating a domain was called *searching*, wherein the outcome of a match determines whether or not a record is a member of the domain.

We also noted that a file can be transformed by altering each individual record, or by altering the sequence in which records appear. In this chapter we expand on this concept and show that record alteration can consist of changing the value of a field, or changing the structure of the record. The alteration of files, or *file maintenance* as it is more commonly known, exerts a large, often dominating, influence on computer time requirements for, hence the cost of, operating an information retrieval system.

The processes of greatest importance in information retrieval, other than searching are: *sorting* (putting all records of a file into a predetermined sequence), *merging* (combining two or more files, each already in sequence on the same key field, into a single file, also in sequence on the same key), and *file maintenance*, which we have just defined. The obviously critical processes of selecting, or removing, certain information has, we feel, been adequately described in Chapter 4. Searching is reviewed here in the context of file processing. Our treatment of these topics is not intended to be exhaustive, but it is of such critical importance in retrieval system planning and cost analysis that some discussion is required. Because the coverage is brief, our aim is to accomplish two things: to demonstrate the essential similarity of what are

255

often viewed as diverse processes and to provide at least a rudimentary basis for cost estimation of every major process.

We shall first review the basic concept of file sequencing. Before discussing how to put a file in sequence, the process of sorting, we shall cover merging because this process is used in almost all large file sort processes. We then cover matching and searching from the file processing point of view.

9.2   FILE SEQUENCE

Let us review, briefly, what is meant by a file being in sequence. A file is in sequence if each record is in position relative to other records according to a sequence specification. When we talk of "sorting a file" we mean to change the positions of records within the file to conform to some sequence specification. The basis for record sequencing is a function of some attribute of the record. Most commonly, it is a *sort key,* a field within the record whose values are used to fix relative record location, the record with the smallest value being first, and the record with the largest value being last. There are many variations possible, including a reversal of record order to run from largest to smallest value. To accomplish either sequencing, we endow all symbols with a precedence, or position, in an ordered set, as we do when we speak of "alphabetical order." In computers, even punctuation and special characters have a rank in the ordering of characters, so that we can sequence on any combination of numbers, letters, or characters.

Order can be based on a function or attribute of a field not explicitly present in the record—for example, the length of the record, number of repetitions of some repeating field, time of arrival of the record at the computer, or salary earned, even if this figure were not present, but hourly rate and hours worked were. In an example in Section 7.3.3, we described sequencing of records (which, in this example, were addresses in a program switch) on the basis of probability of occurrence of field values, to minimize the number of computer instructions needed to select the next processing step on the basis of the content of some input data. The probability was not recorded in the record.

Not all orderings or records are possible. A computer memory, for addressing purposes, is one-dimensional, and is not ideally suited to storing two-dimensional data. For example, suppose we desire to store a large amount of geographic information, perhaps town names and their locations, expressed in latitude and longitude. There is no ordering of such a list that will come even close to preserving distance relationships, guaranteeing that records about towns near each other on the earth's surface are stored near each other in the file. A search, then, for the names of all towns within a specified distance of a given town, cannot be restricted to a small, contiguous area of memory. Such a guarantee can be given for a file ordered on a single variable. See Exercise 1 at the end of this chapter.

Another important concept in file sequencing is that of subordinate sort keys introduced in Section 6.4.2. Suppose a personnel file is sequenced on last name and initials. The file designer who anticipates that there may be more than one person with identical values of these fields can make use of subordinate sort keys to determine relative record position when a group of records have the same value of the primary key. He could use *birthplace* as a second sort key. Even a third key, such as *birth date, sex,* or *department number* may be desirable. Subordinate keys are not always necessary, but often valuable. When subordinate keys are not used, and two or more records can have the same value of the primary key, all such records are in random order relative to fields independent of the primary sort key. Judicious choice of subordinate keys can *usually* put a file in order so that each record's position is uniquely determined. In effect, all the sort keys are chained together to make one long key (e.g., *name-initials-birthplace-sex-age*).

9.3 MERGING

In *merging* we start with two or more files, each in sequence by the same keys. These are combined into a single file, which is also in sequence on the same keys, and which has a number of records equal to the sum of the number of records in the constituent files. A merging process is performed when a new batch of document index records, ordered on accession number, is combined with an existing file, also indexed on access number, to produce a new, corrected file of library accessions. If we were merging files ordered by term, there would be duplication of terms between the existing file and the new data. When this happens, we would usually want to combine the two matching records into a single, resultant record, so the number of output records would be less than the sum of the numbers of input records. We combine the existing record that tells for what existing documents **computer** is an index term with the new record telling for what new documents **computer** is an index term. Strictly speaking, this is not a merge process, by our definition; it is a combination of merging and matching in which we do different things depending on whether records from each stream match each other or not. We pursue this topic in Section 9.5.

The simplest way to carry out a merge of, say, two files on magnetic

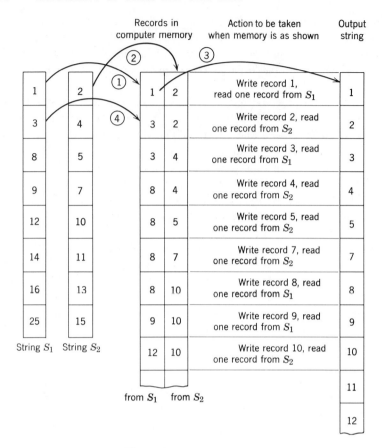

Figure 9.1 File merging.

tape, is to read a record from each into the computer's memory, decide upon the desired relative order between them, write the record with precedence on another tape, replace the record just selected with another from the input tape that originally contributed it, and continue in this fashion until all input records are exhausted. A file merge is illustrated in Figure 9.1. Here steps 1 and 2 represent reading one record from each input file into a working area in computer memory. Step 3 shows the selection of the first ouput record, and Step 4 the replacement of the output record with a new input record. With good programming and the "right" computer configuration, the output tape can be kept continuously in motion, and the entire operation can be completed in just about the amount of time it would take to write the file alone. At worst, a tape will stop after every read or write operation, necessitating

expenditure of a tape start-up time for every input or output record. If
string S_1 contains r_1 records, S_2 contains r_2 records, and so forth, if
an average record is c characters long, read/write rate is k characters
per second, tape start time is t, and input-output operations can be
overlapped, then the total time, T, to perform a merge of n files is
approximately

$$T = r_1\left(\frac{c}{k} + t\right) + r_2\left(\frac{c}{k} + t\right) + r_3\left(\frac{c}{k} + t\right) + \cdots$$

$$= \left(\frac{c}{k} + t\right) \sum_{i=1}^{n} r_i \tag{9.1}$$

We can improve the accuracy of this formula by including a probability
that the tape start time will be required; that is, that the tape cannot
be kept continuously in motion. Thus Eq. 9.1 becomes

$$T = \left(\frac{c}{k} + pt\right) \sum_{i=1}^{n} r_i \tag{9.2}$$

We have included no computation time, this usually being negligible
if the process is a merge by our definition. If other functions are to
be performed on records of the merged file that might consume a significant amount of time, the formula must be corrected to show this. If
input and output operations can be overlapped, the total time is determined by the length R of the output file, and we have

$$T = \left(\frac{c}{k} + pt\right) R \tag{9.3}$$

9.4 SORTING

In Sections 9.2 and 6.4.2 we described the concept of a file in order.
Sorting is a file process which places the records of a file in sequence
according to some stated criterion, such as, "ascending order using field
f as a sort key." We have brought out (Section 7.4.2) the value to
search operations of knowing file sequence when searching a file, and
because of this value, and for ease of housekeeping, files are almost
always put in sequence. Hence sorting is vital to the economy of any
file system.

There are many methods of sorting, and the computer configuration
employed is particularly important in choosing one. The amount of
data to be sorted is also important, and especially critical is whether
or not the file can fit into a computer's internal memory or must
be stored on tape or disks and read in piecemeal. We shall restrict

ourselves, at first, to consideration of data stored on magnetic tape, where the volume is far more than can fit in internal memory. Logic and time estimates for other memories can be derived from this. Then we discuss sorting of sets of records that can be stored in a processor's core memory.

9.4.1   Sorting by Successive Merges

To illustrate the mechanics of sorting, assume a file of records, stored on magnetic tape. The records of the file are to be put in ascending order on a numeric field. The basic approach will be to convert the file into strings, each being a subset of the file, the records within a string being in sequence. We shall increase the length of the strings while reducing their number, until, finally, the whole file is one string—hence, in order. If necessary, the starting strings may consist of as little as a single record each. The logic is illustrated in Figure 9.2. First, we read a single record (sort key value 6) into memory and write

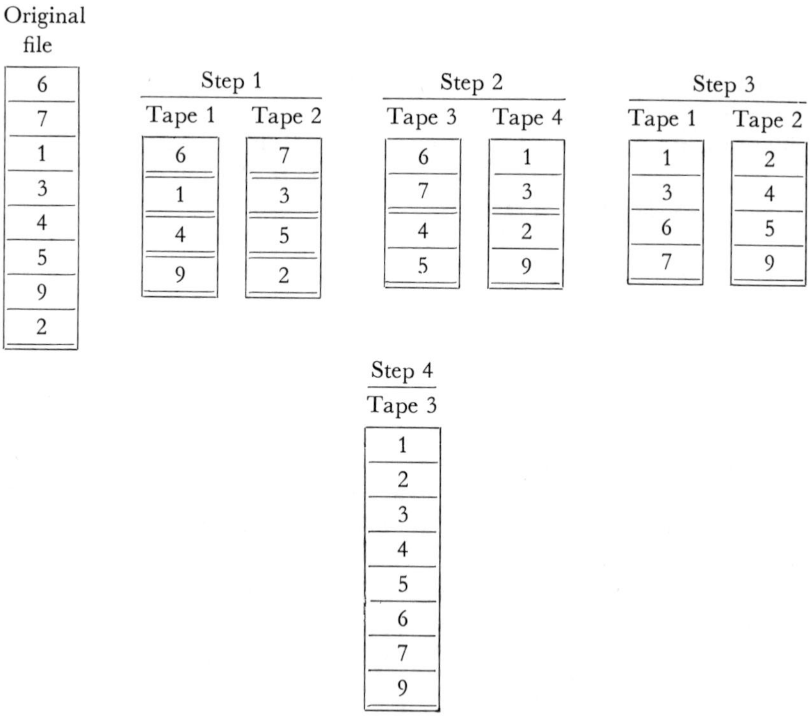

Original file

6
7
1
3
4
5
9
2

Step 1

Tape 1	Tape 2
6	7
1	3
4	5
9	2

Step 2

Tape 3	Tape 4
6	1
7	3
4	2
5	9

Step 3

Tape 1	Tape 2
1	2
3	4
6	5
7	9

Step 4

Tape 3

1
2
3
4
5
6
7
9

Figure 9.2   Two-by-two sorting.

it on the first of two output tapes. Then another record (7) is read in and put on the second output tape. Then a third read (1) followed by a write on tape 1, a fourth read (3) followed by a write on tape 2, and so on, until the entire file is copied, half the records on tape 1 and half on tape 2. The relative order of records on each of these tapes is unchanged; no sorting has yet taken place. Now we have two sets of strings, each containing one record, and there are four strings in each set. We now rewind the tapes and read one record from tape 1 and one from tape 2, with both in memory simultaneously; we then write the "smaller" (6) first on tape 3, followed by the "larger" (7), on the *same tape*. We follow this by reading the second records from tapes 1 and 2 (1 and 3) and placing them in order on tape 4. Repeat now, continuing to switch back and forth from tape 3 to 4 for output and 1 to 2 for input. When all the records have been copied, we have two sets of strings of two records each, in order, on tapes 3 and 4. We now copy these back to tapes 1 and 2, enlarging the output string length to four records, and we repeat this process until there is only one string consisting of the complete file, and it is in order.

The length of the string doubles with each pass, strings having lengths of 2^0, 2^1, 2^2, 2^3 in the four passes shown, meaning that the total number of passes, p, is

$$p = \log_2 r + 1 \qquad (9.4)$$

where r is the number of records in the file. Since r is not always a power of two, we must modify this to

$$p = [\log_2 r] + 1 \qquad (9.5)$$

where the square brackets indicate the "next highest integer" beyond $\log_2 r$ if $\log_2 r$ is not an integer, and $\log_2 r$ if it is an integer.* If, in Figure 9.2, the original file had had nine records, a fifth pass would have been required. The results at the end of pass four would be as shown on tape 3, but tape 4 would contain a single record, to be merged in on the next pass. This method is called *two-by-two sorting*, after the number of tapes required to hold the file after each pass. It is possible to use more than two tapes, for the general expression for the number of passes is†

$$p = [\log_t r] + 1 \qquad (9.6)$$

---

* Thus if $\log_2 r = 2$, $[\log_2 r] = 2$, but if $\log_2 r = 2.1$, $[\log_2 r] = 3$.
† McCracken, Weiss, and Lee[3] and Friend[1] give this and equation 9.5 in the form $p = [\log_t r]$ where p is the number of *merge* passes. The first pass is excluded from the computation on the grounds it is not a merge. We are measuring *total passes,* regardless of type.

where t is the number of tapes over which the file is spread.   Otherwise stated, the first pass produces strings of t^0 records, the second pass t^1, the third pass t^2, . . , until a string length is reached which is greater than or equal to the file size.   This method, of course, is nothing more than a succession of merges.   For timing purposes, the merge equations can be used.

9.4.2   Internal Sorting

A significant saving can be achieved, still using the same basic method, by reading in as large a block of records as possible in pass 1, and sorting them in the computer's internal memory before writing them out again on tape 1.   Putting this set of records in order is called an

Original file	Pass 1		Pass 2	
	Tape 1	Tape 2	Tape 3	Tape 4
69				
12	12	02	02	07
88	69	06	06	10
02	88	68	12	33
06			68	52
68	07	33	69	64
07	10	52	88	70
70	70	64		
10			14	16
33	14	18	18	17
64	40	73	40	21
52	71	82	71	27
14			73	79
71	21	16	82	95
40	79	17		
82	95	27	26	
73				
18	26			
79				
95				
21				
17				
16				
27				
26				

Figure 9.3   Sorting with

internal sort. It can be much faster than the other sort passes that use memory areas external to the main computer, such as tape. Sorts that make use of external memory are called *external sorts.* An internal sort results in a large string at the end of pass 1. Hence, the total number of passes is reduced and much time saved. Figure 9.3 illustrates this process. Here, an original file has 25 records; we read these in three at a time, internally sort them in the computer's memory, and produce, at the end of pass 1, eight strings of three records each, and a ninth string of one record. Having now nine strings to merge into one requires four more passes, for a total of five. Using the first method we described would have required $[\log_2 25] + 1 = 6$ passes. If we increase the initial string size to four, rather than three, we would reduce the total of passes required to four. In practical applications,

Pass 3		Pass 4		Final Pass
Tape 1	Tape 2	Tape 3	Tape 4	
02	14	02	26	02
06	16	06		06
07	17	07		07
10	18	10		10
12	21	12		12
33	27	14		14
52	40	16		16
64	71	17		17
68	73	18		18
69	79	21		21
70	82	27		26
88	95	33		27
26		40		33
		52		40
		64		52
		68		64
		69		68
		70		69
		71		70
		73		71
		79		73
		82		79
		88		82
		95		88
				95

an internal sort pass.

the number of records handled in the first, internal sort pass, can often be far greater than that which we have illustrated, resulting in far more significant savings.

The internal sort pass can be counted upon to put records in sequence at a much greater rate than does successive, external merging, since no significant memory access time is involved. However, there is much scanning and moving of data and the total time to sort a string or records internally is not negligible. We discuss a few such methods in Section 9.4.3.

Having an internal sort pass makes us reconsider our formula for number of passes. The string length, when we are ready for our second pass is s, the number of records internally sorted in a batch. After the second pass, the string length is ts, after the third, t^2s, ... After p passes, we have strings of $t^{p-1}s$ records. If the original file consisted of r records, the number of passes p must be such that

$$t^{p-1}s = r$$

$$p = \log_t \frac{r}{s} + 1$$

or, because r/s is not always a power of t

$$p = \left[\log_t \frac{r}{s}\right] + 1 \tag{9.7}$$

Internal sort timing is so much a function of the individual processor that we shall not consider it here.

There are a number of methods of internal sorting. The reader will find quite comprehensive coverage in McCracken, Weiss, and Lee[4] and in a paper by E. H. Friend,[2] and we shall not repeat these descriptions here. Briefly, however, some of the commonly used techniques are *multiple merging, selection,* and *exchange.* Multiple merging, as an internal sort technique, is logically identical to the external process of multiple merging. The only difference is that records are moved around within core memory and are written on the external memory only when a single, sorted string has been achieved.

Sorting by selection means to search through a set of records to find the smallest, then search for the next smallest, and so on, until all records are in order. This has the advantage of being probably the easiest way to program a sort.

Sorting by exchange means to examine records in pairs, 1 and 2, 2 and 3, 3 and 4, and so on, always placing the two records of a pair in proper sequence. Complete passes through the set of records in core memory are made over and over again until the set is completely in order. This is a good technique to use when a high degree of order is expected in the data, but can be quite cumbersome otherwise.

9.4.3. Taking Advantage of Order in Sorting

Many files are received at the computer partly in order, that is, with only a relatively few records out of sequence. Such would be the case if index records were manually assigned sequential accession numbers by indexers, and turned over to the computer room in batches. Then each batch from a different indexer would be in order (or nearly so, allowance still having to be made for human error). As these batches of records are put on tape, there would be many variable-length strings of records, in some of which there may be a few records out of order. To take advantage of partial ordering, then, the probability that a record has a higher sort key than its predecessor in the file must be substantially higher than would be so if the file were in random order. This does not require that the strings described above be ordered with respect to each other—that is, that indexer number 1 enters his records before indexer number 2—but clearly this is desirable.

One way to take advantage of the order in the input data is to use the exchange method of internal sorting in the first pass. If all the records read into core memory in a batch are already in order, the only time taken is that necessary to verify the order—one pass through the set of records. If a few are out of order, they will quickly be brought up to the "top." However, each exchange of records involves moving records around in memory and this can be time-consuming. An alternative is to skip the internal sort pass altogether and revert to successive merge sorting but using a different way of forming the first set of strings. Strings could be formed by copying records continuously from the input to the output tape as long as the input records are in a continuous sorted string. As soon as a record is found that is out of sequence, it starts a new string on the alternate output tape. When the second string is broken, a change is made back to the first output tape (or onto the third, if available). This method is illustrated in Figure 9.4. The number of passes required in this method is not exactly predictable, for it depends on the particular file being sorted, but limits can be calculated and a probabilistic formula devised.

The worst that can happen is to use this method on a file that is in exactly inverse order, for then all strings are one record long and we would require

$$p = \lceil \log_t r \rceil + 1 \text{ passes} \tag{9.8}$$

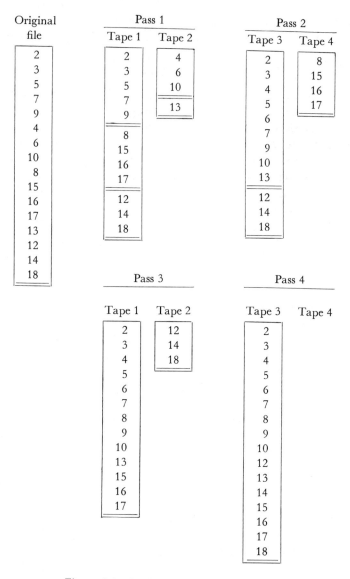

Figure 9.4 Sorting partially ordered data.

In the best case the file would be fully in sort, but the program, not knowing this, would still use one pass to discover it. The string length s is equal to r, the number of records in the file, and $p = (\log_t 1) + 1 = 1$. For other cases the number of passes is

$$p = [\log_t N] + 1 \tag{9.9}$$

where N is the number of sorted strings in the file, a probabilistic variable. For large values of N, near r, which implies that string length is near 1, this method is inefficient, for it does not make use of an internal sort pass which, though time-consuming, is guaranteed to produce long strings at the end of pass 1. The cut-off point is reached when $N = r/s$; that is, when the expected number of strings is equal to the number that would be produced by an internal sort pass. For any N, in this neighborhood or larger, the assumption must be made that there is no order in the data, and an internal sort pass, not relying on order, will prove desirable. For N less than r/s, prior ordering is indicated and can be exploited.

9.5 SEARCHING

A *search* is the process of gaining access to records that are to be matched with queries. More generally, we have a file of query terms, each record constituting a query—the set of terms that specify what records are being sought in another file. We shall see shortly that searching does not always have retrieval as its end result, for searching is a necessary preliminary to many file alteration operations. In preceding chapters we have reviewed several techniques of searching, mostly as illustrations of other concepts. In this section we shall review these techniques and conclude with an example of time estimation for a complex search of a file system.

9.5.1 Principles of Searching

We define a *search plan* as the method used to search a file or file system, examples of which are binary searching and sequential searching. A search plan is selected by a programmer and made a part of the logic of search programs. A search plan differs from *retrieval strategy* as we defined it, in that a retrieval strategy is the plan for the composition and successive use of queries by a searcher in carrying out a particular quest for information. A retrieval strategy is a means of employing resources, one of which is a search plan. A search plan is a function of file and file set organization and of the logic permitted in a query.

Generally, the search plan is fixed within a retrieval system, while retrieval strategy can vary with each individual query.

The principal elements of file organization that affect the search plan are file sequence, storage medium, and file content (the set of record types and fields contained in the file). The availability, somewhere within a file set, of positional information on the principal information files is also of great importance. A major factor, independent of file organization, is the logic used in queries, and another is whether queries can be batched, a subject to be taken up in Section 9.6.

In the simplest search situation we have a single search argument, or query term, and we are guaranteed to find one and only one record in the file which matches it. Furthermore, the file is sequenced by the same field that is used as a search term. An example is the search of a table of logarithms where a preliminary program insures that only those arguments are accepted which are represented in the table; hence, no interpolation is required. At the other end of the spectrum we may have a file system consisting of dictionary, inverted index, index record, and several data files, with queries being permitted that include any combination of any number of values of any field in the file system. It is logically possible to use a query term that is not to be found in the file system.

We are concerned with file sequence because only by having prior knowledge of the location of records in a file being searched can we avoid the time and expense of a search of every record of the file each time we have a query. Placing the file in sequence on the same field as is used in searching is the most common way of accomplishing search economy. Making location tables available which are in sequence on the search term permits fast searching even when the main file is not in the desired sequence. Thus, if searching is expected based on more than one term type, the file can be sequenced by one of them, and location data can be provided for the others. If an index record file is sequenced by access number and an inverted index by subject descriptor, then we can accommodate queries based upon subject or access number with about equal ease, even though the subject query requires two searches. When a file is being searched for a value of its major sort key, we say we have an *ordered search*. It is easy to see that we can also have a *partially ordered search* or an *unordered* or *random search*.

Our concern with storage media is primarily with their accessibility characteristics, rather than with their absolute readout speeds or access times. The dominating characteristic of magnetic tape, for example, is that it is a sequential access storage medium in which we cannot move directly to a desired record, even if we know its exact location. Also of importance is whether reading from the memory or accession to it (such as positioning a disk access arm) can be carried out in parallel with other operations of the computer.

The file structure may dictate or preclude certain methods of file search. Contiguous placement of records encourages the use of binary searching, while use of a list structure indicates a sequential search. On the other hand, some of the disadvantages of some file organizations can be overcome by creating additional, structural information files. A separate location table can be maintained to guide a search through a chain organization without having to burrow through it in a sequential fashion. Such a table could maintain the first sort key value of every track or other memory division devoted to an ordered set of records. Thus to help search for a record whose sort key begins with C we could use a table, each of whose entries is the first sort key value in each track that contains records whose sort key begins with C.

The two major aspects of query logic that affect a search plan are whether more than one term is possible and whether more than one type term is possible in a single query. For most retrieval systems the answers to both questions is yes, but whenever there are restrictions of this type, advantage can be taken of them. If a given file can only be searched by one type term, it can be sequenced on that term. If, as is usually the case with index record file searches, the file can be searched on any of the many fields used in the record, no such simple solution is possible. If more than one query term, whether a repeated value of a single field or a second field, can be used in a query, we are forced into more complicated search logic, but we can then make provisions for batching queries which gives a great potential for time saving.

At the present time no algorithm can accept as input the parameters of a system—file organization, user patterns, query logic, and computer resources available—and produce an optimum search plan.

9.5.2   Basic Search Plans

Each of these plans has been introduced and described elsewhere in the text, so we shall not review them in detail.

1. Full File Search. Each record of the file being searched must be matched against the query record. There is no prior knowledge of the order of the file, nor is there any assurance that a single match ends the search; therefore *all* records must be matched.

2. Sequential Search. The file is in sequence by the term type used as a search term. No location data is available or the file is stored on sequential access memory, so each record must be matched until the desired records are found. If a record is found whose sort key value exceeds that of the query term there will be no retrieval and the search may be terminated. This is described in Section 8.3.1.

3. Binary Search. The file is entered in the middle. The next match is made one-fourth the file "length" away in a direction that depends on the relative values of the query term and the sort key value of the record selected for a test. Called a binary search because a binary (two-valued) decision is made after each test match, it was described in Section 4.3.

4. Direct Access Search. The exact location of at least the first record matching a query term is known in advance of the search (of the file, not the file set, for the location information was probably obtained in a prior file search). This is described in Section 8.4.

As usual, there can be combinations of any of these basic techniques. For example, binary searching may be used to locate only the disk or track containing the desired record, and a sequential search may be carried out of the contents of the lesser memory element to find the exact record sought. Because a track, in most disks, is the minimum element of reading and writing, the entire contents of a track will have to be brought into core memory to make any test, and sequential testing of this relatively small number of records in high-speed memory is no serious burden to total search time.

9.5.3. Time Estimation

We shall consider a single example of how to estimate the time required to carry out a search under a given plan for a given file system. We shall omit any considerations of program timing, for that is not specific to information retrieval, and instead, shall concentrate on timing access to information.

We assume a file system illustrated in Figure 9.5, which is constructed as follows. There is an index record file (IRF) containing R records with an average of r characters each. There is an inverted index file (IVF) of I records with an average of i characters each. Access numbers in these records are in sort. Both files are stored on disk memory whose characteristics are given below. A third file is an index of IRF storage locations. This file, the locator file for the IRF (LF), is stored in core memory. It consists of a list of the access numbers which are

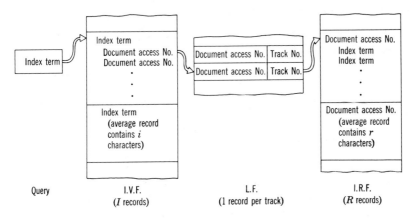

Figure 9.5 Illustrative file system.

in the first record position on each track of the disk memory devoted to IRF storage. This information could have been stored in the IVF, but is separately stored to conserve space by not having to repeat the address for each occurrence of a document number in the IVF.

When a subject descriptor search is to be made, the record in the IVF corresponding to the search term is retrieved first. A modified binary search is employed. The first track of the middle disk of the file is examined and the access arm then moves one-fourth of the way in one direction and samples another first track, and so on. When the correct disk is found, tracks are searched sequentially until the correct track is found. Searching within tracks is done sequentially in core memory.

The set of retrieved access numbers will be in sequence. For each number the track address is retrieved from the LF, using a binary search in core memory. Finally, the index records are recovered from the IRF by going directly to the tracks known to contain desired records and searching in core for the specific records.

The file parameters are

d = number of tracks per disk
c = number of characters per track
k = disk read rate, in characters per second
R = number of index records in the IRF
r = average number of characters in an index record
I = number of records on the IVF
i = average number of characters in an inverted index record
a = average number of access numbers in an inverted index record

Disk timing parameters are the following:

1. Time to move disk arm from the end of one track to the beginning of the adjacent track: m_1

2. Time to move arm from the end of a track across x intervening tracks to the beginning of another track: $m_1 + xm_2$

3. Time to move arm from outer edge of a disk across y intervening disks to another disk: ym_3

The following assumptions are made:

1. At the start of a search of either file stored on disks, the disk access arm is always positioned at the first track of the first disk of the file being searched.

2. The record sought on any given disk, on the average, will be found in the center track; that is, $d/2$ tracks from the edge of the disk.

3. When searching a file on more than one search term, if there are z terms in the query and N records in the file, the records that will be retrieved will be distributed evenly, N/z records apart. Determining the actual distribution of records in a file requires more complex statistical analysis than is in keeping with the level of this book. For example, we should consider the possibility that two or more records will be found in the same track. If this happens, the time and cost of a search will be reduced. We shall, however, proceed with the simplifying assumption of even distribution.

Search timing is computed as follows:

1. Number of brackets in a search of the IVF. A series of matches is made, in which the number of disks traversed is decreased each time until a single disk is isolated. The number of matches M is such that

$$\frac{Ii/cd}{2^M} = 1 \qquad (9.10)$$

where Ii/cd is the number of disks needed for the IVF. Then

$$M = \left[\log_2 \frac{Ii}{cd} \right] \qquad (9.11)$$

2. Time to isolate the single disk. The first step involves traversing $Ii/2cd$ disks, by our first assumption. The time required is $Ii/2cd \cdot m_3$. The time to read the first track of the disk is c/k. Hence the total time for the first leg of the binary search is $Ii/2cd \cdot m_3 + c/k$.

The second leg is the same, except that only half the number of disks is traversed: $Ii/4cd$.   Time, then, is $Ii/4cd \cdot m_3 + c/k$.   The total search requires

$$T = \sum_{n=1}^{M} \left(\frac{Ii}{2^n cd} \cdot m_3 + \frac{c}{k} \right) \tag{9.12}$$

3. Time to search a disk sequentially. Assumption 2 states that we will have to search an average of $d/2$ tracks on the disk finally selected by the bracket search.   This requires $d/2$ moves from one track to the next and $d/2$ reads of a track.   The time for this is $(d/2)\,(m_1 + c/k)$ seconds.

The total time to retrieve an inverted index file record for a single query term, then, is:

$$T = \sum_{n=1}^{M} \left(\frac{Ii}{2^n cd} \cdot m_3 + \frac{c}{k} \right) + \frac{d}{2} \left(m_1 + \frac{c}{k} \right) \tag{9.13}$$

This search will retrieve an average of a records, which are in sequence.   Searching for the disk addresses of each, being a core memory-operation, is negligible by comparison with searches addressed to disk files.

4. Time to retrieve index records.   Having retrieved track addresses for each index record being sought, the final portion of the search is begun.   We again assume the disk arm to be positioned at the start of the IRF, and that a index records are to be recovered.   These are distributed evenly throughout the IRF.   The first search, then, will require moving the access arm across R/a records, or across $(Rr/cda) - 1$ intervening disks.   Each successive search will cover the same number of disks.   The time for each of these moves is:

$$T = \left\{ \left(\frac{Rr}{cda} \right) - 1 \right\} m_3 \tag{9.14}$$

When the desired disk is found, we again assume that, on the average, we must move to the middle track, but we do not need to search through the first $d/2 - 1$ tracks, for we know from the LF exactly what track we want.   The time to acquire and read this track is:

$$T = m_1 + \left(\frac{d}{2} - 1 \right) m_2 + \frac{c}{k} \tag{9.15}$$

Total time to retrieve a records in the IRF is

$$T = a\left(\left\{\left(\frac{Rr}{cda}\right) - 1\right\} m_3 + m_1 + \left(\frac{d}{2} - 1\right) m_2 + \frac{c}{k}\right) \quad (9.16)$$

9.6 BATCH PROCESSING

An important aspect of searching is the number of queries or sets of search arguments that can be processed simultaneously, or nearly so, in a batch. This requires the ability to take two or more queries at a time, each consisting of one or more terms, combine all the terms into a single ordered set, perform a file search, and still produce a separate response at the end for each query. Having this ability can save a great deal of time and expense. Consider a search of, say, a dictionary file on magnetic tape and assume there are an average of n terms in a query. The time to search for the $2n$ terms of a two-query batch is not twice a one-query search time. The search may be extended only very slightly and the percentage of increase will be smaller as more queries are added to a batch.

Whenever there is more than one query term to be matched against a file, search economies are possible. This is true for multiple queries as well as for single queries with multiple terms. The extent of the saving is a function of several variables. Foremost among them are: number of search terms, type memory, organization of data in the file being searched, and programming logic. We shall attempt only to show how to achieve the minimum saving. Without precise specification of the variables, no quantitative answers can be given.

Consider, first, a search of a dictionary stored on magnetic tape, a sequential access memory. The dictionary records, of course, are assumed to be ordered alphabetically. The time to search for a single term in this file is equal to tape start time, plus stop time, plus the access time required to move the tape from its beginning to the point where our term is stored. Access time is dependent upon several variables, such as machine design, programming logic, blocking factor (the number of logical records that constitute a machine record), and the use of structure tables. These variables can be assumed constant for any given problem situation. If we now introduce a second search term, creating a two-term batch, and if these terms are searched for in alphabetical order, without an intervening tape rewind, then the search takes less time than two independent searches by *at least* the access time for the first term. This is shown in Figure 9.6, in which the first search (a) requires a tape to move past seven records and stop at the eighth, as must the second (b), but the first three records of the second search

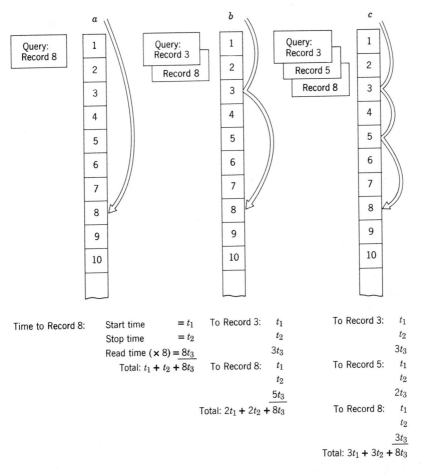

Figure 9.6 Batch processing times.

are "chargeable" to the search for record number 3. The third search, (c) shows an even greater net gain, although the tape is still required to go from its beginning to record eight. The *actual* times to carry out searches (b) and (c) are slightly greater than the time for (a), by the extent of the extra starting and stopping, but the average time per search term is lower, and, it can readily be seen, will continue downward as the batch size increases.*

* There is a point of diminishing return. As the batch gets too big, the time to sort its terms and the memory capacity required to hold them will begin to eat into batch economy. Also, the delay time necessary to accumulate a large batch may be intolerable to some system users.

If we assume tape start time to be t_1, stop time, t_2, and read time, t_3, the time to search for and find record 8, in our first search (a) is:

$$t_1 + t_2 + 8t_3$$

For the second search of Figure 9.6 the time is $t_1 + t_2 + 3t_3 + t_1 + t_2 + 5t_3 = 2t_1 + 2t_2 + 8t_3$, and for the third search $3t_1 + 3t_2 + 8t_3$. Thus the total elapsed time increases as a linear function of the number of starts and stops (read time being constant), not the number of records traversed.

For a disk, or direct access memory, the logic would be the same, provided the file is in order on the search terms. However, the relative saving will generally be less because disk access time (time to position a read mechanism) is far less than tape time to pass over the same amount of data.

For an equal access memory some economy is possible from batching, for there are tables to be searched sequentially even with such a memory available. However, the extent of the potential saving is relatively slight, for there are no access delays.

Maximum saving from batch processing comes when the high-cost, but avoidable, operations are eliminated. In tape searching this is start and stop time, there being no way to avoid scanning the distance from the last stopping place to the farthest descriptor. If, perchance, two or more terms should fall in the same machine record (or, in disk operation, a track), a start and a stop time are saved, as well as some reading time. The larger the machine record, the more probable is this fortuitous occurrence, but this, too, has a point of diminishing return, for larger records exact a price in the making of changes to the file and in the utilization of main memory.

REFERENCES

1. Friend, Edward H., "Sorting on Electronic Computer Systems." *J. Assoc. Computing Machinery,* **3**, 3 (1956), p. 135.
2. *Ibid.,* pp. 134–168.
3. McCracken, Daniel D., Harold Weiss, and Tsai-Hwa Lee, *Programming Business Computers,* John Wiley & Sons, New York, 1959, pp. 298–331.
4. *Ibid.*

EXERCISES

1. Assume that you have a large file of geographic place names and their locations. Describe methods of ordering this file, based on latitude and

longitude, and the corresponding search techniques, assuming there will be frequent questions asking for information on places near other places. Are there sort keys other than latitude and longitude that are useful?

2. Write detailed instructions for sorting playing cards by hand, according to suit and value.   Select a method (e.g., 2 x 2 sort preceded by an "internal" sort pass processing 4 cards at a time), and give instructions to a classmate, instructing him to follow directions exactly and not to assume any instructions he has not been given explicitly.   Do the same for merging strings of sorted cards.   Discuss the methods and results from the points of view of speed of operation and complexity of the "program."

3. Compute the number of passes and number of data record moves involved in the various sort methods briefly described in Section 9.4.2.

4. Devise a search plan for searching a telephone directory (alphabetical and business listings—two files) for a set of query terms which can be names, business types, names of businesses of known type, address only.   Devise retrieval plans for use when the query term cannot be located or it retrieves more than one record.   Flow chart and discuss your results.

CHAPTER 10

File maintenance

10.1 INTRODUCTION

Almost all files are dynamic structures of information, changing often in content, and occasionally in structure, sequence, or storage medium. In many, and possibly the majority of retrieval systems, more time and money are expended on maintaining files than on searching them. Indexing of new accessions, and the posting of new index records to index files and of new documents to document files are examples of file maintenance transactions. The speed and efficiency with which these operations are carried out often determines the cost or feasibility of the entire system. We are often constrained to organize file sets for optimum maintenance efficiency rather than for optimum search efficiency or speed. A system designer should never lose sight of the fact that well-maintained files are as much a user requirement as the ability to do high-speed searching, although he will rarely hear a user say so.

10.2 FILE MAINTENANCE PRINCIPLES

The function of file maintenance consists of, not just one, but a collection of file processes whose results are the incorporation of new records into a file, deletion of obsolete records, and modification of others, or a change in record positioning. Most sorting and merging operations in retrieval systems are performed as part of file maintenance, as are many matching operations. It has been estimated that sorting alone can use as much as 20 to 30 per cent of total machine time in general business applications.[1]

We shall review the foundations upon which maintenance functions are based, and, in the next section, present a few examples to show how maintenance requirements can come to dominate the entire approach to file organization and processing.

10.2.1 Types of Maintenance Transactions

Maintenance transactions can change the membership of a file, the values stored in records of a file, or the structure of a file. Specifically we can perform the following:

1. Add a record to a file
2. Delete a record from a file
3. Change the value of a field in a record
4. Change the structure of a record
5. Change the sequence of records in a file
6. Change the medium on which the file is stored

Adding a record is identical to merging new records with existing records to produce a new file.

Deleting requires a search to find the unwanted records, followed by what amounts to a negative merge, creating a new file without the matched records. In add and delete operations the domain is less than the full file.

Changing the value of a field (such as correcting a spelling error or changing the address of the next record in a chained file) or the structure of a record (by adding or deleting a field in a repeating set, changing the number of digits allocated to a given field, or changing the sequence of fields within a record) can be performed in individual specified records, or these operations can have an entire file as a domain. The latter would be the case if, say, a new coding scheme were initiated for part numbers, requiring more digits than had previously been in use. Then each part number field would be changed in value and in size. Although this type of change does not occur often in any system, it happens occasionally in every system, and ability to handle the requirement of making these changes without completely redesigning or rebuilding the system is a measure of the quality of its design.

Changing record position, or sorting, is an operation performed on an entire file, although individual records can be moved, in effect, by combinations of adding and deleting operations. Sorting of input data, before posting it to a file, is an almost universal system requirement. Resequencing of a file that has already been in operation is rare, but, just like restructuring records, it can be necessary on occasion. Sorting a chained file periodically, to speed searching, is an example.

When we change the medium on which a file is stored, we have changed the file organization and probably the access coefficient of the file. This, in turn, may lead to the adoption of new searching plans

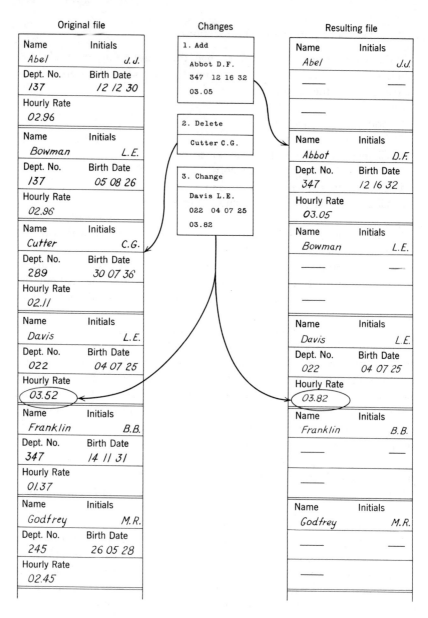

Figure 10.1 File maintenance transactions.

and strategies. In Chapter 6 we gave an example of the necessity for such a change, in the context of a file organization that minimizes the effect of a failure in a computer system component.

10.2.2   Relationship of Maintenance to Searching

Deletion and record structure or field value change operations require a search to isolate the domain of a process. Often addition does also, for many times a new record has its contents combined with an existing record rather than entered as a completely new and separate record. Even when new records are to be merged, intact, into an existing file, we could view this as a search for the correct *position* of the new record. When the new record is to be combined, we look for a match for the new record. A new entry being added to an index record file is almost always a complete record, although such records are sometimes modified after having been stored. An entry to an inverted index usually consists of information to be added to an existing record and will result in combining the new with the old record, or entry of the new record intact if there is no match. Using this approach, then, we may view maintenance operations as consisting of a *search* for a position in a record, a *match* to test whether the position has been found, and some other operation, varying with the specific transaction. A file search operation also meets this description, the last operation being retrieval or copying of the located information. An information retrieval system built in accordance with this unified concept of search and modify can save many programming steps and much operating time by batching file changes and queries into a single program run. Figure 10.1 shows a sample file, a combined list of maintenance transactions to be performed, and the file resulting from these transactions.

10.3   EXAMPLES OF FILE MAINTENANCE PROCESSING

File maintenance is far too complex a function to lend itself easily to the derivation of a neat set of cost equations. Such costs are highly dependent upon the particular computer used, as well as the variables that have been our concern here—file organization, input rate, and query rate. In this section, we shall reconsider some of the file set organizations discussed in Chapter 8, emphasizing the amount of work required for file maintenance compared with that required for file searching. We shall see that in the more elaborate systems the cost of maintenance can be very high compared with search cost and may be the dominant factor in determining the feasibility of a given approach to a problem.

10.3.1   Maintaining a One-File Set

In a file set consisting of only an index file accession numbers can be automatically assigned to records as they are entered, thereby eliminating the need to put new entries into a sequence other than the arrival sequence. To search this file, each record must be examined for its relevance to each query in a batch. There is no advantage to be gained by using a direct access memory because there is no prior knowledge of the location of the desired records (except in the presumably rare case of a search on access number). If queries are batched, then the retrieved records must be sorted by the query number that retrieved them, to permit delivery of an uncluttered list of index records to each requestor. If enough tapes are available, part of this sort can be accomplished during the search by using a different tape for the output of each query, up to the limit of available tape units. The alternative to the sort is to run queries one at a time, necessitating a rewind of the file tape after each pass. For relatively small files, with low query rates, this method is economical. However, when memory permits, batching queries will prove the more economical approach.

Maintenance of this one-file set is trivial. Records are always simply added to the end of the file, and by assigning access numbers automatically as the records are being added to the file we guarantee against sequence errors without the necessity of sorting. If records are to be deleted, the entire file must be recopied, without the undesired records or deleted records can be flagged as such, by changing the value of a field, but not physically removed. This operation can be combined with searching, as can the addition of new records. Changing the contents of an index record can also be handled by deleting the old version and adding the new version with a new access number. At worst, all maintenance transactions can be handled by copying the old file once, making all changes at the appropriate point in the file. This should take no longer than to run a typical batch of queries. Very roughly then, we may say that maintenance adds little to the cost of operating a system of this organization.

In summary, this file set organization results in relatively slow searching. Its use is generally restricted to smaller files, where its inefficiencies are no burden, or to smaller computers which cannot handle more complex structures. Its advantage is that it is an uncomplicated approach that minimizes user training, programming, and administration.

10.3.2   Maintenance with an Inverted Index File

This set consists of the index file, in accession number sequence, and an inverted index file in term sequence. The organizational method is generally for use with larger systems. Searching and maintenance of this file set are illustrated in Figure 10.2. Queries to this set would be broken up and sorted by term, the resulting list of terms being matched against the records of the inverted file. This time an ordered search of inverted file records is possible, and it is advantageous to use a direct access memory. Such a memory is not required to realize the advantage of the organization, however, for even on tape the inverted file approach can improve the efficiency of searching a file set. Once the set of access numbers of the index records containing each term is retrieved, the numbers must be sorted back into a sequence according to the number of the query that requested them (if the queries have

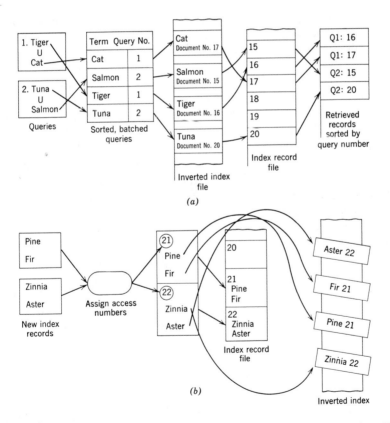

Figure 10.2 Operations with a file system: (*a*) file searching; (*b*) file maintenance.

been batched). Then the Boolean operations are performed on the sets of access numbers pertaining to each query. The result is a single list of access numbers of records that satisfy, or potentially satisfy, each query. These must be sorted by access number (again, assuming queries have been batched), and this list used to search the index file. The index file search now becomes a high-speed, ordered search, in which only the access numbers of index records need be checked, and, when the last record has been found, the search is terminated. This search would also benefit from a direct access memory, but cost usually prohibits the use of one in this manner. At the end, the retrieved index records must be sorted back into query number sequence, just as required for the index file-only method. Although there is a great deal of sorting required, the files being sorted are typically not large. A large memory, for internal sorting, is assumed. This is in keeping with the assumption that this method would be used with large files, justifying the employment of larger, more versatile computers.

To add new records to the file set, as illustrated in Figure 10.2*b*, the index records are annexed to the end of the index file, as before. When the access numbers have been assigned, the new records are sorted by term, and posted to the inverted file. This operation is a bit more complex, requiring either that the inverted file be copied, because records are being added at many points throughout the file, or that a chain or a list structure technique be used to permit noncontiguous placement of records. The latter would speed maintenance, but slow searching and increase storage requirements. Deletion of records requires that both files be recopied, as does making changes in existing records. Processing a set of maintenance transactions should take longer than processing the same number of queries. The method should be used only where a combination of search and maintenance costs, functions of the computer and programs used, indicate a net saving over the single-file approach, or if queries must be answered at very high speed, or if the index file is so long that the single-file approach is economically unfeasible.

In summary, this method is as easy to use as the single-file system, but requires a greater investment in programming and, often, computer equipment. Maintenance costs can be expected to exceed search costs. The method will prove more economical for very large files or for fast-response systems, if "proper" equipment is used.

10.3.3   The Maintenance Problems of a Dictionary

The addition of a dictionary to the file set described above presumes a large vocabulary which is probably complex in the sense of synonyms and homographs. Use of a dictionary also assumes large files with rapid response requirements. The dictionary serves two main purposes: to control quality of input and to tell a requestor how words are related, hence which ones to use. The need for both is characteristic of a large system.

A library user may want to browse through the dictionary before formulating his query to the index files. However many terms he uses or queries he poses, the terms would be sorted alphabetically and the dictionary entries retrieved. Because this would be an ordered search, and a dictionary is normally not too large, direct access memory is indicated, but not required. The result of this kind of dictionary search is nothing more than a list of terms which must then be formed into a query by addition of logical connectives. Each query term would first be used in a dictionary search, both to find synonyms and to ensure that the terms are actually used in the index language. If a match for any query term is not found in the dictionary, the entire query may be rejected. The mechanics of this search are the same as that of the inverted file search, which follows it. Finally, an ordered index file search is conducted.

Searching a file set which includes a dictionary adds just a little to the cost of searching an inverted file, and may pay for itself by detection of errors in queries and consequent prevention of searches which would have resulted in expending computer time to no avail.

In maintenance the dictionary plays an even more significant role in quality control. This brings to mind one of the peculiar side-effects of data processing. Once an error-detecting means is made available in a human communication system such as a library, many errors are found that previously would have been undetected and, being undetected, would have been considered nonexistent. As we pointed out in Section 4.4.3, what suffers in this kind of situation is the net quality of the library's service, a most difficult parameter to measure and, sometimes, even to observe qualitatively. However, now that errors are detected, something must be done about them, and this becomes a factor in the cost of file maintenance. Rejected input must be examined, the errors, if obvious to computer operating personnel, corrected at once, and the data re-entered. If the error is not obvious the record must be returned to an indexer for correction, a time-consuming and expensive process, which may require retrieval and complete re-indexing of the document. The extra scrutiny to which the vocabulary is subjected as a result of this process leads, inevitably, to more dictionary modifications, both to insert common misspellings and equate them to the proper word forms, and to adjust word relationships to reflect an increased awareness of how the index-query language is being used.

Calculator   See *computer*
Computer   Syn: *calculator, processor*
              See also: *electrical accounting machine*
Electrical acounting machine
              Syn: *punched card accounting machine*
              See also: *computer*
Processor   Syn: *computer*

(a)

Calculator   See also: *computer, electrical accounting machine*
Computer   Syn: *processor*
              See also: *calculator, electrical accounting machine*
Electrical accounting machine
              Syn: *punched card accounting machine*
              See also: *calculator, computer*
Processor   Syn: *computer*

(b)

Figure 10.3 Dictionary maintenance: (*a*) dictionary before change; (*b*) dictionary after *calculator* is no longer considered a synonym for *computer*.

Modifying the dictionary may be a more complex operation than modifying an inverted file. We assume the dictionary is fully cross referenced; that is, that every term in the index language is an argument and also is part of the definition of every other term to which it is related. To change the definition of a word, as shown in Figure 10.3, not only must the terms in the definition be changed, but the occurrence of the changed term in every other definition must also be altered. In the illustration we started with **calculator** being a synonym for **computer**. We wish to change this, to show **calculator** as a related, but not identical term. In making the change, we have modified the **computer** record, the **calculator** record, and the **electrical accounting machine** record to fully reflect the new relationship. Thus, if a term is to be deleted, its own entry must be found in an ordered search, and then each term in the definition must be searched for to make any necessary changes in its definition. Since terms in the definition of the deleted term can be anywhere in the file relative to the deleted term, a second pass must be made to change all definitions affected by changes in the first pass.

In summary, the addition of a dictionary to a file system directly induces only a small increase in computer time requirements, and that is about evenly balanced between added search time and added maintenance time. The very availability of a dictionary, however, invites browsing, which increases the number of searches, and indirectly leads to detection of enough errors to cause a significant increase in the number of people required to administer the retrieval system. These errors, of course, are not introduced by the dictionary, but, without it, they might well go undetected.

10.3.4   Indirect Maintenance Costs

As the number of interconnected files increases, which might be caused by combining data files with the index files (e.g., a biomedical library might include tables of biological and chemical data, experimental results, and census data with the bibliographic material), more attention will be focused on maintenance if for no other reason than that more correlation is done among data in different files and more errors detected. It is common in retrieval systems with large files, whether or not the system is mechanized, for there to be a large group of people whose job it is to control the data entering files. These people do not directly perform transcription (key punching, paper tape punching, etc.), nor are they the originators of the data. Their jobs are to supervise their collection, transcription, and entry into the files, study error patterns, and correct errors. They are an indirect part of the cost of file maintenance because complex, interconnected files cannot be effectively maintained without them. For example, as the volume and importance of data handled in an organization increase, more attention can be expected to be paid to such matters as the error rate in transcribing data into machine-readable form, and to the problems of feeding back detected errors to the person best able to correct them. These are essential processes which, although they may precede or follow the actual alteration of computer files, must be considered in any economic analysis of an information retrieval system.

10.4   SUMMARY

In this brief chapter we have reviewed the fundamental processes that are important in information retrieval, principally sorting, merging, and searching. We have tried to give a unified definition to file processes by treating file change operations as combinations of these basic functions.

The principal point to be gained from this chapter is the very important one that searching files is only part of the job in the retrieval of information. Assembling these files and maintaining them, while not necessarily apparent to the retrieval system user, contribute heavily to, in fact can easily dominate, the cost of system operation. It has been shown that the more complex file organizations, although they may speed searching, pay for the speed in extra maintenance costs.

REFERENCES

1. Gotlieb, Calvin C., "General-Purpose Programming for Business Applications," in *Advances in Computers,* Vol. 1, Franz L. Alt (ed.), Academic Press, New York, 1960, p. 17.

EXERCISES

1. Discuss the assignment of document access numbers as a file maintenance problem; e.g., who assigns them, at what stage in the process of entering a document and its index into the files, costs and problems introduced by various approaches and by various file organizations.
2. Make a study of file maintenance in the library you regularly use. Whether or not it is mechanized, try to find out what the processing steps are, and how much time is devoted to maintenance as opposed to indexing or to helping patrons.
3. Devise file organizations and search and maintenance procedures to be used with the following systems
   a. A telephone information service which has 50,000 subscribers, 10,000 of whom wish listings under type of business as well as name. Adds, deletes, and changes in name, address, or telephone number occur at the rate of 5000 per year. Queries are received at the rate of 15,000 per year, 80 per cent on name and 20 per cent on address.
   b. A mail-order house which maintains an inventory averaging 10,000 items. Twenty thousand orders are received daily, with an average of five items requested in each. To process an order the price of the items must be checked, as must the number on hand, to see if the order can be filled. A shipping order must be compiled and transmitted to the appropriate warehouse department, and if the number of items remaining falls below a reorder point specified for each item, a new purchase must be initiated. All sales must be recorded in the item record to enable later analysis of sales trends. There is a customer file which contains records of previous purchases, this purchase, and credit rating (to be checked for all charge orders before shipping), and a supplier file containing information needed to reorder. The customer file lists 90,000 names, of which 5000 are bad credit risks. The supplier file lists 2000 suppliers. File changes, in all files, are approximately 10 per cent of the records per year.
   c. A military intelligence file contains records on 100,000 potential aerial bombardment targets, spread over a broad geographical area. Each record contains 800 characters of information, among the fields of which are *target name, geographic location* in latitude and longitude, and *type*

(e.g., **steel factory, airfield, missile site,** etc.), which is a repeating field since, for example, a factory can produce both tractors and tanks.   Eighty per cent of searches are on the basis of geographic reference, 10 per cent by name, and 5 per cent by type.   The remaining 5 per cent call for an answer to a question such as, "Give me all type_____target records that are within_____miles of a type_____target."   One hundred queries a day and 200 changes a day are processed.   Only sequential access memory is available; except for 32,000 words of magnetic core storage.

Glossary

Abstract: A summary or condensation of a document written in natural language. An abstract serves the same function as an index, but its structure does not lend itself well to mechanized searching. An *extract* is a special case of an abstract, being composed of selected portions of the document being abstracted.

Catalog: "A list of books, maps, etc., arranged according to some definite plan. As distinguished from a bibliography it is a list which records, describes, and indexes the resources of a collection, a library, or a group of libraries."[1]

Character: A character, numeral, punctuation mark, or other sign used to construct semantically meaningful words in a language. A sign may be composed of other signs, as a character in a computer consists of a fixed number of bits.

Citation: "A note of reference to a work from which a passage is quoted or to some source as authority for a statement or proposition."[1]

Citation index: An index whose terms consist of citations taken from the documents being indexed.

Classification: "1. A systematic scheme for the arrangement of books and other material according to subject or form. 2. The assignment of books to their proper places in a system of classification."[1] *As used by author:* The name of a subject or group of subjects in an index language which uses nonoverlapping terms or descriptors and may have a strictly defined subordination relationship among all descriptors of the language.

Classification schedule: "The printed scheme of a particular system of classification."[1]

Concordance: "An index of the principal words in the Bible or the works of an author, showing location in the text, generally giving context, and sometimes defining the words."[1] *As used by author:* The above definition, applied to any work, but without the requirement for definition and not necessarily the need to show context, which presumably can be determined by computer search of the text itself.

Definition: The relationship between a word, or argument, and another word or set of words. The definition need not be in the same language as the argument.

Descriptor: *As used by author:* A word or syntactic unit used as the basic element of an index term. Subdivisions of descriptors, such as the words

291

of a phrase, even though meaningful in natural language, may not be meaningful in the index language. *In more general use:* Variously used in the above sense to imply our meaning of both *descriptor* and *term* or to imply meaning of *key word*.

Dictionary: *As used by author:* A formal device for stating the relationships among the words of a vocabulary or between one vocabulary and another, or a combination. The common, desk-top dictionary relates words of a natural language to other words of that language, expressing their "meaning" in terms of other words of the same language. A French-English dictionary gives the relationship of an English vocabulary to a French vocabulary, and vice versa. The *ASTIA Thesaurus* gives the relationship of words (numbers) of the ASTIA classification vocabulary to other words of the same vocabulary and also gives English language comments; that is, defines when necessary an ASTIA word in terms of English rather than ASTIA language.

Error: In indexing an error is a difference of opinion between indexers that may have been caused by a mistake, such as misreading a classification schedule, or by a difference in indexer point of view.

Facet: That portion of an index record devoted to a specific aspect or attribute of the referent of the record. In our usage we have facets only when we have syntactic index terms, so that the different facets are recognizable and differentiable from each other. A facet of a personnel record may be *name, age,* and so on. A faceted index language is one prescribing that a number of specific facets of the referent of a record be present.

Field: The smallest semantic unit of discourse in a file structure. A field corresponds approximately to a natural language word but can be as little as a single bit.

File: A structure of information, composed of one or more records, such that the records are descriptive of individuals and the file of a class of individuals.

Format: The layout, or scheme for positioning, of elements of an information structure.

Hierarchy: *As used by author:* A manner of grouping words or other information structures, or an instance thereof, whereby the elements or their referents are defined as being contained in one and only one higher order information element.

Index: 1. *As used by author:* A record (hence a document) giving some descriptive information about another record or document, which could be a book, photograph, file, or the like, and some information about its location. 2. *More generally, but somewhat less precisely:* A list or file, or an entry therein, giving the location of a document.

Index record: A record containing descriptive information about a particular document, other index record, or file.

Index file: A set of index records.

Information: There is no precise definition.   In general use it is *news* or *knowledge*.   In information theory it is resolution of uncertainty.

Information retrieval: 1. *As used by author:* Search of a file of information, on the basis of criteria supplied by a searcher, and presentation, to the searcher, of information in the file that met the criteria.   2. The retrieval of documents from a file according to criteria supplied by a requestor.   3. The retrieval of specific references to documents according to search criteria supplied by a requestor.   4. Finding an answer to a question through reference to a file of information, usually using a procedure as defined in 1, 2, or 3.

Key word: A language or a word of such a language whose vocabulary consists of individual, natural language words, or short syntactic units with no hierarchic or other relationship necessarily being given between them.

Language: A set of symbols or words and rules for their usage to communicate ideas.   We treat language as consisting of vocabulary, the basic set of words, and syntax, the rules for combining words into concepts that cannot be represented by the individual words.

Match: The process of comparing a record, or some part, facet, or field of it, with a term or set of terms in a query.

Phrase: A set of vocabulary elements, or words, grouped together into a syntactic unit; that is, with the relationship among the words being determined by some syntactic rule.

Query: A message to an information retrieval system specifying what information is to be retrieved, or giving the criteria by which this information is to be found.

Record: A set of fields, all descriptive of an individual or class of individuals.

Role: 1. *As used by author:* The facet, aspect, or syntactic purpose of a word, field, or term.   2. More generally, the syntactic sense in which a word or descriptor is used in an index.

Search: A procedure for systematic acquisition of records of a file for the purpose of matching them with search criteria stated in a query.

Synonym: A word, field, descriptor, symbol, and so forth, which, in some language is equivalent in meaning to another word, field, and the like.

Syntax: The arrangement of words in a sentence or phrase to show their relationships, or the rules for word arrangement for a given language.   A *syntactic unit* in natural language is a sentence or phrase.   Otherwise, it is any grouping of words which is governed by the syntax of a language.   Two natural language sentences, concatenated, do not constitute a syntactic unit, but two fixed fields may do so.

Term: 1. *As used by author:* A word or syntactic unit of a language which is made up of constituents which are, in turn, words of the vocabulary of a language. By convention a term may have as little as one elementary word, or descriptor, in it. In this case it is, itself, a descriptor. 2. More generally, an entry, or field in an index record, whether an elemental descriptor or a phrase.

Thesaurus: 1. *As used by author:* Synonymous with *dictionary.* 2. As used by others, a book or file relating words of a vocabulary to other words of the vocabulary by relating them both to a common, more abstract concept.

Vocabulary: The set of words or descriptors in use or authorized for use in a given language. Subdivisions of vocabulary words, in any given language, are not necessarily themselves words of the language.

REFERENCES

1. Thompson, Elizabeth H. (Ed.), A. L. A. *Glossary of Library Terms,* American Library Association, Chicago, 1943.

Index

Records, sequence of, 203
  structure of, 159–169, 203
  see also Index records
Redundancy in communication, 206, 209
Referent of a file, 227
Relevance, 118–128
Reliability of storage media, 183–185
Repeating fields, 163–165, 170–172, 194, 239
Replicated index file, 244
Representation of information, 192, 210–216, 219–224
Response time, 191
Retrieval, cyclic, 143–145
  errors, 129–133
  of index records, 106–145
  planning, 120–128
  principles of, 107–120
  strategy, 267
  see also Information retrieval
Role, 293; *see also* Facet

Savage, T. R., 17
Search, binary, 218, 267, 269–270
  by browsing, 191
  direct access, 239, 270
  of files, 107–145, 174–175, 177, 188, 224, 255, 267–274, 293
  logic, 132, 228, 232
  and maintenance, 281
  multifile, 244
  ordered, 268
  plan, 267, 269–270
  program, 228
  random, 268
  of records, 177
  sequence, 228–230
  sequential, 267, 269–270
  time, 203, 230
  variable sequence, 244–252
Selection, of index terms, 86–103
  of information, 108
  sorting by, 264–265
Selective dissemination of information (SDI), 15, 100–101
Semantic ambiguity of a record, 156, 158, 169, 171–172
Semantic attributes of records, 174
Semantic communication, 4, 7, 78, 234

Semantic content of a message, 156
Sequence, of file search, 228–236, 244–252
  of files, 185, 256–257, 259, 268
  of index terms, 232
  information, 218–219
  of records, 174, 185–188, 191–192, 203
Sequential access memory, 181
Sequential searching, 267, 269–270
Shannon, C. E., 3, 5, 6, 7, 204
Shera, J. H., 81, 82
Significance, 70
  measure of, 92–103
Significant words, 87, 92–103
SMART Automatic Document Retrieval System, 124, 128
Sort key, 186–187, 224, 256–257, 259
Sorting, 240, 255–256, 259–267, 278
  exchange, 264–265
  external, 263
  internal, 262–265
  multiple merge, 264–265
  order in, 265–267
  selection, 264–265
  by successive merges, 260–262
  two-by-two, 260–262
Statistical language analysis, 87
Statistical selection of index terms, 86–103
Statistical significance measure, 70
Stiles, H. E., 119, 120
Storage, characteristics of, 174
  of data, 174
  media, 17, 174–181, 268, 279–281
  position of information in, 188–190
  reliability of, 183–185
  of structural information, 203–224
  see also Memory
Strategy for information retrieval, 106, 121
String, 198, 260–267
Structure, of documents, 65–67, 77–86
  files, 228
  of files, 174, 203
  of an index, 67
  of language, 18–20, 160
  of records, 159–172, 203
Structural information, 165–166, 203–224, 236

Date Due